NEW GUIDED MATHEMATICS

CLASS 4

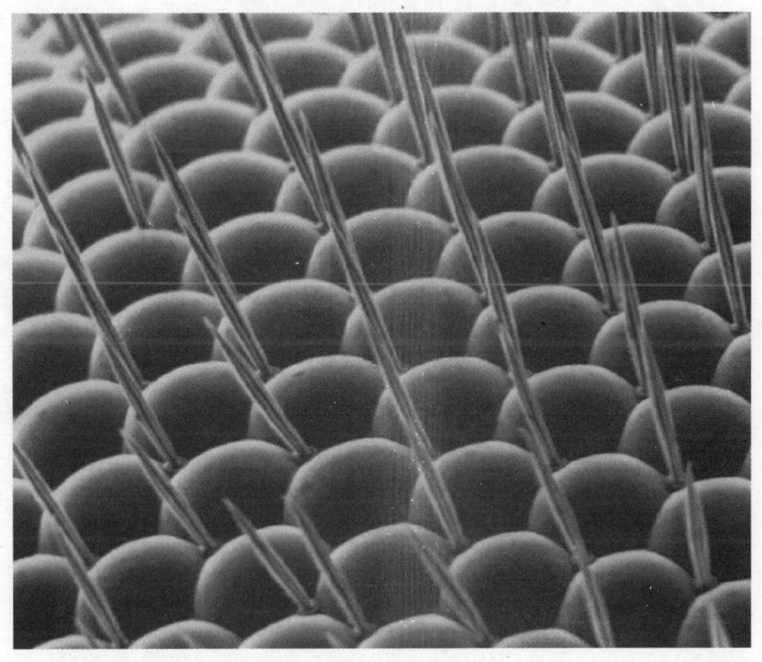

ABHIJIT MUKHERJEA
NEELA GHOSE

OXFORD
UNIVERSITY PRESS

YMCA Library Building, Jai Singh Road, New Delhi 110001

Oxford University Press is a department of the University of Oxford.
It furthers the University's objective of excellence in research, scholarship,
and education by publishing worldwide in

Oxford New York
Auckland Cape Town Dar es Salaam Hong Kong Karachi
Kuala Lumpur Madrid Melbourne Mexico City Nairobi
New Delhi Shanghai Taipei Toronto

With offices in
Argentina Austria Brazil Chile Czech Republic France Greece
Guatemala Hungary Italy Japan Poland Portugal Singapore
South Korea Switzerland Thailand Turkey Ukraine Vietnam

Oxford is a registered trade mark of Oxford University Press
in the UK and in certain other countries.

Published in India
by Oxford University Press

First published 2005
Second revised edition 2008
Ninth impression 2011

ISBN-13: 978-0-19-569056-9
ISBN-10: 0-19-569056-7

Illustrated by Amit John, Gigimon Scaria, Nilabho and Blackleads

The cover illustration (compound eye of a fruit fly)
Showcases the theme patterns in nature

Typeset in Baskerville MT
by innovative Processors, New Delhi 110 002
Printed in India by Print Shop Pvt. Ltd., Chennai 600096
and published by Oxford University Press
YMCA Library Building, Jai Singh Road, New Delhi 110001

Preface

Mathematics is a fascinating subject that has applications in many areas, especially in our day-to-day lives. It underlies processes and patterns in the world around us—the spherical shape of a soap bubble, the ripples on the surface of a pond, the fractal pattern of snowflakes, and the chaotic swirling of a hurricane are but a few examples.

New Guided Mathematics is a well-structured and child-friendly series that aims to draw children into the vibrant world of mathematics. The series aims to engage students in mathematics by providing real-life situations in topic explanations, solved examples, and exercises to ensure that the learner appreciates the applicability of mathematics. This new edition builds upon the strengths of the previous edition.

The key features of the books are listed below.

- Simple language and lively illustrations make the ideas more child-friendly.
- Everyday contexts in solved examples and exercises make students appreciate the need for mathematics.
- Carefully graded exercises are given for practice.
- *Revision exercises,* included after each chapter, provide additional practice.
- *Comprehensive Test Papers*, at the end of each book, prepare students for examination.
- Child-friendly comic strips relating to real-life situations are included at the beginning of each chapter (Classes 3–5).

This new edition has the following additional features.

- *Try this*, given alongside solved examples, tests comprehension of new topics.
- *Worksheets* have been included to provide hands-on practice.
- *Mental Maths*, within each chapter and at the end of each book, trains students to perform quick calculations.
- More numerical questions have been included to facilitate drills and the assignment of tasks for practice.

It is hoped that *New Guided Mathematics* will prove to be an enjoyable companion, as teachers and students proceed on their journey through numbers.

— Authors

Contents

LARGE NUMBERS

Let's Recap

1. Write the number in the expanded form.
   (a) 7814 = ____________________
   (b) 10532 = ____________________
   (c) 67391 = ____________________

2. Write the numbers shown on the following abacus.

(a)

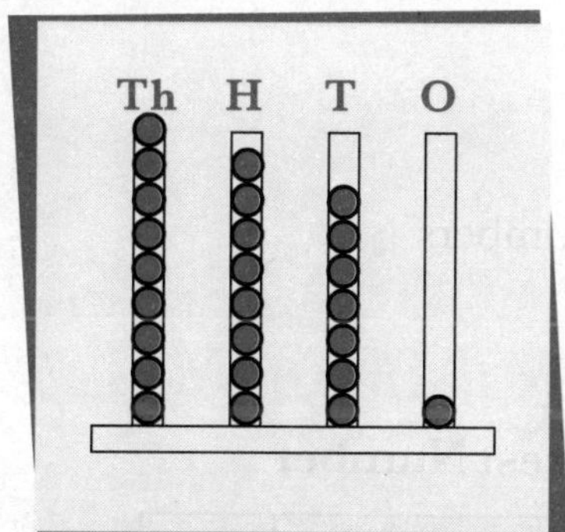

(b)

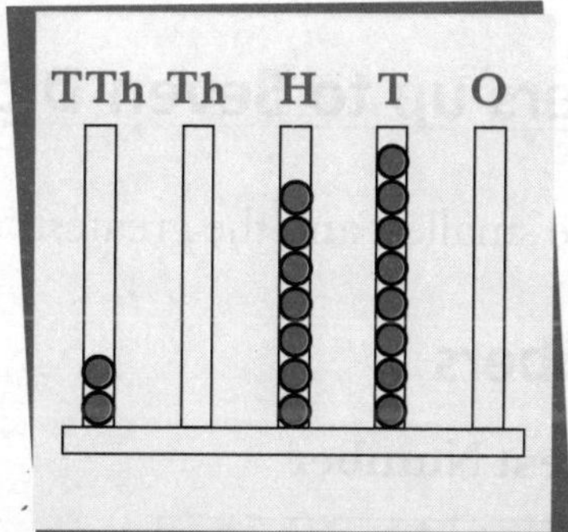

3. Write the place value and the face value of the coloured digits.

	Place Value	Face Value
(a) 23**4**9	________	________
(b) 8**9**43	________	________
(c) 1**3**462	________	________
(d) **5**2984	________	________

4. Arrange the following numbers in ascending order.
   (a) 7563, 7231, 7653, 8930; ____________________
   (b) 11023, 3012, 10123, 1213; ____________________

5. Arrange the following numbers in descending order.
   (a) 2109, 2561, 2980, 2190; ____________________
   (b) 64291, 4382, 4328, 25381; ____________________

Rahul and Priya were discussing their future plans.

Numbers up to Seven Digits

Let us look at the smallest and the greatest 5-, 6- and 7-digit numbers.

5-Digit Numbers

Smallest Number

TTh	Th	H	T	O
1	0	0	0	0

Greatest Number

TTh	Th	H	T	O
9	9	9	9	9

6-Digit Numbers

On adding 1 to the greatest 5-digit number, we get the smallest 6-digit number.

99999 + 1 = 100000. It is read as one lakh.

- One lakh has five zeroes.
- We write L to show the lakhs place in the place-value chart.

Smallest 6-digit Number

L	TTh	Th	H	T	O
1	0	0	0	0	0

In figures: 100000

In words: One lakh

Greatest 6-digit Number

L	TTh	Th	H	T	O
9	9	9	9	9	9

In figures: 999999

In words: Nine lakh, ninety-nine thousand, nine hundred and ninety-nine

7-Digit Numbers

On adding 1 to the greatest 6-digit number, we get the smallest 7-digit number.
999999 + 1 = 1000000. It is read as ten lakhs.

Smallest 7-digit Number

TL	L	TTh	Th	H	T	O
1	0	0	0	0	0	0

In figures: 1000000

In words: Ten lakhs

Greatest 7-digit Number

TL	L	TTh	Th	H	T	O
9	9	9	9	9	9	9

In figures: 9999999

In words: Ninety-nine lakh, ninety-nine thousand, nine hundred and ninety-nine

Some more 6- and 7-Digit Numbers

10000000 is the smallest 8-digit number. It is read as one crore.

Example 1: Write the numbers in words.

215267 = Two lakh fifteen thousand two hundred and sixty-seven.

4325315 = Forty-three lakh twenty-five thousand three hundred and fifteen.

Example 2: Write the numbers in figures.

Six lakh three thousand four hundred and twenty-two = 603422.

Twenty-five lakh eighty-five thousand six hundred and twenty = 2585620.

Try this!

Write the number in words.

564242 = ______________

____

Using an Abacus

Let us now represent large numbers on an abacus.

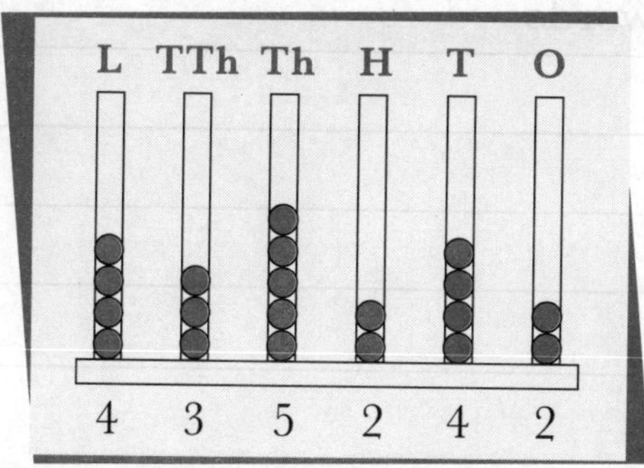

In figures: 435242

In words: Four lakh, thirty-five thousand, two hundred and forty-two

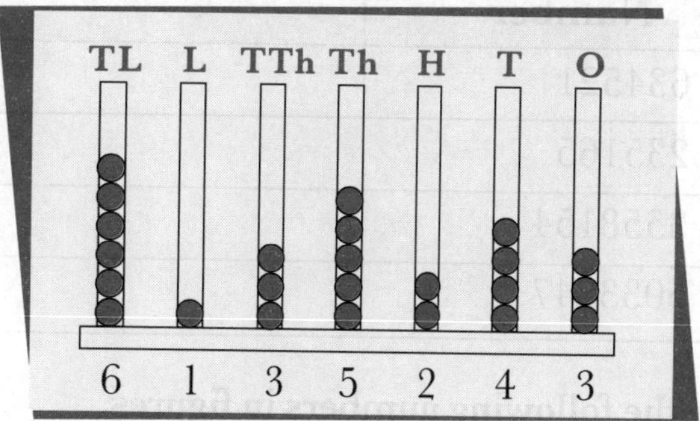

In figures: 6135243

In words: Sixty-one lakh, thirty-five thousand, two hundred and forty-three

Successors and Predecessors

The successor or the number coming just after a given number is 1 more than the given number.

The predecessor or the number coming just before a given number is 1 less than the given number.

To find the **successor** of a number, **add 1.**

To find the **predecessor** of a number, **subtract 1.**

Predecessor	Operation	Number	Operation	Successor
53613	53614 – 1	53614	53614 + 1	53615
638274	638275 – 1	638275	638275 + 1	638276
318518	318519 – 1	318519	318519 + 1	318520
9675009	9675010 – 1	9675010	9675010 + 1	9675011
3688499	3688500 – 1	3688500	3688500 + 1	3688501

Exercise 1.1

1. **Write the following numbers in figures and in words.**

Numbers	In figures	In words
(a) Greatest 5-digit number		
(b) Smallest 6-digit number		
(c) Smallest 7-digit number		
(d) Greatest 7-digit number		
(e) Greatest 6-digit number		

2. **Write the following numbers in words.**

Number	In words
(a) 634521	
(b) 235165	
(c) 3558154	
(d) 5033847	

3. **Write the following numbers in figures.**

Number	In figures
(a) Six lakh thirty-four thousand two hundred and five	
(b) Eight lakh seven thousand nine	
(c) Fifty-three lakh thirty thousand two hundred and forty-nine	
(d) Seventy-seven lakh seven hundred and seven	

4. **Write the number represented on the abacus in figures and in words.**

(a)

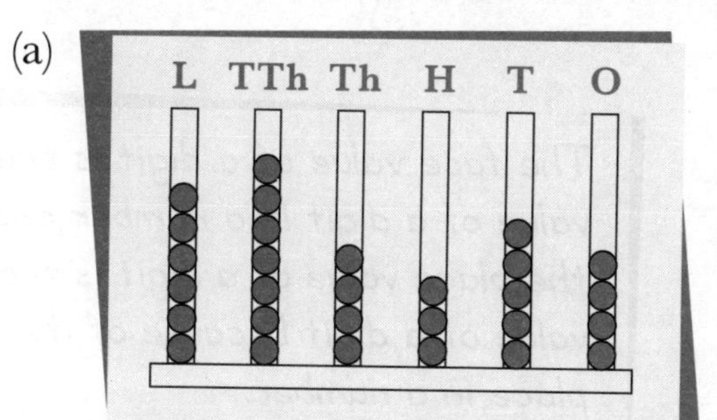

In figures: ____________________

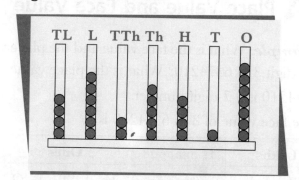

In words: ____________________

(b)

TL L TTh Th H T O

In figures: ____________________

In words: ____________________

5. **Draw beads on the abacus below to represent the following numbers.**

(a)

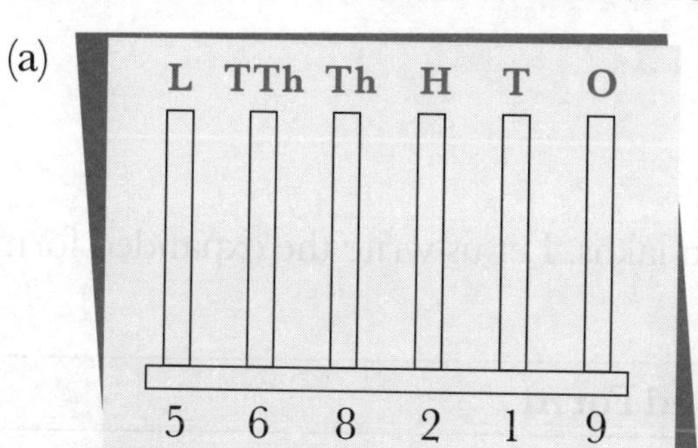

(b)

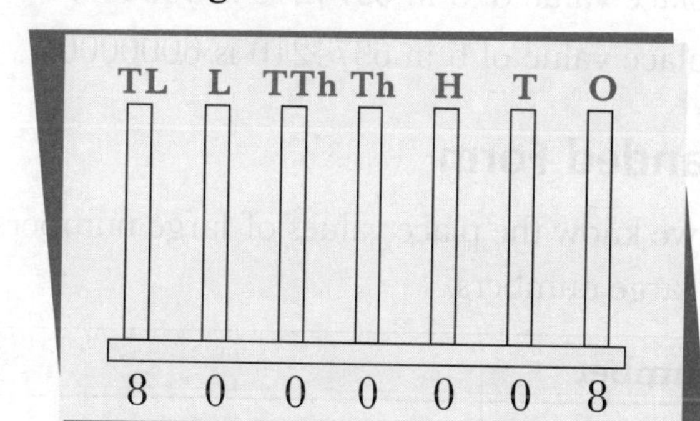

6. **Write the successor in each of the following.**

(a) 321896 ☐

(b) 7348719 ☐

(c) 399999 ☐

(d) 40000 ☐

(e) 867428 ☐

(f) 4875564 ☐

(g) 5689999 ☐

(h) 999999 ☐

7. **Write the predecessor in each of the following.**

(a) 76315 ☐

(b) 6921348 ☐

(c) 1300000 ☐

(d) 300001 ☐

(e) 8823936 ☐

(f) 3748210 ☐

(g) 4388888 ☐

(h) 2100008 ☐

8. **Complete the following series by observing the pattern.**

(a) 421340, 421342, 421344, __________, __________, __________

(b) 381220, 381240, 381260, __________, __________, __________

(c) 461100, 461200, 461300, __________, __________, __________

Place Value and Face Value

Example: What is the face value and the place value of the digit 3 in 6374210? What is the place value of 6?

6374210 is a 7-digit number.

The face value of 3 in 6374210 is 3.

Lakhs		Thousands		Ones		
TL	L	TTh	Th	H	T	O
6	3	7	4	2	1	0

Starting from the right, we see that 3 is in the lakhs place.

The place value of 3 in 6374210 is 300000.

The place value of 6 in 6374210 is 6000000.

The face value of a digit is the value of a digit in a number and the place value of a digit is the value of a digit because of its place in a number.

Expanded Form

Now we know the place values of large numbers upto ten lakhs. Let us write the expanded form of some large numbers.

Number	Expanded Form
56738	5 ten thousands + 6 thousands + 7 hundreds + 3 tens + 8 ones = 50000 + 6000 + 700 + 30 + 8
331421	3 lakhs + 3 ten thousands + 1 thousand + 4 hundreds + 2 tens + 1 one = 300000 + 30000 + 1000 + 400 + 20 + 1
4426798	4 ten lakhs + 4 lakhs + 2 ten thousands + 6 thousands + 7 hundreds + 9 tens + 8 ones = 4000000 + 400000 + 20000 + 6000 + 700 + 90 + 8
2066004	2 ten lakhs + 0 lakhs + 6 ten thousands + 6 thousands + 0 hundreds + 0 tens + 4 ones = 2000000 + 60000 + 6000 + 4
6327712	6 ten lakhs + 3 lakhs + 2 ten thousands + 7 thousands + 7 hundreds + 1 ten + 2 ones = 6000000 + 300000 + 20000 + 7000 + 700 + 10 + 2

Let us summarise:

10 ones = 1 ten	10000 tens = 1 lakh
1000 ones = 1 thousand	1000 hundreds = 1 lakh
1000 tens = 10 thousands	100 thousands = 1 lakh

Indian and International Place-Value Systems

When there are many digits in a number, it becomes confusing to read the number. To avoid mistakes while reading and writing large numbers, the numbers are broken up into **periods** separated by **commas** (,).

Large numbers can be broken up into periods using either the **Indian place-value system** or the **International place-value system.**

The periods are separated by inserting commas between them.

Indian Place-Value System

Periods →	Crores	Lakhs		Thousands		Ones		
Place Value →	Crores C	Ten Lakhs TL	Lakhs L	Ten Thousands TTh	Thousands Th	Hundreds H	Tens T	Ones O
Numbers ↓								
One								1
Ten							1	0
Hundred						1	0	0
1 Thousand					1,	0	0	0
10 Thousands				1	0,	0	0	0
1 Lakh			1,	0	0,	0	0	0
10 Lakhs		1	0,	0	0,	0	0	0
1 Crore	1,	0	0,	0	0,	0	0	0

International Place-Value System

Periods →	Millions		Thousands			Ones		
Place Value →	Ten Millions TM	One Million M	Hundred Thousands HT	Ten Thousands TTh	Thousands Th	Hundreds H	Tens T	Ones O
Numbers ↓								
One								1
Ten							1	0
Hundred						1	0	0
1 Thousand					1,	0	0	0
10 Thousands				1	0,	0	0	0
100 Thousands			1	0	0,	0	0	0
1 Million		1,	0	0	0,	0	0	0
10 Millions	1	0,	0	0	0,	0	0	0

Starting from the right side of the number, according to the Indian place-value system, the first period is the ones period consisting of three place values—ones, tens and hundreds. The other periods to the left of the ones period have two place values each. In the International place-value system all the periods have three place values each.

In the Indian and International place-value systems,

- a 4-digit number like 6438 is written as 6,438.
- a 5-digit number like 54369 is written as 54,369.

Let us now see how 6- and 7-digit numbers are written according to the Indian and International place-value systems.

Indian Place-Value System

Lakhs Period
(6- and 7-digit numbers)

Lakhs		Thousands		Ones			
TL	L	TTh	Th	H	T	O	
	1,	0	0,	0	0	0	1 lakh
1	0,	0	0,	0	0	0	10 lakhs

Examples:

A 6-digit number like 996342 is written as 9,96,342.

A 7-digit number like 6384291 is written as 63,84,291.

> *Try this!*
> *Insert commas according to Indian place-value system.*
> *(a) 165234*
> *(b) 5263108*

International Place-Value System

Millions Period
(6- and 7-digit numbers)

Millions		Thousands			Ones			
TM	M	HTh	TTh	Th	H	T	O	
		1	0	0,	0	0	0	100 thousand
	1,	0	0	0,	0	0	0	1 million

Examples:

A 6-digit number like 996342 is written as 996,342.

A 7-digit number like 6384291 is written as 6,384,291.

> *1 crore (10000000) is written as 1,00,00,000 in Indian place-value system and 10,000,000 in International place-value system.*

Here are a few examples to show how numbers are written on the Indian and the International place-value charts.

Indian Place-Value Chart

Number	Lakhs		Thousands		Ones			Number Name	Written as
	TL	L	TTh	Th	H	T	O		
9012				9	0	1	2	Nine thousand and twelve	9,012
24678			2	4	6	7	8	Twenty-four thousand, six hundred and seventy-eight	24,678

Number	Lakhs		Thousands		Ones			Number Name	Written as
	TL	L	TTh	Th	H	T	O		
164316		1	6	4	3	1	6	One lakh, sixty-four thousand, three hundred and sixteen	1,64,316
3000000	3	0	0	0	0	0	0	Thirty lakhs	30,00,000
2840089	2	8	4	0	0	8	9	Twenty-eight lakh, forty thousand and eighty-nine	28,40,089

International Place-Value Chart

Number	Millions	Thousands			Ones			Number Name	Written as
	M	HTh	TTh	Th	H	T	O		
6372				6	3	7	2	Six thousand, three hundred and seventy-two	6,372
878018		8	7	8	0	1	8	Eight hundred seventy-eight thousand and eighteen	878,018
7002501	7	0	0	2	5	0	1	Seven million two thousand, five hundred and one	7,002,501
9238016	9	2	3	8	0	1	6	Nine million, two hundred thirty-eight thousand and sixteen	9,238,016
4000000	4	0	0	0	0	0	0	Four million	4,000,000

For the purpose of learning, in this book we will follow the Indian place-value system.

Exercise 1.2

1. **Write the following numbers in the Indian place-value chart given below.**

Number	Lakhs		Thousands		Ones		
	TL	L	TTh	Th	H	T	O
(a) 63789							
(b) 700184							
(c) 317042							
(d) 8463921							
(e) 6207581							

2. **Write the following numbers in the International place-value chart given below.**

Number	Millions	Thousands			Ones		
	M	HTh	TTh	Th	H	T	O
(a) 378921							
(b) 600000							
(c) 505050							
(d) 1738492							
(e) 2381710							

3. **Fill in the blanks.**

(a) 1 million = __________ lakhs.

(b) 70 lakhs = __________ million.

(c) 3 hundred thousands = __________ lakhs.

(d) 26 lakhs = __________ million __________ hundred thousands.

4. **Put commas to break up the following numbers into periods and write them in words according to the Indian place-value system.**

(a) 1873 __________ (b) 29365 __________ (c) 632786 __________

(d) 7342630 __________ (e) 5498139 __________ (f) 4210367 __________

5. **Put commas to break up the following numbers into periods and write them in words according to the International place-value system.**

(a) 3490 __________ (b) 88314 __________ (c) 378177 __________

(d) 653210 __________ (e) 1789360 __________ (f) 7304059 __________

6. **Write the face value and the place value of the digit 3 and the period it belongs to in the following numbers.**

	Face Value	Place Value	Period
(a) 6,96,347	3	300	Ones
(b) 3,80,172			
(c) 2,38,491			
(d) 3,95,476			
(e) 47,00,853			
(f) 53,04,658			

7. **Write the following numbers in expanded form.**

Number	Expanded Form
(a) 68,481	
(b) 5,23,784	
(c) 9,65,412	
(d) 7,51,314	
(e) 13,41,187	
(f) 68,00,218	
(g) 41,29,703	
(h) 39,61,455	
(i) 80,36,000	
(j) 8,67,000	

8. **Fill in the blanks for the following conversions.**

(a) 10 thousands = ________ tens.
(b) 1000 thousands = ________ lakhs.
(c) 1 lakh = ________ tens.
(d) 1000 tens = ________ thousands.
(e) 10,000 hundreds = ________ lakhs.
(f) 10,00,000 ones = ________ lakhs.

Comparison of Numbers

Recollect the checklist for comparison of numbers.

1. The number with more digits is the greater number.
2. The number that comes later in the number line is the greater number.
3. The number with the greater digit in the same place is the greater number.

Example 1: Compare the numbers 63,89,210 and 2,16,430.

First, write the periods and place value of the numbers.

Lakhs		Thousands		Ones		
TL	L	TTh	Th	H	T	O
6	3	8	9	2	1	0
	2	1	6	4	3	0

The number 63,89,210 has more digits than 2,16,430. So, it is the greater number.

Thus, 63,89,210 > 2,16,430.

Example 2: Compare the numbers 8,71,263 and 8,71,491.

First, write the periods and place value of the numbers.

Lakhs		Thousands		Ones		
TL	L	TTh	Th	H	T	O
	8	7	1	2	6	3
	8	7	1	4	9	1

Both the numbers have the same number of digits.

So we start from the left and compare the digits until we find two digits that are different. We then compare them to decide which is the smaller or the greater number.

8 7 1 2 6 3

8 7 1 4 9 1

Same ← (8 7 1)   (2, 4) → Different

As 2 < 4,   8,71,263 < 8,71,491   *or*   8,71,491 > 8,71,263

Try this!
Fill in the box with < or >.
2,52,461 ☐ 2,52,468

Some More Examples:

85,23,161 > 5,31,185   2,36,787 < 4,38,213

52,13,181 > 52,13,157   5,65,128 > 5,65,127

Ordering of Numbers

Let us arrange the numbers 1,73,281; 1,83,821; 1,37,128; 1,32,723; 1,38,712 and 1,78,213 in ascending and descending order.

First, let us write the periods and place value of the numbers.

Lakhs		Thousands		Ones		
TL	L	TTh	Th	H	T	O
	1	7	3	2	8	1
	1	8	3	8	2	1
	1	3	7	1	2	8
	1	3	2	7	2	3
	1	3	8	7	1	2
	1	7	8	2	1	3

Since all the numbers are 6-digit numbers, the place values of the digits are compared.

1. We begin with the **lakhs** place. All the numbers have the digit 1 in the lakhs place.
2. We move to the digits in the **ten thousands** place.
   The smallest digit is 3. The numbers with the digit 3 in the **ten thousands** place are: 1,37,128; 1,32,723; 1,38,712.
3. We then compare the digits in the **thousands** place of these numbers. The smallest digit is 2 in 1,32,723. So, the smallest number is 1,32,723.
4. Similarly, we find the next smallest number. Thus the numbers in ascending order are:
   1,32,723; 1,37,128; 1,38,712; 1,73,281; 1,78,213; 1,83,821

For arranging the digits in descending order, start and look for the greatest digit in the ten thousands place, then the thousands place and so on. So, the numbers in descending order are: 1,83,821; 1,78,213; 1,73,281; 1,38,712; 1,37,128; 1,32,723

Example: Arrange the numbers 1,75,623; 2,35,421; 1,46,381 and 3,56,421 in descending order.

Lakhs		Thousands		Ones		
TL	L	TTh	Th	H	T	O
	1	7	5	6	2	3
	2	3	5	4	2	1
	1	4	6	3	8	1
	3	5	6	4	2	1

Following the steps given above, the numbers in descending order are:

3,56,421; 2,35,421; 1,75,623; 1,46,381

Arrangement of Digits

Arrange the digits from 1 to 7 to make the greatest and the smallest 7-digit numbers without repetition of digits.

1. Since repetition of digits is not allowed, starting from the left, we write the greatest digit available to make the greatest number possible.

TL	L	TTh	Th	H	T	O
7	6	5	4	3	2	1

So, the greatest number is 76,54,321.

2. Since repetition of digits is not allowed, starting from the left, we write the smallest digit available.

TL	L	TTh	Th	H	T	O
1	2	3	4	5	6	7

So, the smallest number is 12,34,567.

When repetition of digits is not allowed,
- to write the greatest number possible, write the digits in descending order.
- to write the smallest number possible, write the digits in ascending order.

Exercise 1.3

1. Fill in the boxes with > or < to compare the numbers.

(a) 8,72,694 ☐ 88,72,694 (b) 75,38,101 ☐ 99,999

(c) 3,37,228 ☐ 3,73,828 (d) 78,36,174 ☐ 78,36,274

(e) 2,38,961 ☐ 2,39,816 (f) 52,86,419 ☐ 52,68,149

2. **Encircle the smallest number in each of the following.**

(a) 8,59,614; 2,99,510; 7,36,512; 5,37,816; 4,28,917

(b) 17,645; 2,93,168; 2,99,587; 29,27,456; 65,847

(c) 21,46,846; 12,64,486; 21,64,486; 12,46,846; 21,64,846

3. **Encircle the largest number in each of the following.**

(a) 9,69,543; 9,96,453; 9,69,453; 9,69,345; 9,96,543

(b) 3,74,357; 5,86,145; 1,99,065; 4,63,888; 27,01,010

(c) 72,85,306; 7,28,536; 7,28,530; 72,58,360; 78,25,306

4. **Arrange the following numbers in ascending order.**

(a) 3,33,333; 33,333; 33,33,333; 3,33,033; 33,03,303

____

(b) 7,25,845; 7,25,548; 7,25,854; 7,25,584; 7,25,485

____

(c) 8,12,939; 7,37,241; 7,98,147; 8,92,347; 8,21,120

____

(d) 54,52,761; 45,22,671; 55,22,176; 54,52,716; 44,25,617

____

5. **Arrange the following numbers in descending order.**

(a) 6,83,576; 6,83,657; 6,83,675; 6,83,567; 6,83,765

____

(b) 76,88,462; 73,88,462; 79,88,462; 75,88,462; 77,88,462

____

(c) 78,93,174; 38,71,348; 29,84,562; 8,36,245; 2,76,209

____

6. **Write the greatest and the smallest 6-digit numbers possible by using the following digits only once.**

	Greatest	Smallest
(a) 6, 8, 7, 5, 4, 1	____________	____________
(b) 9, 3, 2, 4, 0, 7	____________	____________

7. **Write the greatest and the smallest 7-digit numbers possible by using the following digits only once.**

	Greatest	Smallest
(a) 4, 2, 9, 3, 8, 6, 1	____________	____________
(b) 5, 0, 7, 4, 3, 6, 2	____________	____________

Revision Exercise

Do these sums in your notebook.

1 Write the numbers with commas according to the Indian place-value system.

(a) 563249 (b) 3862539 (c) 5632738 (d) 9875432

2 Write the numbers with commas according to the International place-value system.

(a) 326542 (b) 8432124 (c) 756329 (d) 6321825

3 Write the following in words according to the Indian place-value system.

(a) 6,73,429 (b) 5,86,321 (c) 45,32,655 (d) 22,35,001

4 Write the following in words according to the International place-value system.

(a) 353,429 (b) 7,652,312 (c) 1,605,595 (d) 135,681

5 Write the place value of 5 in each of the following numbers.

(a) 5,18,237 (b) 4,53,621 (c) 52,31,023 (d) 15,27,008

6 Write the predecessor and the successor in each of the following.

(a) 2,18,375 (b) 3,64,008 (c) 99,99,995 (d) 89,36,779

7 Write the greatest and the smallest number in each of the following list.

(a) 2,28,412; 3,25,152; 42,13,532; 36,83,129; 3,32,521

(b) 58,62,301; 8,52,800; 63,25,012; 31,92,409; 1,86,006

8 Arrange the following numbers in ascending order.

(a) 1,75,423; 7,12,432; 3,42,171; 4,32,711; 4,32,117

(b) 32,41,500; 41,32,005; 50,03,224; 30,61,003; 31,60,421

9 Arrange the following numbers in descending order.

(a) 3,14,278; 3,00,142; 2,40,001; 6,29,508; 3,42,106

(b) 67,42,000; 31,80,003; 52,19,620; 30,08,217; 25,08,669

10 Arrange the following digits to make the greatest and the smallest 6-digit numbers possible without repeating any digit.

(a) 3, 8, 7, 5, 4, 2 (b) 8, 3, 0, 5, 2, 6 (c) 5, 3, 6, 2, 0, 9 (d) 7, 9, 5, 8, 3, 2

11 Arrange the following digits to make the greatest and the smallest 7-digit number possible without repeating any digit.

(a) 7, 1, 0, 5, 8, 6, 2 (b) 3, 2, 4, 1, 9, 8, 5 (c) 2, 0, 6, 7, 5, 4, 3 (d) 9, 1, 6, 7, 4, 0, 3

12 What is 1 more than the greatest 7-digit number?

13 What is 1 less than the smallest 6-digit number?

ROMAN NUMERALS

The two friends (Rahul and Priya) decided to visit a zoo. On their way to pick up their friend Rohan, they passed a village fair.

Roman Numerals

The ten digits 0, 1, 2, 3, 4, 5, 6, 7, 8 and 9 that we are familiar with, are called Hindu–Arabic numerals. The Hindu–Arabic numeral system uses these ten digits to make all other numerals. These numerals are also called international numbers.

In this chapter we will learn about the Roman system of numeration. The Romans had seven basic symbols represented by the following letters:

Roman	I	V	X	L	C	D	M
Hindu–Arabic	1	5	10	50	100	500	1000

The Romans did not have a symbol to represent the digit 0. They used a combination of the above given letters to build all other numbers.

Rules for Forming Roman Numerals

Rule 1: When the same symbol is repeated one after the other, the product of the value of the symbol and the number of times it is repeated is the value of the numeral.

III = 1 × 3 = 3
XX = 10 × 2 = 20

Exception:

The symbols V, L and D are never repeated. So if we want to write 10 in Roman numerals, we use the symbol X (and not VV). Similarly, if we want to write 100 or 1000 in Roman numerals, we use the symbols C and M, respectively (and not LL or DD).

Rule 2: If a symbol is written to the right of another symbol (i.e., after the symbol) of greater value, the value of the numeral is the **sum** of the values of the symbols.

VI = 5 + 1 = 6

VIII = 5 + 1 + 1 + 1 = 8

XXVIII = 10 + 10 + 5 + 1 + 1 + 1 = 28

Rule 3: If a symbol is written to the left of another symbol (i.e., before the symbol) of greater value, the value of the numeral is the **difference** of the values of the symbols.

IV = 5 – 1 = 4

IX = 10 – 1 = 9

Rule 4: If the symbols are combined, the value of a symbol of smaller value in the middle of two symbols of greater values is **subtracted** from the value of the symbol on its right.

XIV = 10 + (5 – 1)

= 10 + 4

= 14

(Here both X and V have greater values than I. So the value of I is subtracted from V, which is to its right. The difference is added to the value of the numeral to the left. So the value of IV = 5 – 1 = 4. Now, add 10 and 4; 10 + 4 = 14.)

XXIX = 10 + 10 + (10 – 1) = 10 + 10 + 9 = 29

Remember!

- *A letter can be repeated up to a maximum of three times only.*
- *A symbol of smaller value can be written to the left of the symbol of greater value only once. So Roman numerals can never be IIV or IIIX.*

Exercise 2.1

A. Complete the tables.

1	I	1
2	II	1 + 1
3	III	1 + 1 + 1
4	IV	5 – 1
5	V	5
6	VI	5 + 1
7	VII	
8	VIII	
9	IX	10 – 1
10	X	
11	XI	10 + 1
12		
13		
14	XIV	10 + 4
15		
16		
17		
18		
19	XIX	10 + 9
20	XX	10 + 10

21	XXI	10 + 10 + 1
22		
23		
24		
25		
26	XXVI	10 + 10 + 6
27		
28		
29		
30	XXX	
31		
32		
33		
34		
35		
36		
37	XXXVII	10 + 10 + 10 + 7
38		
39		
40	XL	

B. Write the corresponding Roman numerals.

(a) 7 ☐ (b) 18 ☐ (c) 25 ☐

(d) 30 ☐ (e) 49 ☐ (f) 100 ☐

C. Write the corresponding Hindu–Arabic numerals.

(a) VI ☐ (b) IX ☐ (c) XXV ☐

(d) XXVII ☐ (e) X ☐ (f) LXI ☐

Revision Exercise

Do these sums in your notebook.

1 Match the Hindu–Arabic numerals to the Roman numerals of the same value.

Roman Numerals	Hindu–Arabic Numerals
IX	36
XX	23
VII	32
XXVIII	18
XVIII	7
XXXII	14
XIV	28
XXIII	9
XXXVI	20

2 Write the corresponding Hindu–Arabic numeral for the following Roman numerals.

(a) IV (b) XXXV (c) XII (d) XL
(e) III (f) XIX (g) XXIV (h) XXXVI

3 Write the corresponding Roman numeral for the following Hindu–Arabic numerals.

(a) 8 (b) 27 (c) 15 (d) 35
(e) 19 (f) 11 (g) 32 (h) 10

4 Put $<$ or $>$ signs to compare the following Roman numerals.

(a) IX [$<$] XI (b) XV [ ] XX
(c) XXX [ ] XL (d) C [ ] D
(e) L [ ] C (f) M [ ] D

5 Which of the following are not Roman numerals as their combination of symbols is against the rules?

(a) IIIX (b) XIII (c) VIII (d) IIV
(e) VVI (f) LLII (g) XXI (h) VXV

6 Tick the correct Roman numeral for the following Hindu–Arabic numerals.

(a) We write the number 4 as: IIII [ ] IV [✓]
(b) We write the number 9 as: VIIII [ ] IX [ ]
(c) We write the number 14 as: XIV [ ] XIIII [ ]
(d) We write the number 29 as: XXVIIII [ ] XXIX [ ]
(e) We write the number 40 as: XL [ ] XXXX [ ]

ADDITION AND SUBTRACTION

Let's Recap

1. Fill in the boxes.

(a) 1,435 + 0 = ☐

(b) 58,699 + 1 = ☐

(c) 1 + 78,645 = 78,645 + ☐

(d) 4,790 + 3,865 = 3,865 + ☐

(e) 56,836 – 1 = ☐

(f) 9,743 – 0 = ☐

(g) 48,769 – 0 = ☐

Do you remember?

```
  7 5 2 ⟶ Addend
+ 2 3 4 ⟶ Addend
  9 8 6 ⟶ Sum

  8 6 9 ⟶ Minuend
– 3 5 6 ⟶ Subtrahend
  5 1 3 ⟶ Difference
```

2. Add the following.

(a)
```
  Th H T O
   3 2 5 1
 + 4 0 3 6
```
(b)
```
  Th H T O
   2 4 1 6
 + 7 3 4 3
```
(c)
```
  Th H T O
   6 8 0 4
 + 3 6 8 7
```
(d)
```
  Th H T O
   4 1 6 9
 + 4 5 1 0
```
(e)
```
  TTh Th H T O
     2  5 3 2 6
 +   3  1 4 3 0
```
(f)
```
  TTh Th H T O
     3  4 6 9 2
 +   1  3 4 2 9
```
(g)
```
  TTh Th H T O
     2  5 2 6 8
 +   4  2 9 7 5
```
(h)
```
  TTh Th H T O
        4 1 0 2
 +   4  0 5 8 8
 +   3  9 6 9 3
```

3. Subtract the following.

(a)
```
  Th H T O
   6 1 4 5
 – 2 0 2 3
```
(b)
```
  Th H T O
   9 7 5 8
 – 3 5 4 7
```
(c)
```
  Th H T O
   2 7 5 8
 – 1 8 6 7
```
(d)
```
  Th H T O
   5 2 7 1
 – 3 8 4 3
```
(e)
```
  TTh Th H T O
     7  7 2 9 9
 –   3  7 2 2 3
```
(f)
```
  TTh Th H T O
     5  1 2 4 6
 –   2  0 1 4 3
```
(g)
```
  TTh Th H T O
     3  7 5 2 3
 –   2  9 2 8 4
```
(h)
```
  TTh Th H T O
     4  3 5 6 1
 –   1  6 8 8 2
```

Priya and Rahul are on their way to Rohan's house.

Addition of Large Numbers

To add large numbers, the addends are arranged in columns according to the place values of the digits.

Addition without Carrying

Example 1: Add 3,24,012 and 73,952

	L	TTh	Th	H	T	O
	3	2	4	0	1	2
+		7	3	9	5	2
	3	9	7	9	6	4

Thus, 3,24,012 + 73,952 = 3,97,964

Example 2: Add 1,00,000 and 10,000

	L	TTh	Th	H	T	O
	1	0	0	0	0	0
+		1	0	0	0	0
	1	1	0	0	0	0

Thus, 1,00,000 + 10,000 = 1,10,000

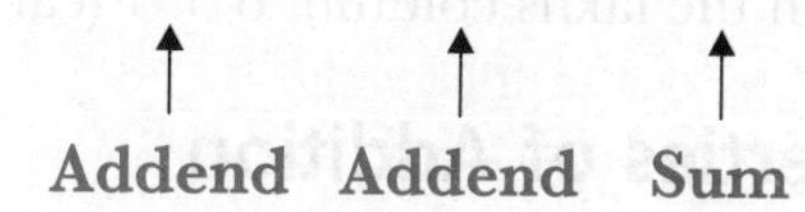

Example 3: Fill in the correct digits in the boxes.

	L	TTh	Th	H	T	O
	2	8	7	1	3	4
+		0	1	7		
	3		8	8	8	7

> *On adding two addends we get the sum*
> *or, addend 1 + addend 2 = sum*
> *This can be written as:*
> *sum – addend 1 = addend 2*
> *or sum – addend 2 = addend 1*

In the **ones** column, 7 – 4 = **3**

In the **tens** column, 8 – 3 = **5**

In the **ten thousands** column, 8 + 0 = **8**

In the **lakhs** column, 3 – 2 = **1**

	L	TTh	Th	H	T	O
	2	8	7	1	3	4
+	[1]	0	1	7	[5]	[3]
	3	[8]	8	8	8	7

Addition with Carrying

Example 1: Add 6,42,791 and 3,37,286

	L	TTh	Th	H	T	O
		(1)	(1)	(1)		
	6	4	2	7	9	1
+	3	3	7	2	8	6
	9	8	0	0	7	7

Thus, 6,42,791 + 3,37,286 = 9,80,077

Example 2: Add: 1,87,632 + 24,715 + 82,163

	L	TTh	Th	H	T	O
	(1)	(1)	(1)	(1)	(1)	
	1	8	7	6	3	2
+		2	4	7	1	5
+		8	2	1	6	3
	2	9	4	5	1	0

Thus, 1,87,632 + 24,715 + 82,163 = 2,94,510

Example 3: Fill in the correct digits in the boxes.

	8	5	9	7	6	5
	+	[ ]	3	[ ]	5	[ ]
	[ ]	4	3	3	2	3

Try this!

Add

```
  3 4 2 1 6 7
+ 2 7 8 8 9 5
```

In the ones column, 3 < 5. So, 13 – 5 = **8**

Thus, in the tens column, 6 + 5 + 1 (carried over) = 12. *1 is carried over to the hundreds column.* Now, 3 < (7 + 1) or 3 < 8. So, in the hundreds column, 13 – 8 = **5**. Thus, in the thousands column, 9 + 3 + 1 (carried over) = **13**. *1 is carried over to the ten thousands column.*

Now, 4 < (5 + 1) or 4 < 6.

So, in the ten thousands column, sum – addend = 14 – 6 = **8**

Thus, in the lakhs column, 8 + 1 (carried over) = **9**

	L	TTh	Th	H	T	O
	(1)	(1)	(1)	(1)	(1)	
	8	5	9	7	6	5
+		[8]	3	[5]	5	[8]
	[9]	4	3	3	2	3

Properties of Addition

1. Changing the order of adding the addends does not change the sum.

Example:

```
  6 3 7 1 2 8          1 8 9 3 4 6
+ 1 8 9 3 4 6   →    + 6 3 7 1 2 8
  8 2 6 4 7 4    =     8 2 6 4 7 4
```

So, 6,37,128 + 1,89,346 = 8,26,474 = 1,89,346 + 6,37,128.

2. **Changing the grouping of numbers when adding more than two numbers does not change the sum.**

Example: Add 27,385; 14,716 and 35,028

(i) *Step 1:* Add 27,385 and 14,716

	2	7	3	8	5
+	1	4	7	1	6
	4	2	1	0	1

Step 2: Add 35,028 to the sum

	4	2	1	0	1
+	3	5	0	2	8
	7	7	1	2	9

So, 27,385 + 14,716 + 35,028 = 77,129

(ii) *Step 1:* Add 27,385 and 35,028

	2	7	3	8	5
+	3	5	0	2	8
	6	2	4	1	3

Step 2: Add 14,716 to the sum

	6	2	4	1	3
+	1	4	7	1	6
	7	7	1	2	9

So, 27,385 + 35,028 + 14,718 = 77,129

(iii) *Step 1:* Add 14,716 and 35,028

	1	4	7	1	6
+	3	5	0	2	8
	4	9	7	4	4

Step 2: Add 27,385 to the sum

	4	9	7	4	4
+	2	7	3	8	5
	7	7	1	2	9

So, 14,716 + 35,028 + 27,385 = 77,129

We see that,

(27,385 + 14,716) + 35,028

= (27,385 + 35,028) + 14,716

= (14,716 + 35,028) + 27,385 = 77,129

Try this!

Fill in the boxes.

(a) 2,56,789 + 8,74,302 = ☐ + 2,56,789

(b) 8,92,030 + ☐ = 8,92,030

3. **Adding zero to a number gives the number itself.**

Example: 5,18,064 + 0 = 5,18,064

Exercise 3.1

1. **Add the following.**

(a)

	L	TTh	Th	H	T	O
	1	4	0	3	5	7
+	6	4	8	6	3	2

(b)

	L	TTh	Th	H	T	O
	2	5	4	3	2	6
+		3	2	5	1	7

(c)

	L	TTh	Th	H	T	O
	2	6	4	8	1	9
+		7	9	6	3	6

(d)

	L	TTh	Th	H	T	O
	3	9	8	7	4	9
+	1	4	6	3	8	6

(e)

	L	TTh	Th	H	T	O
	5	6	4	2	4	3
+		1	3	5	2	6

(f)

	L	TTh	Th	H	T	O
	6	2	8	4	3	2
+	3	1	0	4	4	6

2. Add the following.

(a)

	L	TTh	Th	H	T	O
	1	6	7	3	9	4
+	2	4	1	5	7	3
+	4	0	8	9	2	0

(b)

	L	TTh	Th	H	T	O
	6	9	8	1	4	6
+			2	3	7	8
+		4	6	1	3	5
+	2	5	3	2	1	0

(c)

	L	TTh	Th	H	T	O
	6	2	3	8	1	6
+		3	8	2	4	3
+		6	6	8	1	7

(d)

	L	TTh	Th	H	T	O
	1	8	2	4	3	8
+	3	2	5	6	7	4
+		6	8	6	3	4

(e)

	L	TTh	Th	H	T	O
	3	4	6	3	9	1
+	5	2	1	8	7	0
+		1	8	0	0	5

(f)

	L	TTh	Th	H	T	O
	6	5	6	1	3	4
+	2	3	2	1	5	1
+		1	1	2	4	3

3. Fill in the missing numbers in the boxes.

(a) 2,87,643 + 6,93,210 = □ + 2,87,643

(b) 7,96,310 + 1,49,812 = 1,49,812 + □

(c) (36,789 + 44,952) + 71,164 = 36,789 + (□ + 71,164)

(d) 4,38,691 + (2,87,346 + 1,60,079) = (4,38,691 + 2,87,346) + □

(e) 6,87,140 + □ = 6,87,140

(f) □ + 0 = 7,79,346

4. Fill in the missing digits to complete the following additions.

(a)

	TTh	Th	H	T	O
	6	8	7	3	5
+	□	1	□	4	□
	9	□	8	7	5

(b)

	L	TTh	Th	H	T	O
	3	2	6	1	0	4
+	4	□	□	3	2	□
	7	9	9	4	2	6

(c)

	TTh	Th	H	T	O
	2	0	0	0	0
+	□	1	□	3	□
	6	1	5	3	2

(d)

	TTh	Th	H	T	O
	4	3	□	1	9
+	1	□	2	0	3
+	1	7	4	□	6
	□	6	2	5	□

Subtraction of Large Numbers

To subtract large numbers, the minuend and subtrahend are arranged in columns according to the place values of the digits. Like in addition, we always start from the ones place.

Subtraction without Borrowing

Example 1: Subtract 2,14,054 from 6,85,398

	L	TTh	Th	H	T	O
	6	8	5	3	9	8
–	2	1	4	0	5	4
	4	7	1	3	4	4

Thus, 6,85,398 – 2,14,054 = 4,71,344

Minuend Subtrahend Difference

Example 2: Subtract 3,21,307 from 6,73,948

	L	TTh	Th	H	T	O
	6	7	3	9	4	8
–	3	2	1	3	0	7
	3	5	2	6	4	1

Thus, 6,73,948 – 3,21,307 = 3,52,641

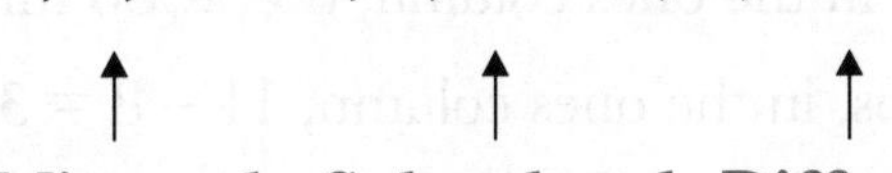

Minuend Subtrahend Difference

Example 3: Fill in the correct digits in the boxes.

	TTh	Th	H	T	O
	3	7	9	8	6
–	2	□	4	□	□
	1	5	5	4	2

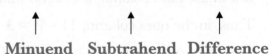

minuend – subtrahend = difference
or, difference + subtrahend = minuend
or, minuend – difference = subtrahend

In the **ones** column, 6 – 2 = 4

In the **tens** column, 8 – 4 = 4

In the **thousands** column, 7 – 5 = 2

	TTh	Th	H	T	O
	3	7	9	8	6
–	2	2	4	4	4
	1	5	5	4	2

Subtraction with Borrowing

Example 1: Subtract 1,82,645 from 3,24,378

Arrange the minuend and subtrahend in columns according to the place values of the digits.

	L	TTh	Th	H	T	O
	(2)	(12)	(3)	(13)		
	~~3~~	~~2~~	~~4~~	~~3~~	7	8
–	1	8	2	6	4	5
	1	4	1	7	3	3

Thus, 3,24,378 – 1,82,645 = 1,41,733

Example 2: Subtract 38,747 from 1,00,000

Arrange the minuend and subtrahend in columns according to the place values of the digits.

	L	TTh	Th	H	T	O
		(9)	(9)	(9)	(9)	(10)
	1	~~0~~	~~0~~	~~0~~	~~0~~	~~0~~
–		3	8	7	4	7
		6	1	2	5	3

Thus, 1,00,000 – 38,747 = 61,253

Example 3: Fill in the correct digits in the boxes.

	L	TTh	Th	H	T	O
	2	6	3	4	5	1
–		☐	2	☐	7	☐
	☐	7	1	3	7	8

Try this!

Subtract

6	7	3	2	5	0
– 2	4	5	0	7	1

We know, minuend – difference = subtrahend

But in the ones column, 8 > 1. So minuend must be 11 with 10 ones borrowed from 5 tens.

Thus, in the ones column, 11 – 8 = **3**

The tens column has also borrowed 10 tens from 4 hundreds and that is how 14 – 7 = **7**

In the hundreds column, 3 – 3 = **0**

In the ten thousands column, 6 < 7. So the minuend must be 16 ten thousands with 10 ten thousands borrowed from 2 lakhs.

Thus, in the ten thousands column, 16 – 7 = **9**

In the lakhs column, the minuend has 2 – 1 = **1** lakh left

	L	TTh	Th	H	T	O
	(1)	(16)		(3)	(14)	(11)
	~~2~~	~~6~~	3	~~4~~	~~5~~	~~1~~
–		9	2	0	7	3
	1	7	1	3	7	8

Try this!

Fill in the blank spaces.

5	6	3	2	7	3
– _	_	_	_	_	_
2	3	0	1	5	2

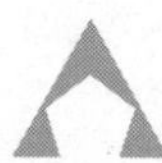

Addition and Subtraction Together

Look at the following example.

Example: 5,63,218 + 1,88,395 – 3,56,719

Step 1:

	L	TTh	Th	H	T	O
	5	6	3	2	1	8
+	1	8	8	3	9	5
	7	5	1	6	1	3

Step 2:

	L	TTh	Th	H	T	O
	7	5	1	6	1	3
–	3	5	6	7	1	9
	3	9	4	8	9	4

Thus, 5,63,218 + 1,88,395 – 3,56,719 = 3,94,894

Try this!

Add and subtract

```
  6 2 3 0 5 3
+ 2 0 8 3 9 6

– 3 5 2 0 7 8
```

Exercise 3.2

1. Subtract the following.

(a)

	L	TTh	Th	H	T	O
	5	7	3	6	8	5
–	3	1	1	5	3	2

(b)

	L	TTh	Th	H	T	O
	6	8	8	9	4	6
–	5	1	4	5	0	4

(c)

	L	TTh	Th	H	T	O
	8	9	7	5	8	6
–	3	6	3	2	5	4

(d)

	L	TTh	Th	H	T	O
	2	7	6	5	9	5
–		4	5	1	6	3

(e)

	L	TTh	Th	H	T	O
	5	7	9	6	8	4
–	2	5	4	3	7	0

(f)

	L	TTh	Th	H	T	O
	8	7	7	5	8	2
–	2	2	3	2	6	8

(g)

	L	TTh	Th	H	T	O
	7	3	8	4	2	3
–	4	1	5	9	3	5

(h)

	L	TTh	Th	H	T	O
	7	4	5	1	7	3
–	2	6	8	7	7	9

(i)

	L	TTh	Th	H	T	O
	6	3	1	8	4	7
–	2	1	0	8	5	9

(j)

	L	TTh	Th	H	T	O
	5	3	5	6	6	4
–	2	4	7	6	8	6

(k)

	L	TTh	Th	H	T	O
	6	0	0	0	0	0
–	3	7	5	0	0	0

(l)

	L	TTh	Th	H	T	O
	9	8	5	0	0	0
–	4	1	8	5	2	7

2. Subtract the following. *(Do these sums in your notebook.)*

(a) 3,78,943 – 1,26,712 (b) 57,128 – 25,017 (c) 4,73,581 – 96,329

(d) 6,38,000 – 5,69,000 (e) 6,83,129 – 4,15,073 (f) 1,00,000 – 73,278

(g) 9,00,000 – 5,98,347 (h) 5,37,689 – 2,12,267 (i) 8,57,128 – 2,50,174

3. Add and then subtract the following. *(Do these sums in your notebook.)*

(a) 3,00,000 + 30,000 – 1,00,000 (b) 5,50,000 + 50,000 – 1,10,000

(c) 2,80,000 + 80,000 – 1,20,000 (d) 3,50,000 + 35,000 – 53,000

(e) 63,500 + 1,54,505 – 98,000 (f) 2,11,540 + 3,24,800 – 4,00,000

(g) 5,62,399 + 1,24,851 – 2,05,565 (h) 3,65,943 + 2,34,057 – 1,50,000

(i) 2,12,856 + 3,50,000 – 4,06,752 (j) 1,89,774 + 4,55,000 – 3,96,719

4. Fill in the missing digits to complete the following subtractions.

(a)

	9	7	5	8	4
–	☐	4	☐	4	☐
	6	3	1	4	2

(b)

	3	8	5	7	6
–	1	7	☐	☐	☐
	2	1	1	4	2

(c)

	6	☐	7	☐	9
–	☐	3	2	7	☐
	4	2	☐	1	7

(d)

	5	9	☐	5	7
–	☐	2	4	3	☐
	3	☐	4	☐	1

Word Problems

Example 1: The population of Bahamas is 2,76,000. The population of Barbados is 2,64,000 and that of Seychelles is 72,000. What is the population of the three countries taken together?

Population of Bahamas	=	2,76,000
Population of Barbados	= (+)	2,64,000
Population of Seychelles	= (+)	72,000
		6,12,000

The population of the three countries taken together is 6 lakh 12 thousand.

Example 2: The area of New Zealand is 2,70,534 square kilometres. The area of Venezuela is 6,41,516 square kilometres more than the area of New Zealand. What is the area of Venezuela?

Area of New Zealand	=	2,70,534 sq. km
Area to be added	= (+)	6,41,516 sq. km
Area of Venezuela	=	9,12,050 sq. km

The area of Venezuela is 9,12,050 sq. km.

Example 3: The population of Bhutan is 6,00,000 and the population of Maldives is 3,62,000 less than that of Bhutan. What is the population of Maldives?

Population of Bhutan	=	6,00,000
Number to be subtracted	= (–)	3,62,000
Population of Maldives	=	2,38,000

The population of Maldives is 2,38,000.

Example 4: Norway's area is 3,23,752 square kilometres, whereas Portugal's area is 91,905 square kilometres. By how much is Norway bigger in area than Portugal?

Area of Norway	=	3,23,752 sq. km
Area of Portugal	= (–)	91,905 sq. km
Norway is bigger by	=	2,31,847 sq. km

Norway is bigger in area than Portugal by 2,31,847 sq. km.

Example 5: Find the number which is 52,702 less than the greatest 6-digit number.

The greatest 6-digit number	=	9,99,999
Less	= (–)	52,702
The number which is 52,702 less than 9,99,999	=	9,47,297

Thus, the number which is 52,702 less than the greatest 6-digit number is 9,47,297.

Exercise 3.3

1. A florist sold 47,386 roses, 18,794 tulips and 23,217 chrysanthemums in a year. How many flowers did the florist sell in all, that year?	Number of roses sold = _____ Number of tulips sold = _____ Number of chrysanthemums sold = _____ Total number of flowers sold = _____
2. Circus A earned Rs 3,73,500 in the year 2006. Circus B earned Rs 58,720 less than Circus A earned in that year. How much did Circus B earn in 2006?	Circus A earned Rs _____ in 2006. Circus B earned Rs _____ less than Circus A in 2006. Circus B earned Rs _____ in 2006.
3. In a year, a factory produced 3,84,740 bulbs, out of which it sold 2,96,800 bulbs. How many bulbs were left unsold?	Number of bulbs produced = _____ Number of bulbs sold = _____ Number of bulbs unsold = _____
4. A library had 37,652 works of fiction, 58,127 magazines and many reference books in its total stock of 1,34,897 books and magazines. How many reference books were there in the library?	Works of fiction = _____ Magazines = _____ Magazines and works of fiction = _____ Total no. of books in the library = _____ Magazines and works of fiction = _____ No. of reference books = _____
5. The population of a town is 53,784. If 28,325 of them are males, then find the number of females in the town.	Population of the town = _____ Number of males = _____ Number of females = _____
6. The sum of two numbers is 8,21,025. If one of the numbers is 3,10,150, find the other number.	Sum of two numbers = _____ One number = _____ The other number = _____

Revision Exercise

Do these sums in your notebook.

1 Add the following.

(a) 7,36,154 + 2,62,431 (b) 3,78,194 + 2,16,035 (c) 5,81,620 + 2,15,318

(d) 24,610 + 9,13,289 (e) 6,13,847 + 3,22,783 (f) 1,63,499 + 6,50,012

(g) 2,64,171 + 1,05,301 + 3,20,216

(h) 1,82,438 + 3,25,674 + 68,634

2 Subtract the following.

(a) 7,23,680 – 4,81,732 (b) 8,00,000 – 6,28,711 (c) 5,13,414 – 1,23,126

(d) 5,21,473 – 2,79,368 (e) 6,00,000 – 99,999 (f) 8,13,120 – 2,35,160

(g) 7,30,000 – 5,86,790 (h) 5,92,600 – 2,99,999 (i) 3,00,009 – 2,66,095

3 Fill in the boxes.

(a) 5,68,423 + ☐ = 5,68,423 (b) 2,34,156 + 93,245 = 93,245 + ☐

(c) 3,24,031 + 12,549 = 12,549 + 3,24,031 + ☐

(d) 0 + ☐ = 8,09,341

4 Fill in the missing digits.

(a)

	1	2	5	9	3
+	☐	☐	☐	☐	☐
+	7	3	2	4	4
	9	8	2	7	1

(b)

	3	0	0	0	0	0
–	1	☐	6	☐	4	☐
	1	4	3	8	5	3

5 The area of France is 5,43,965 sq. km and that of Germany is 3,56,974 sq. km. What is the area of France and Germany taken together?

6 3,46,218 men, 3,39,464 women and 1,12,894 children live in a town. What is the total population of the town?

7 Ashok's father earned Rs 89,237 in 2005 and Rs 1,04,578 in 2006. How much did Ashok's father earn in the years 2005 and 2006?

8 1,41,732 students appeared for an examination, out of which 80,497 were boys. How many girls appeared for the examination?

9 A man had Rs 5 lakhs to spend on a house. He bought a plot of land for Rs 2,36,000 and spent the rest of the money building a house on it. How much did he spend on building the house?

10 A number is 86,376 more than the greatest 5-digit number. What is the number?

11 The sum of two numbers is 7,51,356. If one of the numbers is 2,00,008, find the other number.

MULTIPLICATION

Let's Recap

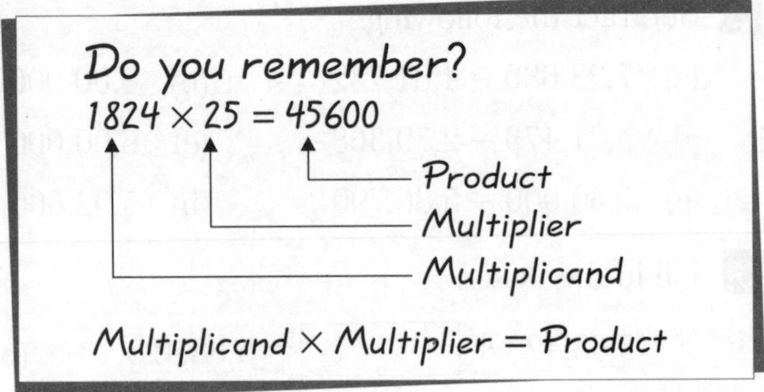

Do you remember?
1824 × 25 = 45600
Product
Multiplier
Multiplicand
Multiplicand × Multiplier = Product

1. Fill in the boxes.
   (a) 57 × 0 = ☐
   (b) 658 × 10 = ☐
   (c) 245 × 100 = ☐
   (d) 32 × 1,000 = ☐
   (e) 642 × 83 = ☐ × 642
   (f) 194 × 461 = 461 × ☐

2. Fill in the boxes.
   (a) 219 + 219 + 219 + 219 + 219 + 219 + 219 = 1533; 219 × 7 = ☐
   (b) 17,893 + 17,893 + 17,893 + 17,893 = 71,572; 17,893 × ☐ = 71,572
   (c) 18,947 + 18,947 + 18,947 = 56,841; ☐ × 3 = 56,841
   (d) 17,286 + 17,286 + 17,286 + 17,286 + 17,286 = ☐ ; 17,286 × 5 = 86,430

3. Multiply the following.

(a)

	Th	H	T	O
	2	4	1	3
×				2

(b)

	Th	H	T	O
	3	1	0	2
×				3

(c)

	Th	H	T	O
	9	4	5	8
×				3

(d)

	Th	H	T	O
	8	1	2	7
×				8

(e)

	TTh	Th	H	T	O
	4	2	1	0	3
×					2

(f)

	TTh	Th	H	T	O
	1	2	0	3	2
×					3

(g)

	TTh	Th	H	T	O
	1	6	7	4	5
×					5

(h)

	TTh	Th	H	T	O
	1	5	3	2	7
×					6

(i)

	H	T	O
	4	5	3
×		2	7

(j)

	H	T	O
	2	3	6
×		4	5

(k)

	H	T	O
	3	8	6
×	2	0	5

(l)

	H	T	O
	7	9	5
×	1	2	0

As Rahul, Priya and their friend Rohan came out of Rohan's house, Rahul looked bored.

Multiplication Properties

Let us learn the various properties of multiplication. You already know some of them.

1. **When a number is multiplied by zero, the product is zero.**

   For example, $2{,}549 \times 0 = 0$

   and $49{,}738 \times 0 = 0$

2. **When a number is multiplied by 1, the product is the number itself.**

   For example, $1{,}938 \times 1 = 1{,}938$

   and $6{,}45{,}201 \times 1 = 6{,}45{,}201$

Mental maths

(a) $6{,}822 \times 0 =$ ☐

(b) $46{,}302 \times 1 =$ ☐

(c) $2{,}31{,}564 \times 0 =$ ☐

3. **When more than two numbers are multiplied, a change in the order of multiplication does not change the product.**

   For example, $(6 \times 3) \times 2 = 36 = 6 \times (3 \times 2) = (6 \times 2) \times 3$

   $(110 \times 2) \times 30 = 6{,}600 = 110 \times (2 \times 30) = (110 \times 30) \times 2$

4. **Multiplication by Numbers with Zeroes**

   (a) When a number is multiplied by 10, one zero is added to its right to make the product.

   For example, $136 \times 10 = 1{,}360$

   and $5{,}721 \times 10 = 57{,}210$

   (b) To multiply a number by tens, like 30, 40, 70, etc., we multiply the number by the first digit of the multiplier and then add one zero to its right to make the product.

For example, $342 \times 20 = ?$

First, multiply 342 and 2: $342 \times 2 = 684$

Then, add one zero to its right. We get 6,840.

So, $342 \times 20 = 6,840$

Similarly, $2,321 \times 30 = 69,630$

(c) When a number is multiplied by 100, we add two zeroes to its right to make the product.

For example, $228 \times 100 = 22,800$

and $4,310 \times 100 = 4,31,000$

(d) To multiply a number by hundreds, like 200, 800, etc., we multiply the number by the first digit of the multiplier and then add two zeroes to its right to make the product.

For example, $114 \times 200 = ?$

First multiply 114 and 2: $114 \times 2 = 228$

Then, add two zeroes to its right, we get 22,800

So, $114 \times 200 = 22,800$

Similarly, $4,322 \times 200 = 8,64,400$

(e) Similarly, when a number is multiplied by 1000, we add three zeroes to its right to make the product.

When the first digit of the multiplier is 1 and all the other digits are 0, the product will be the multiplicand with that many number of zeroes to its right as the number of zeroes in the multiplier.

More Examples:

$6 \times 10,000$

Number of zeroes after 1 in multiplier = 4

6	×	10,000	=	60,000
↑		↑		↑
Multiplicand		**Multiplier**		**Product**

Thus, product = 60,000 (*Four zeroes after the multiplicand*)

$7 \times 1,00,000$

Number of zeroes after 1 in multiplier = 5

So, $7 \times 1,00,000 = 7,00,000$ (*Five zeroes after the multiplicand*)

Mental maths

(a) $348 \times 0 =$ ☐

(b) $6,250 \times 100 =$ ☐

(c) $4,108 \times 1,000 =$ ☐

Exercise 4.1

1. Multiply the following.

(a) 6,394 × 0 = ______ (b) 5,591 × 1 = ______

(c) 0 × 98,145 = ______ (d) 2,785 × 10 = ______

(e) 3,477 × 10 = ______ (f) 47,609 × 10 = ______

(g) 5,864 × 100 = ______ (h) 7,192 × 100 = ______

(i) 22,100 × 100 = ______ (j) 3,551 × 1,000 = ______

(k) 3,878 × 1,000 = ______ (l) 1,623 × 1,000 = ______

(m) 87,190 × 1,000 = ______ (n) 52,215 × 10,000 = ______

(o) 312 × 1,00,000 = ______ (p) 58,967 × 1,00,000 = ______

2. Multiply the following.

(a) 223 × 20 = ______ (b) 213 × 30 = ______

(c) 1,221 × 40 = ______ (d) 4,312 × 200 = ______

(e) 332 × 300 = ______ (f) 202 × 400 = ______

(g) 2,431 × 2,000 = ______ (h) 920 × 3,000 = ______

(i) 1,200 × 5,000 = ______ (j) 2,403 × 4,000 = ______

3. Fill in the blanks.

(a) 7 × 9 = 9 × ______

(b) 869 × 27 = ______ × 869

(c) (3 × 7) × 9 = (9 × ______) × 7

(d) 49 × (22 × 8) = (______ × 49) × 8

(e) (643 × 24) × 46 = (24 × 46) × ______

Multiplication of Large Numbers

In Class III you have learnt how to multiply 2- and 3-digit numbers. Let us now learn multiplication of some larger numbers.

Multiplication without Carrying

Example 1: Multiply 2,324 by 12.

```
    2 3 2 4
  ×     1 2
  ---------
    4 6 4 8
  2 3 2 4 ×
  ---------
  2 7 8 8 8
```

Example 2: Multiply 1,021 by 23.

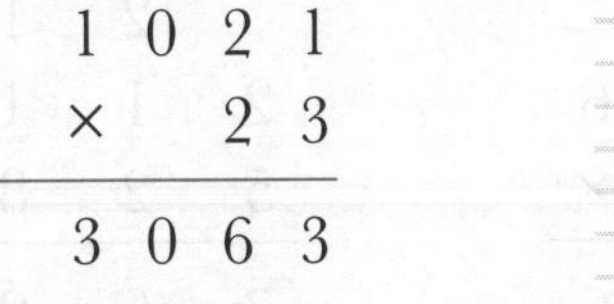

```
    1 0 2 1
  ×     2 3
  ---------
    3 0 6 3
  2 0 4 2 ×
  ---------
  2 3 4 8 3
```

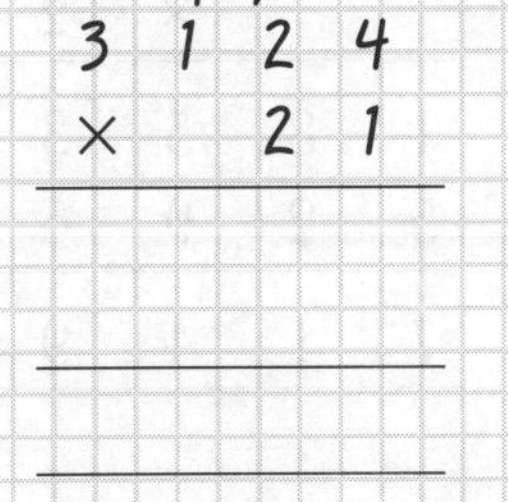
Try this!
Multiply
3 1 2 4
× 2 1

In such multiplications we know that the product of the multiplicand and the tens of the multiplier will be in tens. So, the ones place of the product will have a zero. Sometimes, when in a hurry, we might forget to put a zero. So to avoid making a mistake, we mark the ones place with a cross.

Example 3: Multiply 3,012 by 113.

```
      3 0 1 2
    × 1 1 3
    ---------
      9 0 3 6
    3 0 1 2 ×
  3 0 1 2 × ×
  -----------
  3 4 0 3 5 6
```

Example 4: Multiply 1,014 by 122.

```
      1 0 1 4
    × 1 2 2
    ---------
      2 0 2 8
    2 0 2 8 ×
  1 0 1 4 × ×
  -----------
  1 2 3 7 0 8
```

Mental maths

Study the pattern and fill in the blanks.

37 × 3 = 111
37 × 6 = 222
37 × 9 = 333
37 × 12 = ________
37 × 15 = ________
37 × 18 = ________

Example 5: Multiply 40,123 by 12.

```
    4 0 1 2 3
  ×       1 2
  -----------
    8 0 2 4 6
  4 0 1 2 3 ×
  -----------
  4 8 1 4 7 6
```

Try this!

Multiply

```
  3 1 2 3 1
  ×   1 3 2
  ---------
```

Multiplication with Carrying

Example 1: 2,648 × 27 = ?

```
    (4)(3)(5)
    2  6  4  8
       ×  2  7
  ------------
 1  8  5  3  6
 5  2  9  6  ×
  ------------
 7  1  4  9  6
```

Example 2: 5,283 × 144 = ?

```
        5 2 8 3
      × 1 4 4
  -------------
      2 1 1 3 2
    2 1 1 3 2 ×
  5 2 8 3 × ×
  -------------
  7 6 0 7 5 2
```

Try and avoid writing the amounts carried over. Instead, try and remember what you carry over and add it with the products.

Exercise 4.2

1. Multiply the following.

(a) 1364×16

(b) 7361×19

(c) 2109×17

(d) 4538×21

(e) 4020×21

(f) 1330×30

(g) 1375×36

(h) 1324×32

(i) 5050×37

(j) 2817×44

(k) 3407×45

(l) 2763×50

(m) 1010×88

(n) 1101×77

(o) 11011×90

(p) 22341×38

2. Multiply the following.

(a) 5362×118

(b) 2135×109

(c) 4328×200

(d) 3036×204

(e) 1 8 7 6 × 2 2 7

(f) 2 7 3 8 × 2 6 1

(g) 3 0 0 1 × 2 7 5

(h) 1 4 4 2 × 2 9 0

(i) 1 7 5 4 × 5 1 8

(j) 1 6 8 8 × 3 7 2

(k) 1 2 3 5 × 7 4 0

(l) 2 1 7 4 × 4 5 4

Word Problems

Example 1: There are 350 toffees in a tin. How many toffees are there in 24 such tins?

Number of toffees in one tin = 350

Number of toffees in 24 such tins = 350 × 24

```
   3 5 0
  ×  2 4
 -------
 1 4 0 0
 7 0 0 ×
 -------
 8 4 0 0
```

Thus, there are 8,400 toffees in 24 tins.

Example 2: A television set costs Rs 8,955. How much would 86 such television sets cost?

Cost of one television set = Rs 8,955

Cost of 86 such television sets = Rs 8,955 × 86

```
    Rs 8 9 5 5
     ×     8 6
  ------------
     5 3 7 3 0
   7 1 6 4 0 ×
  ------------
 Rs 7 7 0 1 3 0
```

Thus, 86 television sets would cost Rs 7,70,130.

Exercise 4.3

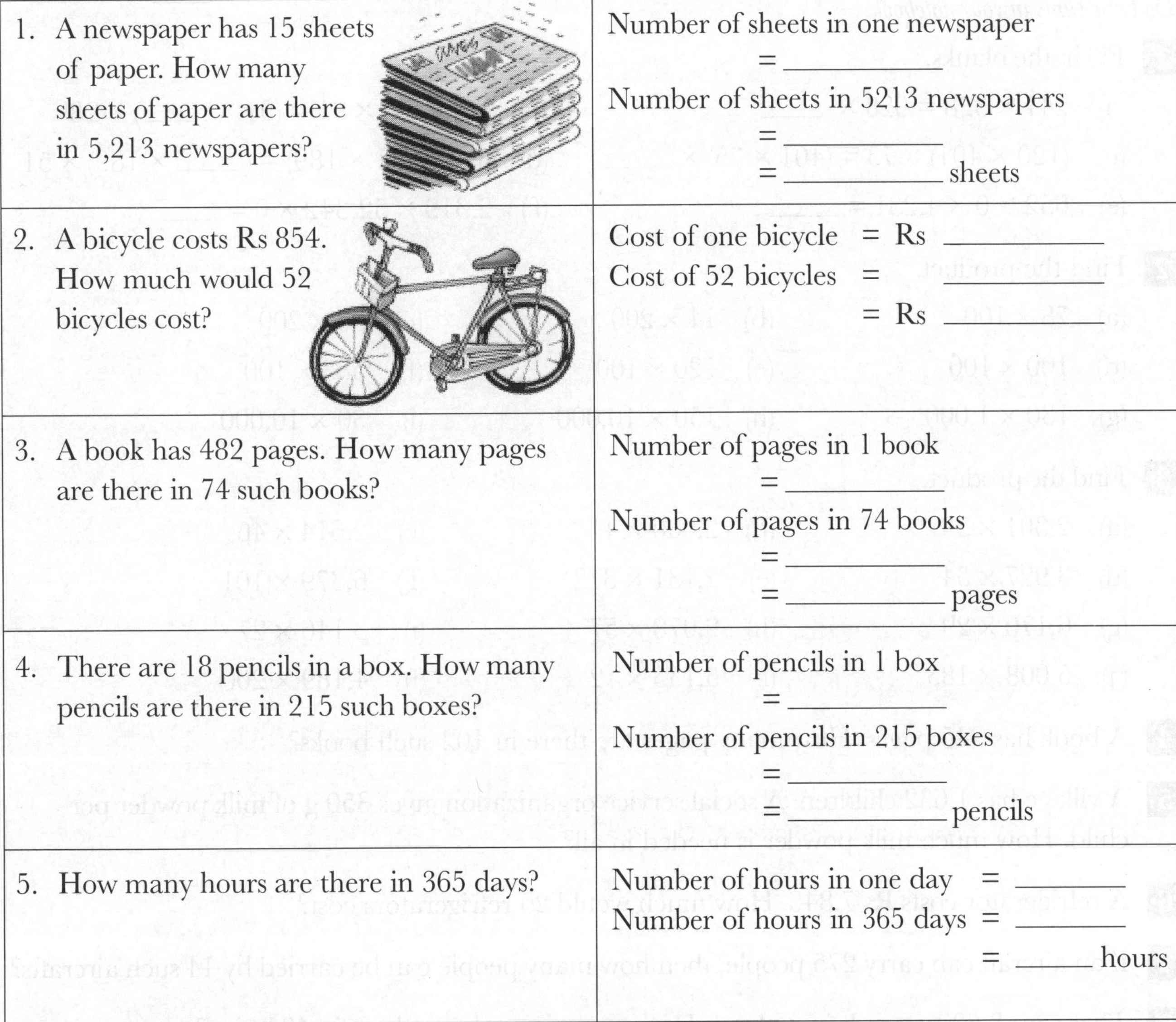

1. A newspaper has 15 sheets of paper. How many sheets of paper are there in 5,213 newspapers?	Number of sheets in one newspaper = ________ Number of sheets in 5213 newspapers = ________ = ________ sheets
2. A bicycle costs Rs 854. How much would 52 bicycles cost?	Cost of one bicycle = Rs ________ Cost of 52 bicycles = ________ = Rs ________
3. A book has 482 pages. How many pages are there in 74 such books?	Number of pages in 1 book = ________ Number of pages in 74 books = ________ = ________ pages
4. There are 18 pencils in a box. How many pencils are there in 215 such boxes?	Number of pencils in 1 box = ________ Number of pencils in 215 boxes = ________ = ________ pencils
5. How many hours are there in 365 days?	Number of hours in one day = ________ Number of hours in 365 days = ________ = ________ hours

Revision Exercise

Do these sums in your notebook.

1 Fill in the blanks.

(a) $241 \times 328 = 328 \times$ _____ (b) $(28 \times 62) \times 91 = (91 \times$ _____ $) \times 28$

(c) $(120 \times 401) \times 75 = (401 \times 75) \times$ _____ (d) $394 \times (51 \times 189) = ($ _____ $\times 189) \times 51$

(e) $652 \times 0 \times 4{,}231 =$ _____ (f) $2{,}319 \times 52{,}342 \times 0 =$ _____

2 Find the product.

(a) 78×100 (b) 14×200 (c) 90×200

(d) 100×100 (e) 720×100 (f) 583×100

(g) $130 \times 1{,}000$ (h) $150 \times 10{,}000$ (i) $30 \times 10{,}000$

3 Find the product.

(a) $2{,}301 \times 33$ (b) $2{,}000 \times 41$ (c) $2{,}614 \times 46$

(d) $3{,}927 \times 54$ (e) $2{,}131 \times 312$ (f) $6{,}379 \times 101$

(g) $6{,}170 \times 29$ (h) $2{,}078 \times 57$ (i) $3{,}146 \times 27$

(j) $5{,}008 \times 183$ (k) $5{,}135 \times 12$ (l) $4{,}189 \times 200$

4 A book has 245 pages. How many pages are there in 102 such books?

5 A village has 1,632 children. A social service organization gives 350 g of milk powder per child. How much milk powder is needed in all?

6 A refrigerator costs Rs 7,846. How much would 25 refrigerators cost?

7 If an aircraft can carry 275 people, then how many people can be carried by 14 such aircrafts?

8 There are 3,600 seconds in an hour. How many seconds are there in 48 hours?

9 There are 1,756 children on board a passenger ship. The captain decides to present each child with 12 bars of chocolate. How many bars of chocoloate will the captain need?

10 There are 50 apartments in one block. How many apartments are there in a colony of 17 blocks of apartments?

11 There are 26 letters in the English alphabet. A child is asked to write the entire English alphabet 150 times. How many letters will the child have to write?

12 What is the product of the smallest 4-digit number and the greatest 2-digit number?

13 What is the product of the greatest 3-digit number and the greatest 2-digit number?

5 DIVISION

Let's Recap

1. Fill in the boxes.

   (a) $15 \times 8 = 120$; $120 \div \square = 15$, $120 \div 15 = \square$

   (b) $60 \times 7 = 420$; $420 \div \square = 7$, $\square \div 7 = 60$

   (c) $120 \times 10 = 1,200$; $1,200 \div 10 = \square$, $1,200 \div \square = 10$

   (d) $0 \div 241 = \square$

   (e) $\square \div 538 = 0$

   (f) $575 \div 575 = \square$

   (g) $\square \div 361 = 1$

   (h) $2,000 \div 10 = \square$

   (i) In $649 \div 10$, quotient = $\square$, remainder = $\square$

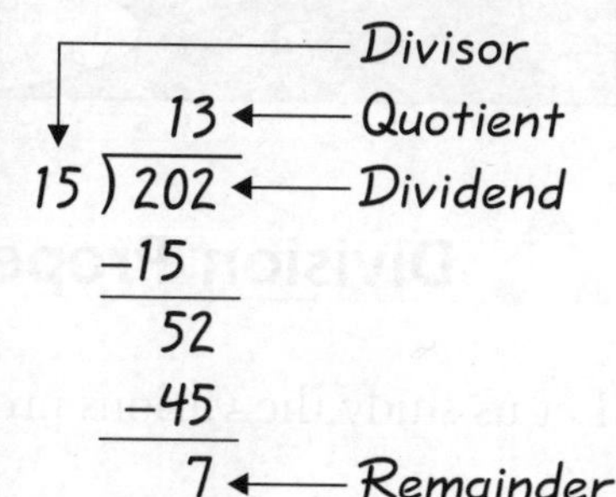

Do you remember?

Divisor

13 ← Quotient

15) 202 ← Dividend

−15

52

−45

7 ← Remainder

Divisor × Quotient + Remainder = Dividend

2. Divide the following.

(a) 2) 420	(b) 3) 6960	(c) 5) 2585	(d) 7) 8143

3. Divide the following.

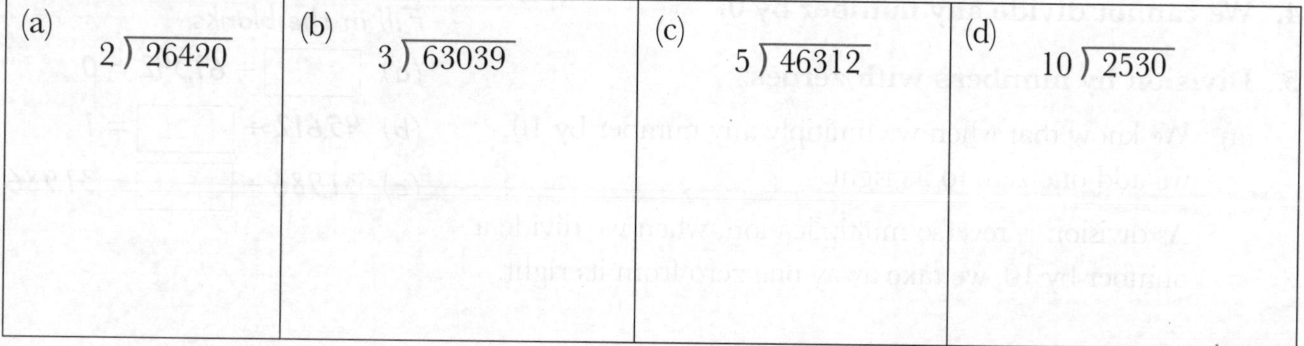

(a) 2) 26420	(b) 3) 63039	(c) 5) 46312	(d) 10) 2530

While on their way to the zoo, the kids met Priya's father, who offered them a lift in his car.

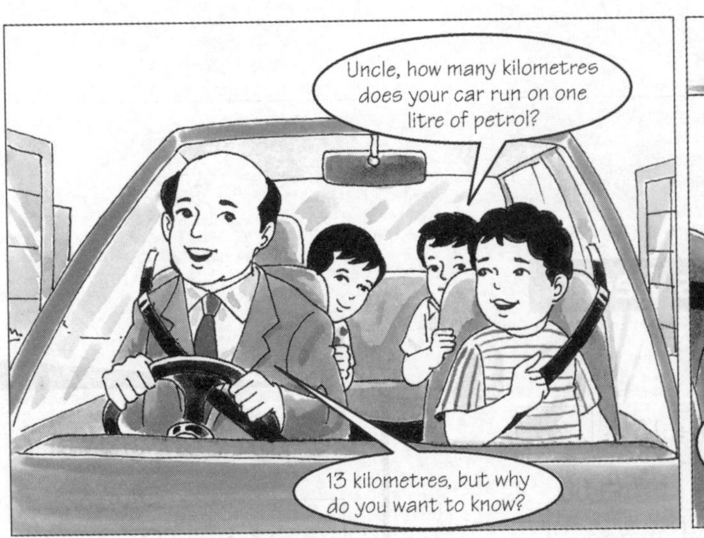

Uncle, how many kilometres does your car run on one litre of petrol?
13 kilometres, but why do you want to know?

That's right. See, my car has already covered 34,450 kilometres. If you divide that by 13, you'll know that a car indeed consumes a great deal of petrol.
Okay, so now I know why my father says a car is expensive to run!

Division Properties

Let us study the various properties of division.

1. **We know that any number multiplied by 0 gives 0 as the product. As division is reverse multiplication, zero divided by any number gives 0 as the quotient.**

   As $2{,}314 \times 0 = 0$,

   $0 \div 2{,}314 = 0$

   Similarly, $0 \div 58{,}642 = 0$

2. **Any number divided by 1 is the number itself.**

   For example, $525 \div 1 = 525$ because $525 \times 1 = 525$

   Similarly, $3{,}502 \div 1 = 3{,}502$; $24{,}316 \div 1 = 24{,}316$

3. **Any number divided by itself gives 1 as the quotient.**

   For example, $525 \div 525 = 1$ because $1 \times 525 = 525$

   Similarly, $2{,}806 \div 2{,}806 = 1$; $31{,}251 \div 31{,}251 = 1$

4. **We cannot divide any number by 0.**

5. **Division by numbers with zeroes.**

   (a) We know that when we multiply any number by 10, we add one zero to its right.

   As division is reverse multiplication, when we divide a number by 10, we take away one zero from its right.

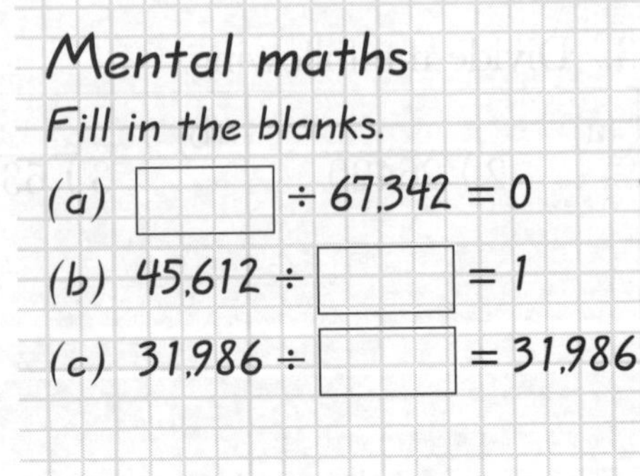

Mental maths

Fill in the blanks.

(a) ☐ ÷ 67,342 = 0

(b) 45,612 ÷ ☐ = 1

(c) 31,986 ÷ ☐ = 31,986

As $200 \times 10 = 2{,}000$

So, $2{,}000 \div 10 = 2{,}00\not{0} = 200$

Let us check this
by long divison.

```
    200
10 |2000     20 ÷ 10 = 2 (quotient), no remainder
   -20↓
     ×0      0 ÷ 10 = 0 (quotient), no remainder
     -0↓
      ×0     0 ÷ 10 = 0 (quotient), no remainder
      -0
       ×
```

Thus, $2{,}000 \div 10 = 200$

(b) We know that when we multiply a number by 100, we add two zeroes to its right. As division is reverse multiplication, when we divide a number by 100, we take away two zeroes from its right.

Similarly, when we divide a number by 1,000 we take away three zeroes from its right.

So, $2{,}000 \div 100 = 20\not{0}\not{0} = 20$

and $2{,}000 \div 1{,}000 = 2\not{0}\not{0}\not{0} = 2$

Division of Large Numbers

In this chapter you will learn how to divide 4- and 5-digit numbers by 2-digit numbers. But before that let us revise the division of 3-digit numbers.

Example 1: Divide 684 by 2.

```
   342
2 |684      6 ÷ 2 = 3 (quotient)
  -6↓
   ×8       8 ÷ 2 = 4 (quotient)
   -8↓
    ×4      4 ÷ 2 = 2 (quotient)
    -4
     ×      This division leaves no remainder.
```

Check:
Divisor × Quotient = Dividend
$2 \times 342 = 684$

Thus, $684 \div 2 = 342$

Example 2: Divide 286 by 3.

```
    95      As 2 cannot be divided by 3, we move right along the dividend
3 |286      to the tens place.
  -27↓      28 ÷ 3 = 9 (quotient), 1 (remainder)
    16      16 ÷ 3 = 5 (quotient), 1 (remainder)
   -15
     1      This division leaves 1 as remainder.
```

Check: Divisor × Quotient + Remainder = Dividend

$3 \times 95 + 1 = 285 + 1 = 286$

Thus, $286 \div 3 = 95$ (quotient), 1 (remainder)

Division of 4-Digit Numbers

Division of 4-digit numbers is similar to division of smaller numbers.

Example 1: Divide 1,644 by 12.

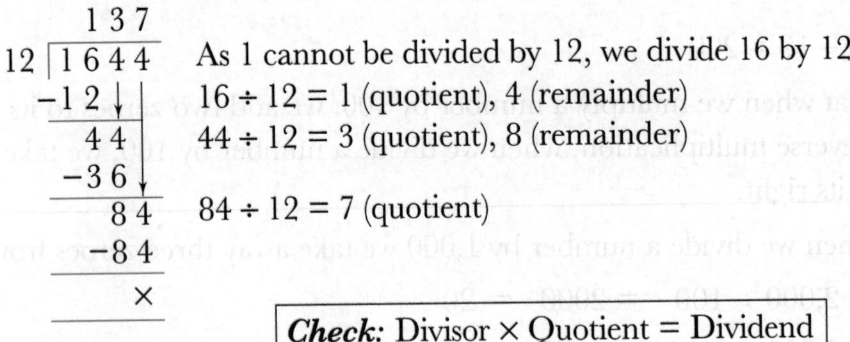

As 1 cannot be divided by 12, we divide 16 by 12.

$16 \div 12 = 1$ (quotient), 4 (remainder)

$44 \div 12 = 3$ (quotient), 8 (remainder)

$84 \div 12 = 7$ (quotient)

Try this!
Divide

$11 \overline{)1540}$

Thus, $1{,}644 \div 12 = 137$

Check: Divisor × Quotient = Dividend

$12 \times 137 = 1{,}644$

Example 2: Divide 3,240 by 15.

```
      2 1 6
15 | 3 2 4 0
   -3 0
      2 4
     -1 5
        9 0
       -9 0
          ×
```

As 3 cannot be divided by 15, we divide 32 by 15.

$32 \div 15 = 2$ (quotient), 2 (remainder)

$24 \div 15 = 1$ (quotient), 9 (remainder)

$90 \div 15 = 6$ (quotient)

Thus, $3{,}240 \div 15 = 216$

Check: $15 \times 216 = 3{,}240$

Some More Examples

Till now we have been dividing numbers by reciting the multiplication tables of the divisors. This is because the divisors we have used till now were from 1 to 20. Let us now learn how to divide using divisors greater than 20.

Example 1: Divide 5,152 by 28.

As we do not know the multiplication table of 28, it would help if we work it out in the margin for rough work.

```
      1 8 4
28 | 5 1 5 2
    -2 8↓
      2 3 5
    -2 2 4↓
        1 1 2
       -1 1 2
           ×
```

Rough Work

28 × 1 = 28	28 × 2 = 56	28 × 3 = 84
28 × 4 = 112	28 × 5 = 140	28 × 6 = 168
28 × 7 = 196	28 × 8 = 224	28 × 9 = 252
28 × 10 = 280		

Step 1: As 28 × 2 = 56 and 56 > 51,

we have 51 ÷ 28 = 1 (quotient), 23 (remainder)

Step 2: As 28 × 8 = 224 and 224 < 235,

we have 235 ÷ 28 = 8 (quotient), 11 (remainder)

Step 3: As 28 × 4 = 112,

112 ÷ 28 = 4 (quotient), no remainder

Thus, 5,152 ÷ 28 = 184

Check: 28 × 184 = 5,152

Example 2: Divide 9,389 by 38.

```
      2 4 7
38 | 9 3 8 9
    -7 6↓
      1 7 8
     -1 5 2↓
        2 6 9
       -2 6 6
            3
```

Rough Work

38 × 1 = 38	38 × 2 = 76	38 × 3 = 114
38 × 4 = 152	38 × 5 = 190	38 × 6 = 228
38 × 7 = 266	38 × 8 = 304	38 × 9 = 342
38 × 10 = 380		

Check: Divisor × Quotient + Remainder = Dividend

38 × 247 + 3 = 9,389

Thus, 9,389 ÷ 38 = 247 (quotient), 3 (remainder)

Example 3: Divide 86,434 by 46.

```
      1 8 7 9
46 | 8 6 4 3 4
    -4 6↓
      4 0 4
     -3 6 8↓
        3 6 3
       -3 2 2↓
          4 1 4
         -4 1 4
              ×
```

Rough Work

46 × 1 = 46

46 × 2 = 92	46 × 3 = 138	46 × 4 = 184	46 × 5 = 230
46 × 6 = 276	46 × 7 = 322	46 × 8 = 368	46 × 9 = 414

46 × 10 = 460

Check: 46 × 1,879 = 86,434

Thus, 86,434 ÷ 46 = 1,879

Exercise 5.1

Do these sums in your notebook.

1. Find the quotient.

(a) 984 ÷ 6	(b) 952 ÷ 7	(c) 916 ÷ 4
(d) 959 ÷ 7	(e) 928 ÷ 8	(f) 972 ÷ 9

2. Divide by the following tens.

(a) 6,720 ÷ 10	(b) 5,000 ÷ 100	(c) 7,000 ÷ 1,000
(d) 8,000 ÷ 10	(e) 7,000 ÷ 100	(f) 6,000 ÷ 1,000

3. Find the quotient in the following divisions.

Check your answer.

(a) 782 ÷ 23	(b) 837 ÷ 31	(c) 903 ÷ 43
(d) 8,294 ÷ 29	(e) 4,830 ÷ 35	(f) 6,909 ÷ 47
(g) 7,000 ÷ 50	(h) 8,250 ÷ 33	(i) 90,000 ÷ 60
(j) 7,128 ÷ 27	(k) 6,426 ÷ 34	(l) 5,564 ÷ 52
(m) 31,987 ÷ 29	(n) 85,716 ÷ 36	(o) 71,853 ÷ 43

4. Find the quotient and remainder in the following divisions.

Check your answer.

(a) 859 ÷ 7	(b) 977 ÷ 3	(c) 968 ÷ 21
(d) 967 ÷ 37	(e) 1,550 ÷ 6	(f) 2,390 ÷ 8
(g) 3,794 ÷ 10	(h) 2,579 ÷ 20	(i) 3,863 ÷ 12
(j) 3,311 ÷ 13	(k) 7,675 ÷ 16	(l) 6,778 ÷ 18
(m) 6,040 ÷ 26	(n) 5,921 ÷ 33	(o) 4,496 ÷ 42
(p) 38,238 ÷ 38	(q) 77,777 ÷ 46	(r) 79,599 ÷ 48

Word Problems

Example 1: 18 ceiling fans cost Rs 7,830. How much does one ceiling fan cost?

Cost of 18 ceiling fans = Rs 7,830

Cost of 1 ceiling fan = Rs 7,830 ÷ 18

```
      4 3 5
18 | 7 8 3 0
    -7 2
    ------
      6 3
     -5 4
    ------
        9 0
       -9 0
    ------
          ×
```

Thus, one ceiling fan costs Rs 435.

Example 2: A poultry farm needs to pack 6,552 eggs in cartons of 12 eggs each. How many cartons are required to pack all the eggs?

Number of eggs to be packed = 6,552

Number of eggs in each carton = 12

Number of cartons required = 6,552 ÷ 12

```
      5 4 6
12 | 6 5 5 2
    -6 0
    ------
      5 5
     -4 8
    ------
        7 2
       -7 2
    ------
          ×
```

Thus, 546 cartons are required to pack all the eggs.

Example 3: A number when divided by 62 gives 157 as quotient and 6 as remainder. Find the number.

We know that Divisor × Quotient + Remainder = Dividend

or, 62 × 157 + 6 = Dividend

```
    1 5 7
  ×   6 2
  -------
    3 1 4
  9 4 2 ×
  -------
  9 7 3 4  + 6 = 9,740
```

Check:

```
       1 5 7
62 | 9 7 4 0
    -6 2
    --------
     3 5 4
    -3 1 0
    --------
       4 4 0
      -4 3 4
    --------
           6
```

Thus, 9,740, when divided by 62 gives 157 as quotient and 6 as remainder.

Exercise 5.2

1. 16 books cost Rs 1,840. How much does one book cost?	Cost of 16 books = Rs ________ Number of books = Rs ________ Cost of 1 book = Rs ________
2. 240 cold drink bottles are to be arranged in rows of 12 each. How many rows will be formed?	Number of cold drink bottles = ________ Number of bottles in 1 row = ________ Number of rows = ________
3. Four chefs in a restaurant baked 280 pizzas in one day. How many pizzas did each of them bake, if all four baked an equal number of pizzas?	Number of pizzas baked = ________ Number of chefs = ________ Number of pizzas baked by 1 chef = ________
4. 50,000 tiles are fitted equally in 100 residential flats. How many tiles are fitted in each flat?	Number of tiles = ________ Number of flats = ________ Number of tiles in each flat = ________
5. A number when divided by 30 gives 275 as quotient. Find the number.	Divisor = ________ Quotient = ________ Dividend = ________
6. A number when divided by 22 gives 258 as quotient and 4 as remainder. Find the number.	Divisor = ________ Quotient = ________ Remainder = ________ Dividend = ________

Revision Exercise

Do these sums in your notebook.

1 Divide the following.

(a) 5,000 ÷ 10	(b) 6,800 ÷ 10	(c) 8,800 ÷ 10
(d) 4,500 ÷ 100	(e) 9,000 ÷ 100	(f) 76,000 ÷ 100
(g) 8,000 ÷ 1,000	(h) 7,000 ÷ 1,000	(i) 81,000 ÷ 1,000

2 Find the quotients in the following divisions.

(a) 1,540 ÷ 20	(b) 2,262 ÷ 13	(c) 1,653 ÷ 19	(d) 5,968 ÷ 16
(e) 5,796 ÷ 28	(f) 8,416 ÷ 32	(g) 7,452 ÷ 69	(h) 9,271 ÷ 73
(i) 1,700 ÷ 85	(j) 8,100 ÷ 90	(k) 1,900 ÷ 95	(l) 8,633 ÷ 97

3 Find the quotient (Q) and remainder (R) in the following divisions.

(a) 3,070 ÷ 14	(b) 4,775 ÷ 15	(c) 2,150 ÷ 17	(d) 1,830 ÷ 19
(e) 6,713 ÷ 52	(f) 9,999 ÷ 63	(g) 6,830 ÷ 82	(h) 8,757 ÷ 84
(i) 1,509 ÷ 90	(j) 5,379 ÷ 96	(k) 6,850 ÷ 21	(l) 8,123 ÷ 52

4 Rahul, Rohan and Priya go to a restaurant and decide to share the bill equally. If the total bill was for Rs 270, how much did each of them have to pay?

5 1500 tiles are to be packed in boxes of 25 each. How many boxes are needed?

6 A farmer needed to plant 5,016 seeds equally in 33 rows. How many seeds can be planted in each row?

7 A restaurant storekeeper needs to divide 600 kg of rice into sacks of 25 kg each. How many sacks are required to pack the rice?

8 8,000 $m\ell$ of cold drink is to be poured equally into 40 glasses. How much cold drink will be poured in each glass?

9 A number when divided by 35 gives 264 as quotient. Find the number.

10 A number when divided by 73 gives 129 as quotient and 3 as remainder. Find the number.

11 Which number would divide 5,250 such that the quotient is 57 and remainder is 6?

12 To get a quotient of 58, what number should be divided by 17?

13 How many dozens make 7,476? (**Hint:** One dozen = a set of 12)

14 How many scores make 6,380? (**Hint:** One score = a set of 20)

6 MULTIPLES AND FACTORS

The three friends stopped by at a confectionery shop to have some cookies.

Multiples

Let us recollect the multiplication table of 2.

$2 \times 1 = 2$
$2 \times 2 = 4$
$2 \times 3 = 6$
$2 \times 4 = 8$
$2 \times 5 = 10$
$2 \times 6 = 12$
$2 \times 7 = 14$
$2 \times 8 = 16$
$2 \times 9 = 18$
$2 \times 10 = 20$
…, and so on.

Try this!
Write the first five multiples of 6.

The numbers 2, 4, 6, 8, etc., are the numbers that we get when 2 is multiplied by numbers 1, 2, 3, 4, etc. These numbers 2, 4, 6, 8, … are called the **multiples** of 2.

So, *the product of a number and a counting number (1, 2, 3,.., etc.) is called the multiple of that number.*

Similarly, multiples of 4 are 4, 8, 12, 16, 20,…

Properties of Multiples

Given below are the first 7 multiples of 1, 3, 5 and 7:

1 × 1 = 1
1 × 2 = 2
1 × 3 = 3
1 × 4 = 4
1 × 5 = 5
1 × 6 = 6
1 × 7 = 7

3 × 1 = 3
3 × 2 = 6
3 × 3 = 9
3 × 4 = 12
3 × 5 = 15
3 × 6 = 18
3 × 7 = 21

5 × 1 = 5
5 × 2 = 10
5 × 3 = 15
5 × 4 = 20
5 × 5 = 25
5 × 6 = 30
5 × 7 = 35

7 × 1 = 7
7 × 2 = 14
7 × 3 = 21
7 × 4 = 28
7 × 5 = 35
7 × 6 = 42
7 × 7 = 49

1. Consider the first multiple of the numbers 1, 3, 5 and 7. We find that the multiples are the same as the multiplicands (i.e., the number itself).

   For example, 3 × 1 = 3, 7 × 1 = 7, etc.

   Thus, **every number is a multiple of itself.**

2. Consider the multiples of 1. We find that the multiples are the same as the multiplier.

   For example, 1 × 3 = 3, 1 × 5 = 5, 1 × 7 = 7, ..., and so on.

   So, **every number is a multiple of 1.**

3. Consider the product of 5 and 7.

   As 5 × 7 = 35, 35 is a multiple of 5.

   As 7 × 5 = 35, 35 is a multiple of 7 too.

   Now, consider the product of 2, 3 and 5.

   2 × 3 × 5 = 30

   Also, as 2 × 15 = 30, 30 is a multiple of 2.

   As 3 × 10 = 30, 30 is a multiple of 3 too.

   As 5 × 6 = 30, 30 is a multiple of 5 too.

   So, **the product of two or more numbers is a multiple of each of the numbers.**

> ➤ *Every number is a multiple of itself.*
> ➤ *Every number is a multiple of 1.*
> ➤ *There is no limit to the number of multiples of a number.*
> ➤ *Every multiple of a number is greater than or equal to the number.*

Common Multiples

Consider the multiplication tables of 2 and 3 again.

2	×	1	=	2
2	×	2	=	4
2	×	3	=	(6)
2	×	4	=	8
2	×	5	=	10
2	×	6	=	(12)
2	×	7	=	14
2	×	8	=	16
2	×	9	=	(18)
2	×	10	=	20
2	×	11	=	22
2	×	12	=	(24)
2	×	13	=	26
2	×	14	=	28

3	×	1	=	3
3	×	2	=	(6)
3	×	3	=	9
3	×	4	=	(12)
3	×	5	=	15
3	×	6	=	(18)
3	×	7	=	21
3	×	8	=	(24)
3	×	9	=	27
3	×	10	=	30
3	×	11	=	33
3	×	12	=	36
3	×	13	=	39
3	×	14	=	42

Take the first few multiples of 2 and 3.

Multiples of 2: 2, 4, **6**, 8, 10, **12**, 14, 16, **18**, 20, **24**, 26,...

Multiples of 3: 3, **6**, 9, **12**, 15, **18**, 21, **24**, 27,...

The numbers 6, 12, 18 and 24 appear in both the list of multiples.

They are the **common multiples** of 2 and 3.

Thus, *a number that is a multiple of two or more numbers is known as the common multiple of those numbers.*

Alternatively, we can find the common multiples as follows:

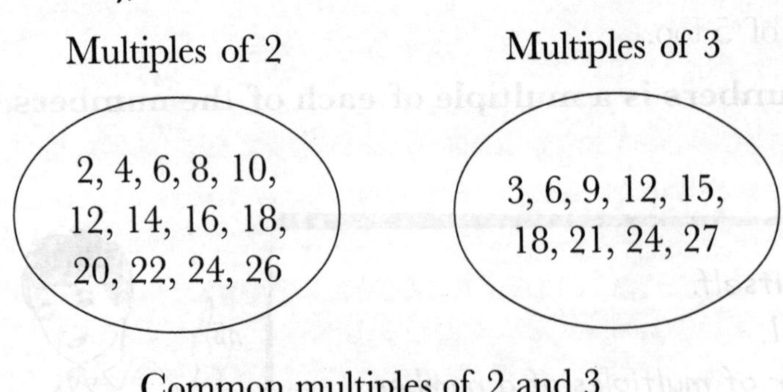

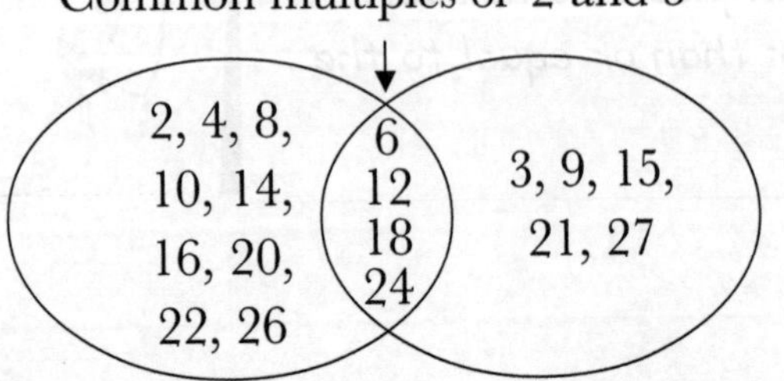

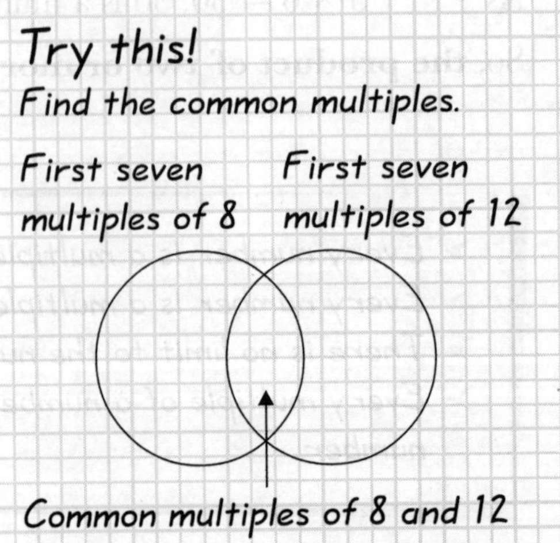

Try this!
Find the common multiples.
First seven multiples of 8
First seven multiples of 12
Common multiples of 8 and 12

Example: What are the first five common multiples of 3 and 4?

Method 1: Write the first few multiples of both the numbers.

Multiples of 3: 3, 6, 9, 12, 15, 18, 21, 24, 27, 30, 33, 36, 39, 42, 45, 48, 51, 54, 57, 60, 63, 66, ...

Multiples of 4: 4, 8, 12, 16, 20, 24, 28, 32, 36, 40, 44, 48, 52, 56, 60, 64, 68, ...

We encircle the common multiples till 5 common multiples of 3 and 4 are found.

Thus, the first five multiples of 3 and 4 are **12, 24, 36, 48** and **60**.

Method 2: Find the multiples of the product of 3 and 4.

A product of 3 and 4 will also be a multiple of both 3 and 4.

$3 \times 4 = 12$. We now multiply 12 with 1, 2, 3, 4 and 5.

Now, $12 \times 1 = 12$; 12 is the first common multiple.

$12 \times 2 = 24$; 24 is the second common multiple.

$12 \times 3 = 36$; 36 is the third common multiple.

$12 \times 4 = 48$; 48 is the fourth common multiple.

$12 \times 5 = 60$; 60 is the fifth common multiple.

So, the first five common multiples of 3 and 4 are **12, 24, 36, 48, 60.**

Note: This method can only be used if one of the given numbers is not a multiple of the other. For example, the first common multiple of 2 and 4 will be 4 and not 8 (i.e., 2×4).

Exercise 6.1

1. Write the first five multiples of:

(a) 8 ______ (b) 9 ______

(c) 10 ______ (d) 11 ______

(e) 12 ______ (f) 15 ______

(g) 20 ______ (h) 22 ______

2. Encircle the numbers that are multiples of 7:

(a) 71 (b) 17 (c) 35 (d) 7 (e) 27

3. Encircle the numbers that are multiples of 5:

(a) 40 (b) 51 (c) 55 (d) 551 (e) 5,553

4. **Encircle the numbers that are multiples of 1:**

(a) 27 (b) 38 (c) 263 (d) 311 (e) 7,074

5. **Encircle the numbers that are not multiples of 3:**

(a) 60 (b) 23 (c) 36 (d) 13 (e) 43

6. **Write the greatest:**

(a) 2-digit multiple of 3 ________ (b) 3-digit multiple of 2 ________

7. **Encircle the numbers that are multiples of 3. Put a square around the multiples of 6. List their common multiples.**

1	2	3	4	5	6	7	8	9	10
11	12	13	14	15	16	17	18	19	20
21	22	23	24	25	26	27	28	29	30

Common multiples of 3 and 6: ________________________________

8. **Encircle the numbers that are multiples of 2. Put a square around the multiples of 4. List their common mutiples.**

1	2	3	4	5	6	7	8	9	10
11	12	13	14	15	16	17	18	19	20
21	22	23	24	25	26	27	28	29	30

Common multiples of 2 and 4: ________________________________

9. **Find the first two common multiples of:**
(Do these sums in your notebook.)

(a) 4 and 5 (b) 7 and 9 (c) 5 and 7 (d) 6 and 8

(e) 9 and 12 (f) 9 and 10 (g) 2, 3 and 5 (h) 4, 5 and 6

10. **Write the common multiples of the given number pairs in the shaded areas.**

(a) Multiples of 3, up to 39 — Multiples of 4, up to 40

Common multiples

(b) Multiples of 3, up to 48 — Multiples of 5, up to 50

Common multiples

Factors

We know that $6 \times 7 = 42$ or multiplicand × multiplier = product

We say that 6 and 7 are **factors** of 42.

So, *the numbers that are multiplied to get a product are called the factors of the product.*

Example: $\underbrace{2 \times 3 \times 4 \times 5 \times 6}_{\text{Factors of 720}} = \underset{\text{Product}}{720}$

Properties of Factors

1. Consider the multiplication table of 1. We see that the products are the same as the multipliers.

   For example,

   $1 \times 3 = 3$, $1 \times 6 = 6$, $1 \times 9 = 9$, ..., and so on

   So, **every number is a factor of itself.**

2. If we multiply any number with 1, the product is the same as the multiplicand.

   For example,

   $4 \times 1 = 4$, $7 \times 1 = 7$, $10 \times 1 = 10$, ..., and so on

   So, **1 is a factor of every number.**

> ➤ *Every number is a factor of itself. It is also the greatest factor of that number.*
>
> ➤ *1 is a factor of every number. It is also the smallest factor of a number.*
>
> ➤ *The factor of a number is less than or equal to the number.*

Finding Factors of a Number

We can find the factors of a number by recalling multiplication tables.

Product	12	14	60	276	6,868
Factors	3 × 4	2 × 7	3 × 20	12 × 23	17 × 404

Other factors can also go on to make the same product. Consider the number 12. It has the following factors.

Product	12	12	12
Factors	3 × 4	2 × 6	2 × 3 × 2

Example 1: Find four factors of 60.

We know that every number is a factor of itself.

We also know that 1 is a factor of every number.

So, 1 × 60 = 60 or 1 and 60 are factors of 60.

Now take the bigger factor (60) and see if two other factors can be found.

2 × 30 = 60

So, 2 and 30 are also factors of 60.

Thus, four factors of 60 are 1, 60, 2 and 30.

Try this!

Find all the factors of 18.

Example 2: Find all the factors of 60.

1 × 60 = 60 *or* 60 × 1 = 60

2 × 30 = 60 *or* 30 × 2 = 60

3 × 20 = 60 *or* 20 × 3 = 60

4 × 15 = 60 *or* 15 × 4 = 60

5 × 12 = 60 *or* 12 × 5 = 60

6 × 10 = 60 *or* 10 × 6 = 60

Thus, all the factors of 60 are:

1, 2, 3, 4, 5, 6, 10, 12, 15, 20, 30 and 60.

Steps:

- From Example 1, we know that 1, 2, 30 and 60 are factors of 60.
- Now take the next smaller number after 2.
  3 × 20 = 60 or 20 × 3 = 60
- Now take the next smaller number 4, and so on.

Example 3: Find two factors and two multiples of 24.

6 × 4 = 24

Thus, 6 and 4 are two factors of 24.

We know that 24 × 2 = 48 and 24 × 3 = 72

Thus, 48 and 72 are two multiples of 24.

The two factors would be within and less than the number and the two multiples would be outside and greater than the number.

To Find Out if a Number is a Factor of Another Number

Example 1: Find if 13 is a factor of 3,107.

13 will be a factor of 3,107 if we get 3,107 as the product on multiplying 13 with a number, i.e., when 13 × [?] = 3,107. To find the other factor we divide 3,107 by 13. If the division leaves no remainder, then 13 is a factor of 3,107.

```
      2 3 9
13 | 3 1 0 7
    -2 6
      5 0
     -3 9
      1 1 7
     -1 1 7
          ×
```

Check:

```
      2 3 9
    × 1 3
      7 1 7
  + 2 3 9 ×
    3 1 0 7
```

When a number is divided by the other leaving a remainder zero, the divisor and the quotient are the factors of the first number.

As the division leaves no remainder, 13 is a factor of 3,107, the other factor being 239.

Example 2: Find if 23 is a factor of 1,354.

```
         5 8
23 | 1 3 5 4
    -1 1 5
       2 0 4
      -1 8 4
         2 0
```

The division leaves 20 as remainder.
So, 23 is not a factor of 1,354.

Try this!
Is 15 a factor of 135?

Common Factors

Let us consider the factors of 9 and 15.

Factors of 9:

1 × 9 = 9 *or* 9 × 1 = 9

3 × 3 = 9

Factors of 9: 1, 3 and 9

Factors of 15:

1 × 15 = 15 *or* 15 × 1 = 15

3 × 5 = 15 *or* 5 × 3 = 15

Factors of 15: 1, 3, 5 and 15

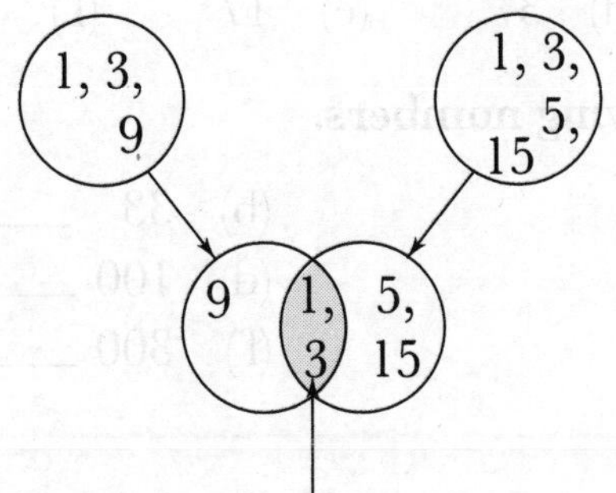

Common factors of 9 and 15

Try this!
Find common factors of 10 and 15.

Thus, *factors common to two or more numbers are known as the common factors of those numbers.*

Exercise 6.2

1. Write 'T' for True and 'F' for False for the following statements.

(i) $7 \times 5 = 35$ and $35 \times 3 = 105$

(a) 7 is a factor of 35. ______ (b) 5 is a multiple of 7. ______

(c) 35 is a multiple of 5. ______ (d) 105 is a multiple of 3. ______

(e) 105 is a factor of 3. ______ (f) 7 is a factor of 105. ______

(g) 5 is a factor of 105. ______ (h) 35 is a multiple of 105. ______

(ii) $20 \times 10 = 200$ and $200 \times 2 = 400$

(a) 200 and 2 are factors of 400. ______

(b) 20 and 10 are multiples of 200. ______

(c) 200 is a multiple of 10. ______

(d) 200 is a factor of 20. ______

(e) 400 is the first multiple of 200. ______

(f) 400 is the second multiple of 200. ______

(g) 200 is a common multiple of 20 and 10. ______

(h) 400 is not a common multiple of 20 and 10. ______

2. Encircle the numbers that are factors of 56.

(a) 2 (b) 7 (c) 6 (d) 5 (e) 10 (f) 3 (g) 8

3. Encircle the numbers that are factors of 28.

(a) 2 (b) 7 (c) 6 (d) 5 (e) 10 (f) 3 (g) 8

4. Encircle the numbers that are factors of 70.

(a) 2 (b) 7 (c) 6 (d) 5 (e) 10 (f) 3 (g) 8

5. Encircle the numbers that are factors of 847.

(a) 77 (b) 121 (c) 21 (d) 37 (e) 17 (f) 7 (g) 22

6. Write two factors of each of the following numbers.

(a) 18 ______ (b) 33 ______

(c) 72 ______ (d) 100 ______

(e) 350 ______ (f) 300 ______

7. Write 2 multiples and 2 factors of:

(a) 32 ______ (b) 40 ______

(c) 25 ______ (d) 50 ______

(e) 100 ______ (f) 150 ______

8. Find the common factors of: (*Do these sums in your notebook.*)

(a) 6 and 8 (b) 6 and 9 (c) 5 and 7 (d) 5 and 10

(e) 12 and 14 (f) 12 and 18 (g) 10 and 20 (h) 13 and 26

Even and Odd Numbers

In earlier classes you have learnt that even numbers are divisible by 2, while odd numbers are not. The following table lists all the odd and even numbers between 1 and 20.

Odd		**Even**	
1	**11**	**2**	**12**
3	**13**	**4**	**14**
5	**15**	**6**	**16**
7	**17**	**8**	**18**
9	**19**	**10**	**20**

Numbers that have **2**, **4**, **6**, **8** and **0** in the ones place are called **even numbers**.

Numbers that have **1**, **3**, **5**, **7** and **9** in the ones place are called **odd numbers**.

Finding Even and Odd Multiples

Let us now define even and odd numbers in terms of multiples.

Numbers which are multiples of 2 are called even numbers.

Numbers which are not multiples of 2 are called odd numbers.

Example 1: Find the first three even multiples of 3.

The first few multiples of 3 are: 3, **6**, 9, **12**, 15, **18**, 21,...

Thus, the first three even multiples of 3 are 6, 12 and 18.

Example 2: Find the first four odd multiples of 3.

Looking at the multiples of 3 listed in the previous example, we find that the first four odd multiples of 3 are 3, 9, 15 and 21.

Mental maths

Find the sums. Say whether they are odd or even.

(a) 2 + 4 = 6 [E]

(b) 3 + 5 = ______ [ ]

(c) 2 + 5 = ______ [ ]

Now, fill in the blanks.

even + even = ______

odd + odd = ______

even + odd = ______

Tests of Divisibility

A number is said to be **divisible by** another number if upon dividing, no remainder is left. There are ways to determine if a number is divisible by a certain number without carrying out the actual division.

Divisibility by 2, 5, 10

A number is divisible by	If the last digit is
2	0, 2, 4, 6, 8
5	0, 5
10	0

Number	Divisible by		
	2	5	10
10	✓	✓	✓
22	✓	✗	✗
35	✗	✓	✗

Even numbers are divisible by 2 and odd numbers are not divisible by 2.

Divisibility by 3 and 9

A number is divisible by	If the sum of the digits is divisible by
3	3
9	9

Number	Sum of the digits	Divisible by	
		3	9
27	2 + 7 = 9	✓	✓
33	3 + 3 = 6	✓	✗

Divisibility by 4 and 6

A number is divisible by	If the
4	number formed by the last two digits of a number is divisible by 4.
6	number is divisible by both 2 and 3.

Number	Divisible by	
	4	6
108	✓	✓
18	✗	✓
16	✓	✗

Some More Examples

Example 1: Which of the following numbers are divisible by 2?

603; 500; 226; 314; 437; 2498

The numbers 603 and 437 have odd digits, 3 and 7, respectively, in the ones place. Thus, these numbers are not divisible by 2.

The numbers 500; 226; 314 and 2,498 have even digits or 0 in the ones place. Thus, these numbers are divisible by 2.

We can check this by the long division method:

```
    1  1  3                          2  1  8
2 | 2  2  6                      2 | 4  3  7
   -2                               -4
   ---------                        ---------
       2                               3
      -2                              -2
   ---------                        ---------
          6                            1  7
         -6                           -1  6
   ---------                        ---------
          ×   No Remainder                1   Remainder = 1
```

Thus, 226 is divisible by 2 and 437 is not divisible by 2.

Example 2: Which of the following numbers are divisible by 3?

337; 219; 4,614; 3,729

Number	Sum of the digits	Divisible by 3
337	13	✗
219	12	✓
4,614	15	✓
3,729	21	✓

Let us check our answer for the numbers 337 and 3,729 by the long division method.

```
    1  1  2                   1  2  4  3
3 | 3  3  7               3 | 3  7  2  9
   -3                        -3
   ---------                 ------------
   ×  3                      ×  7
     -3                        -6
   ---------                 ------------
      ×  7                      1  2
        -6                     -1  2
   ---------                 ------------
         1   Remainder = 1         ×  9
                                     -9
                             ------------
                                      ×   No Remainder
```

You can check by long division if the numbers 219 and 4,614 are divisible by 3.

Thus, 3,729 is divisible by 3 and 337 is not divisible by 3.

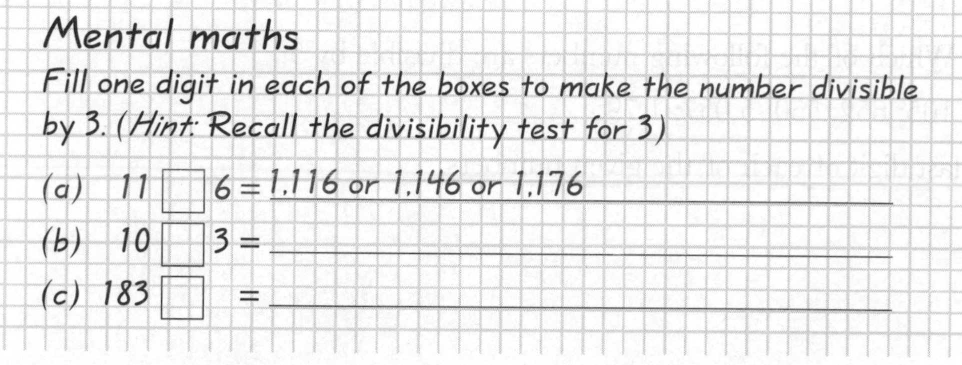

Mental maths

Fill one digit in each of the boxes to make the number divisible by 3. (Hint: Recall the divisibility test for 3)

(a) 11 ☐ 6 = 1,116 or 1,146 or 1,176

(b) 10 ☐ 3 = ____________

(c) 183 ☐ = ____________

Example 3: Which of the following numbers are divisible by 4?

439; 6,317; 7,824; 9,936; 21,208

Number	Number formed by the last two digits	Divisible by 4
4**39**	39	✗
6,3**17**	17	✗
7,8**24**	24	✓
9,9**36**	36	✓
21,2**08**	08	✓

Let us check our answer for the numbers 439 and 21,208.

```
      1 0 9              5 3 0 2
  4 | 4 3 9          4 | 2 1 2 0 8
     -4                 -2 0
     -----              ---------
      3 9               × 1 2
     -3 6                -1 2
     -----              ---------
      × 3                 × 0
                           -0
  Remainder 3           ---------
                            × 8
                             -8
                        ---------
                              ×   No Remainder
```

You can check by long division if the numbers 6,317; 7,824 and 9,936 are divisible by 4?

Thus, 439 is not divisible by 4 and 21,208 is divisible by 4.

Mental maths

Fill one digit in each of the boxes to make the number divisible by 2 as well as 3. (*Hint:* Recall the divisibility tests of 2 and 3)

(a) 84☐ = 840 or 846

(b) 93☐8 = ____________

(c) 6☐78 = ____________

Example 4: Which of the following numbers are divisible by 5?

105; 652; 550; 5,057; 1,795

Observe the last digit of each of the given numbers.

Number	Last digit is	Divisible by 5
105	5	✓
652	2	✗
550	0	✓
5,057	7	✗
1,795	5	✓

Example 5: Which of the following numbers are divisible by 6?

6,384; 2,007; 644, 7,296; 138

Recollect the divisibility tests of 2 and 3.

Number	Divisible by 2	Divisible by 3	Divisible by 6
6,384	✓	✓	✓
2,007	✗	✓	✗
644	✓	✗	✗
7,296	✓	✓	✓
138	✓	✓	✓

Example 6: Which of the following numbers are divisible by 9?

7,218; 6,301; 4,968; 2,009; 9,009

Number	Sum of the digits	Divisible by 9
7,218	18	✓
6,301	10	✗
4,968	27	✓
2,009	11	✗
9,009	18	✓

Example 7: Which of the following numbers are divisible by 10?

6,310; 9,000; 4,003; 7,867

If the digit in the ones place in a number is zero, the number is divisible by 10.

Thus, 6,310 and 9,000 are divisible by 10.

Example 8: Which of the following numbers are divisible by 100?

70,000; 6,730; 2,800; 9,103; 6,001; 8,330; 8,400

If the digits in the ones place and tens place in a number are zero, the number is divisible by 100.

Thus, 70,000; 2,800 and 8,400 are divisible by 100.

- ➤ All even numbers are divisible by 2.
- ➤ A number is divisible by 3 if the sum of its digits is divisible by 3.
- ➤ A number is divisible by 4 if the number formed by its last two digits is divisible by 4.
- ➤ All numbers ending with 0 or 5 are divisible by 5.
- ➤ Numbers that are divisible by both 2 and 3 are divisible by 6.
- ➤ A number is divisible by 9 if the sum of its digits is divisible by 9.

Exercise 6.3

1. Encircle the numbers which are even numbers.

(a) 4 (b) 8 (c) 17 (d) 25 (e) 100

2. Encircle the numbers which are odd numbers.

(a) 5 (b) 7 (c) 6 (d) 37 (e) 46

3. Write the first 4 even multiples of:

(a) 2 ______ (b) 3 ______
(c) 4 ______ (d) 5 ______
(e) 6 ______ (f) 7 ______

4. Encircle the numbers which are divisible by 2.

7,963; 8,472; 9,008; 1,340; 4,823; 8,706; 9,110; 3,744

5. Encircle the numbers which are divisible by 3.

39; 71; 282; 636; 929; 4,174; 3,796; 8,808

6. Encircle the numbers which are divisible by 4.

54; 48; 732; 834; 9,124; 10,722; 18,764; 99,812

7. Encircle the numbers which are divisible by 5.

50; 360; 553; 4,955; 8,612; 98,340; 49,385; 9,177

8. Encircle the numbers which are divisible by 6.

2,934; 6,003; 7,288; 7,206; 83,184; 2,199; 40,006; 68,754

9. Encircle the numbers which are divisible by 9.

216; 343; 666; 7,281; 9,999; 1,377; 6,716; 9,036

10. **Encircle the numbers which are divisible by 10 as well as 100.**

300; 4,730; 89,100; 20,000; 68,001; 73,600; 89,707; 65,550

11. **Encircle the numbers which are divisible by 3 as well as 5.**

600; 750; 215; 700; 555; 55; 1,785; 1,945

Composite and Prime Numbers

We know that even numbers are those numbers that are divisible by 2. We also know that odd numbers are those numbers that are not divisible by 2.

When we learnt about factors we observed that some numbers were divisible by two or more numbers other than 1 and the number itself. Such numbers are called **composite numbers**

Examples of composite numbers:

6 (divisible by 3, 2), 15 (divisible by 3, 5), 21 (divisible by 3, 7), etc.

We also have numbers that are divisible only by 1 and the number itself. Such numbers are called **prime numbers**. Thus, a number is either a prime number or a composite number. The only exception to the above statement is the number 1.

> *1 is neither a prime number nor a composite number, although 1 is divisible by 1 and the number itself.*

Examples of prime numbers:

Look at the numbers 2, 7, 29, 47, etc. These numbers cannot be divided by any number other than 1 or the number itself.

Factors of 2: 1 and 2

Factors of 29: 1 and 29

Factors of 47: 1 and 47

Thus, 2, 29 and 47 are prime numbers.

Example 1: Find all the prime and composite numbers from 1 to 10.

The following table lists the factors of the numbers from 1 to 10.

Number	Factors
1	1
2	1, 2
3	1, 3
4	1, 2, 4
5	1, 5
6	1, 2, 3, 6
7	1, 7
8	1, 2, 4, 8
9	1, 3, 9
10	1, 2, 5, 10

> *2 is the only even prime number.*

Observe that the numbers 2, 3, 5 and 7 have only two factors each—1 and the number itself. So 2, 3, 5 and 7 are prime numbers.

The numbers 4, 6, 8, 9 and 10 have more than two factors each. So they are composite numbers.

Primes Between 1 and 100

In the previous section we identified the primes between 1 and 10 by listing out the factors of each number.

Eratosthenes was a Greek mathematician who found a method to find the prime numbers between 1 and 100. The method is popularly known as the **Sieve of Eratosthenes** as the table of numbers so formed is full of crosses or gaps.

1	2	3	4	5	6	7	8	9	10
11	12	13	14	15	16	17	18	19	20
21	22	23	24	25	26	27	28	29	30
31	32	33	34	35	36	37	38	39	40
41	42	43	44	45	46	47	48	49	50
51	52	53	54	55	56	57	58	59	60
61	62	63	64	65	66	67	68	69	70
71	72	73	74	75	76	77	78	79	80
81	82	83	84	85	86	87	88	89	90
91	92	93	94	95	96	97	98	99	100

Step 1: As 1 is not a prime number it is crossed out.

Step 2: The next number 2 is left as it is and all multiples of 2 (4, 8, 24, etc.–all even numbers except 2) are crossed out.

Step 3: The next number 3 is left as it is and all multiples of 3 (9, 27, etc.), that have not already been crossed out, are crossed out.

Step 4: The next number 5 is left as it is and all multiples of 5 (25, 55, etc.), that have not already been crossed out, are crossed out.

Step 5: The next number 7 is left as it is and all multiples of 7 (49, 91, etc.), that have not already been crossed out, are crossed out.

After crossing out 1 and all the composite numbers, we are left with 25 prime numbers between 1 and 100. The 25 prime numbers between 1 and 100 are:

2, 3, 5, 7, 11, 13, 17, 19, 23, 29, 31, 37, 41,

43, 47, 53, 59, 61, 67, 71, 73, 79, 83, 89, 97

In the Sieve of Eratosthenes we find seven sets of two prime numbers between 2 and 100 which are separated by one composite number.

For example, 3 and 5, 5 and 7, 11 and 13, 17 and 19, 41 and 43, 59 and 61, 71 and 73, etc. Such prime numbers which differ by 2 are known as **twin prime numbers.**

If two numbers have only 1 as a common factor, they are known as **coprime numbers.**

Thus, *all prime numbers are coprime numbers, but all coprime numbers need not be prime numbers.*

Example 2: Are 15 and 12 coprime numbers?

The factors of 15 are 1, 15, 3 and 5.

The factors of 12 are 1, 12, 2, 3, 4 and 6.

15 and 12 have 1 and 3 as common factors. Hence they are not coprime numbers.

Example 3: Are 12 and 13 coprime numbers?

The factors of 12 are 1, 12, 2, 3, 4 and 6.

The factors of 13 are 1 and 13.

As 1 is the only common factor between 12 and 13, they are coprime numbers. Notice that in this set of coprime numbers, 13 is a prime number and 12 is a composite number.

Exercise 6.4

1. Given below is a table of numbers from 1 to 200. Cross out the composite numbers to make a Sieve of Eratosthenes and answer the questions that follow.

[**Hint:** *Instead of prime numbers upto 7, you will now have to go upto 17.*]

1	2	3	4	5	6	7	8	9	10	11	12	13	14	15	16	17	18	19	20
21	22	23	24	25	26	27	28	29	30	31	32	33	34	35	36	37	38	39	40
41	42	43	44	45	46	47	48	49	50	51	52	53	54	55	56	57	58	59	60
61	62	63	64	65	66	67	68	69	70	71	72	73	74	75	76	77	78	79	80
81	82	83	84	85	86	87	88	89	90	91	92	93	94	95	96	97	98	99	100
101	102	103	104	105	106	107	108	109	110	111	112	113	114	115	116	117	118	119	120
121	122	123	124	125	126	127	128	129	130	131	132	133	134	135	136	137	138	139	140
141	142	143	144	145	146	147	148	149	150	151	152	153	154	155	156	157	158	159	160
161	162	163	164	165	166	167	168	169	170	171	172	173	174	175	176	177	178	179	180
181	182	183	184	185	186	187	188	189	190	191	192	193	194	195	196	197	198	199	200

(a) Write all the prime numbers between 80 and 100.

____

(b) Write all the prime numbers between 120 and 130.

____

(c) Write all the prime numbers between 150 and 200.

____

(d) How many prime numbers are there between 1 and 100?

____

(e) How many prime numbers are there between 100 and 200?

____

(f) Write five sets of twin prime numbers.

____

(g) Write five sets of prime numbers whose difference is 4.

____

2. Write whether the following statements are true or false.

(a) After 197 and 199, the next set of twin primes is 209 and 211. ☐

(b) 189 and 160 are coprime numbers. ☐

(c) 36 and 63 are coprime numbers. ☐

(d) If 3 and 5 are twin primes and 5 and 7 are twin primes, then 3 and 7 are also twin primes. ☐

(e) 4 is the smallest composite number. ☐

(f) 1 is the smallest prime number. ☐

(g) 97 is the greatest 2-digit composite number. ☐

(h) 98 is the greatest 2-digit composite number. ☐

(i) 101 is the smallest 3-digit prime number. ☐

(j) 405 and 392 are coprime numbers. ☐

3. Write the factors of the given number and state whether they are composite or prime.

	Number	Factors	Prime or Composite
(a)	12	1, 2, 3, 4, 6, 12	Composite number
(b)	41	1, 41	Prime number
(c)	7		
(d)	16		
(e)	23		
(f)	27		
(g)	42		
(h)	43		
(i)	55		
(j)	91		
(k)	101		
(l)	108		

Factorisation

Factorisation involves finding out all the possible factors of a number.

Earlier in this chapter we learnt how all the factors of a number can be found by repeated factorisation of the bigger numbers.

Example 1: Find all the possible factors of 70.

Factorisation	Factors
$1 \times 70 = 70$	1 and 70
$2 \times 35 = 70$	2 and 35
70 is not divisible by 3 and 4.	
$5 \times 14 = 70$	5 and 14
70 is not divisible by 6.	
$7 \times 10 = 70$	7 and 10
70 is not divisible by 8 and 9. The factor 10 has already been found.	

Thus, all the factors of 70 are 1, 2, 5, 7, 10, 14, 35 and 70.

Prime Factorisation

In the previous example, we found that upon factorisation of 70, we get some prime numbers and some composite numbers as factors. We know that composite numbers can be expressed as products of prime numbers.

For example, $35 = 7 \times 5$ and $70 = 7 \times 5 \times 2$

Prime factorisation is the expression of a number as the product of only prime numbers.

Prime factorisation can be done by two methods—factor tree method and successive division method.

Example 2: Obtain the prime factorisation of 360.

Method 1: Prime factorisation by building a factor tree

If the factors of a number are shown as branching out, as shown below, we get a **factor tree**

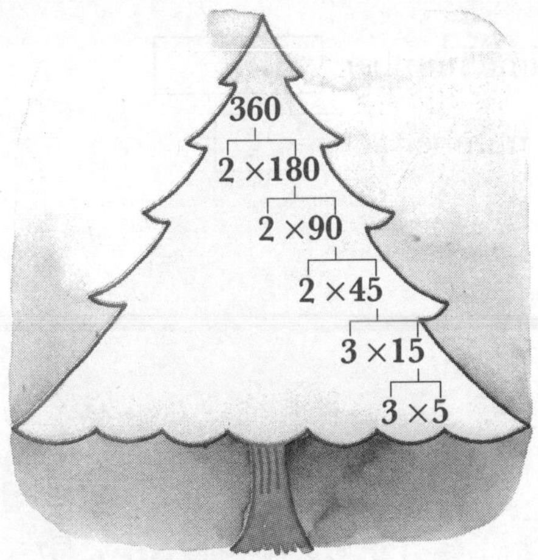

Step 1: Start with the smallest prime factor of 360.

$$2 \times 180 = 360$$

Step 2: Next, find the smallest prime factor of 180.

$$2 \times 90 = 180$$

Step 3: Continue to find the smallest prime factor at every step.

Step 4: Stop when the last row has only prime numbers.

Thus, prime factorisation of 360 = $2 \times 2 \times 2 \times 3 \times 3 \times 5$

The result will be the same even if the factor tree branches out differently.

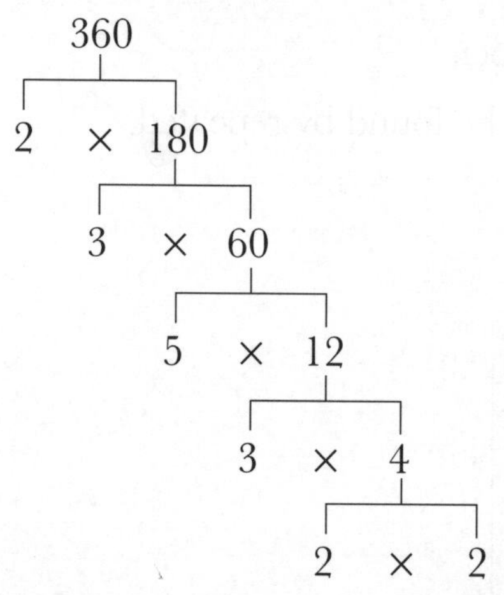

360
3 × 120
5 × 24
3 × 8
2 × 4
2 × 2

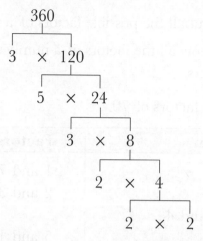

$360 = 2 \times 3 \times 5 \times 3 \times 2 \times 2$ $\quad$ $360 = 3 \times 5 \times 3 \times 2 \times 2 \times 2$

Try this!
Use factor tree method to find the prime factors of 60.

Method 2: Prime factorisation by successive division

Here we divide the number successively by the smallest prime number possible till the quotient is 1.

2	360
2	180
2	90
3	45
3	15
5	5
	1

- ➤ Divide by the smallest prime number 2. Write the quotient below the dividend.
- ➤ Continuing with 2, divide the quotient again.
- ➤ Continuing with 2, divide the quotient again.
- ➤ Next smallest prime number is 3, so divide the quotient by 3.
- ➤ Continuing with 3, divide the quotient again.
- ➤ Next smallest prime number is 5, so divide the quotient by 5.
- ➤ Stop when the quotient is 1.

Thus, 360 = $2 \times 2 \times 2 \times 3 \times 3 \times 5$

Exercise 6.5

1. State whether the following are true or false.

(a) The product of two prime numbers is a prime number. [F]

(b) The sum of two prime numbers is a prime number. [F]

(c) 1 is a prime number. [F]

(d) 2 is the only even prime number. [T]

2. **Fill in the boxes to complete the factor trees.**

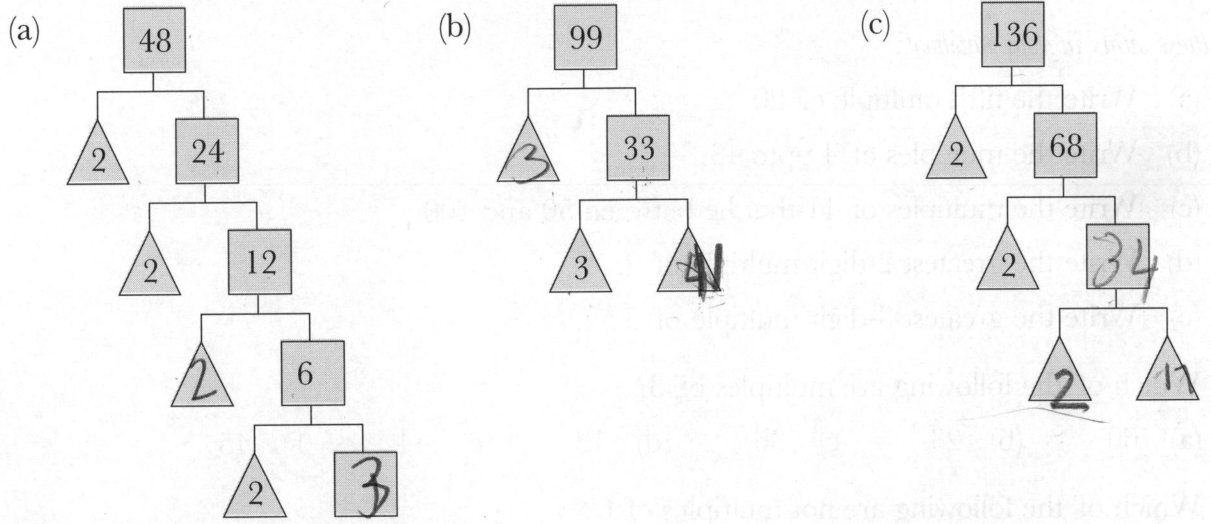

3. **Obtain the prime factorisation by using the successive division method in each of the following.**

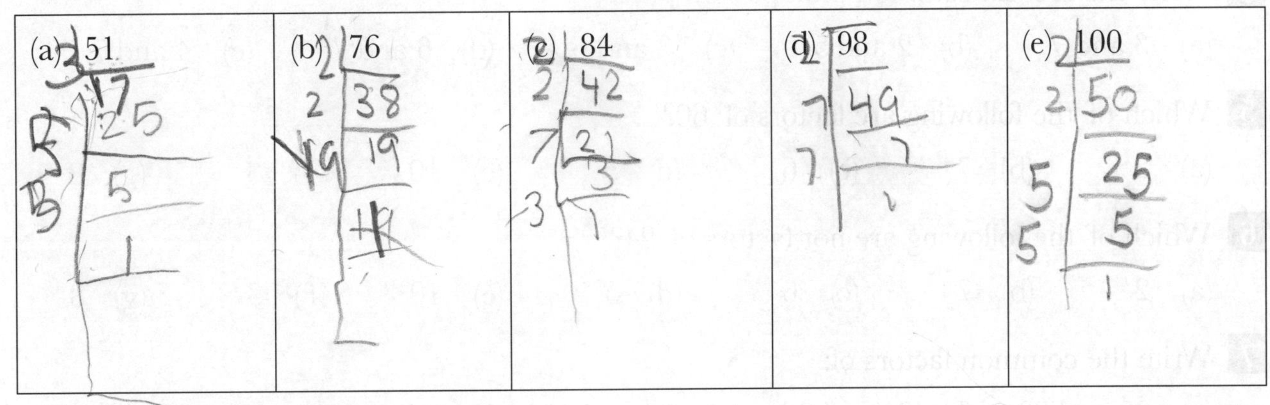

(a) 51	(b) 76	(c) 84	(d) 98	(e) 100

Do these sums in your notebook.

(f) 185 (g) 364 (h) 640 (i) 635 (j) 672

4. **Obtain the prime factorisation by using the factor tree method in each of the following.**

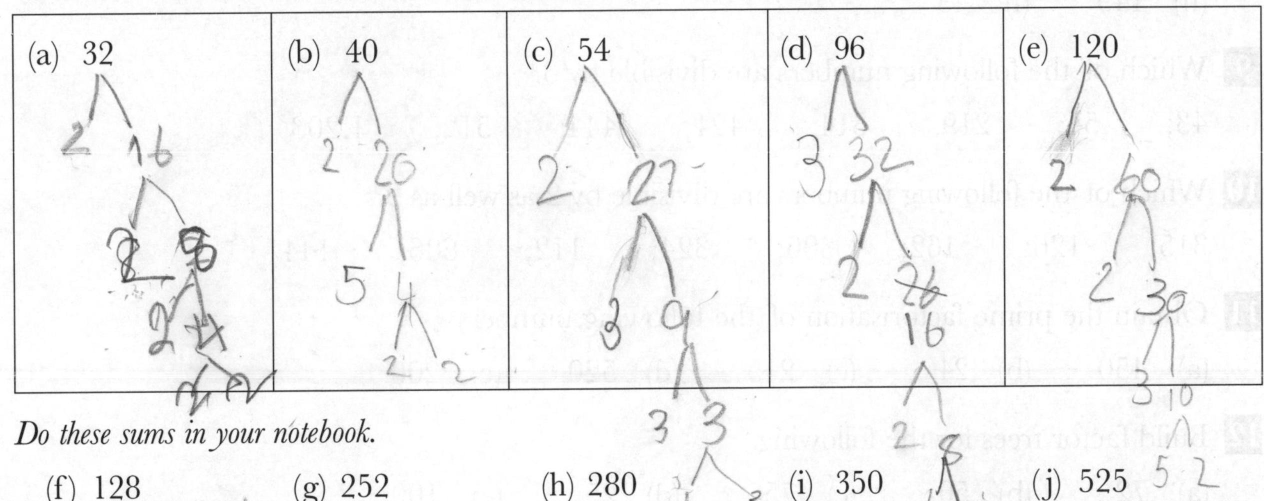

(a) 32	(b) 40	(c) 54	(d) 96	(e) 120

Do these sums in your notebook.

(f) 128 (g) 252 (h) 280 (i) 350 (j) 525

Revision Exercise

Do these sums in your notebook.

1 (a) Write the fifth multiple of 20.

(b) Write the multiples of 4 upto 48.

(c) Write the multiples of 11 that lie between 50 and 100.

(d) Write the greatest 2-digit multiple of 2.

(e) Write the greatest 3-digit multiple of 3.

2 Which of the following are multiples of 3?

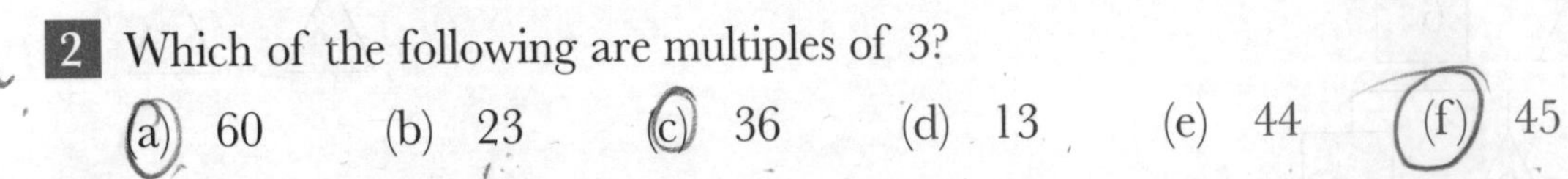

(a) 60 (b) 23 (c) 36 (d) 13 (e) 44 (f) 45

3 Which of the following are not multiples of 6?

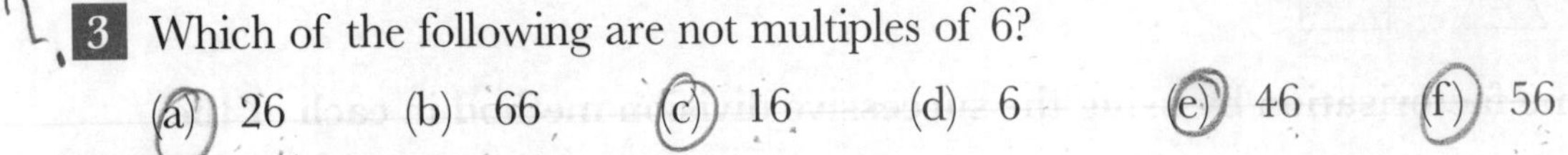

(a) 26 (b) 66 (c) 16 (d) 6 (e) 46 (f) 56

4 Write the first six common multiples of:

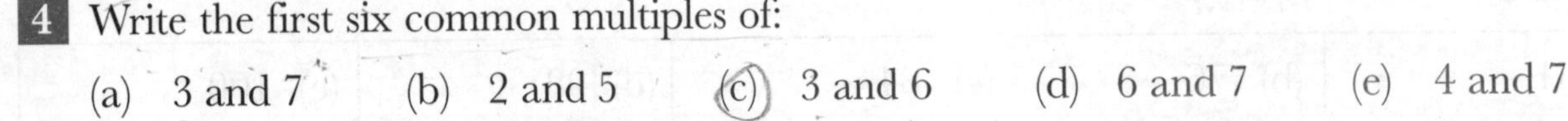

(a) 3 and 7 (b) 2 and 5 (c) 3 and 6 (d) 6 and 7 (e) 4 and 7

5 Which of the following are factors of 60?

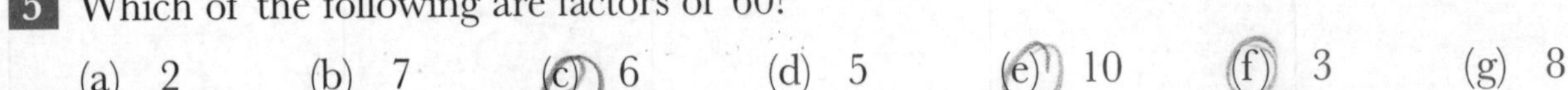

(a) 2 (b) 7 (c) 6 (d) 5 (e) 10 (f) 3 (g) 8

6 Which of the following are not factors of 24?

(a) 2 (b) 7 (c) 6 (d) 5 (e) 10 (f) 3 (g) 8

7 Write the common factors of:

(a) 25 and 30 (b) 21 and 36 (c) 24 and 48 (d) 45 and 75 (e) 56 and 64

8 Which of the following are factors of 975?

(a) 39 (b) 15 (c) 26 (d) 45 (e) 195 (f) 9 (g) 25
(h) 149 (i) 45

9 Which of the following numbers are divisible by 3?

43; 54; 219; 314; 421; 444; 512; 1,203

10 Which of the following numbers are divisible by 2 as well as 9?

315; 126; 162; 306; 324; 112; 686; 144

11 Obtain the prime factorisation of the following numbers.

(a) 450 (b) 24 (c) 215 (d) 520 (e) 200

12 Build factor trees for the following.

(a) 72 (b) 50 (c) 75 (d) 25 (e) 100

7 HCF AND LCM

Inside the zoo, the three friends wanted to feed the monkeys. Rahul had 56 peanuts and Priya had 40 peanuts for the monkeys.

You have learnt about factors and multiples in the previous chapter. You are also familiar with common factors and common multiples. In this chapter you will learn about the highest common factor (HCF) and the lowest common multiple (LCM) of two given numbers.

Highest Common Factor

Look at the numbers 56 and 40.

The factors of 56 are 1, 2, 4, 7, 8, 14, 28 and 56.

The factors of 40 are 1, 2, 4, 5, 8, 10, 20 and 40.

Common factors of 56 and 40 are 1, 2, 4 and 8. Of these four common factors, 8 is the highest number or the greatest number that will divide 56 and 40 without leaving any remainder. So 8 is the **highest common factor** or **HCF** of 56 and 40.

Common factors

Factors of 56	Common	Factors of 40
7	1	5
14	2	10
28	4	20
56	8	40

Thus, the highest common factor or HCF of two or more numbers is the greatest number that divides all the numbers without leaving any remainder.

Example 1: Find the HCF of 24 and 36.

Let us first find out the factors of 24 and 36.

Factors of 24	1, 2, 3, 4, 6, 8, 12 and 24
Factors of 36	1, 2, 3, 4, 6, 9, 12, 18 and 36
Common factors of 24 and 36	1, 2, 3, 4, 6 and 12

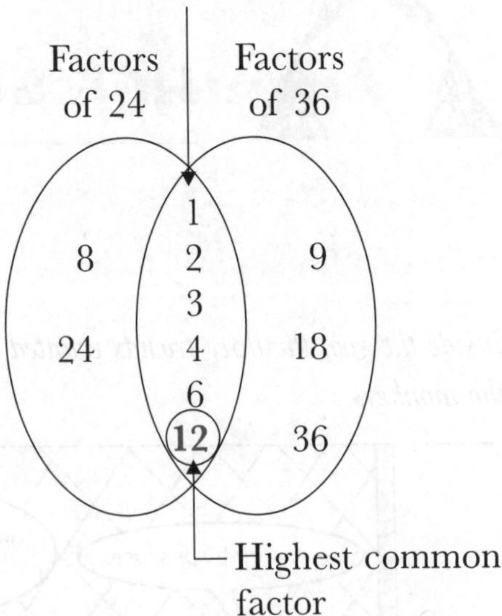

Of all the common factors of 24 and 36, 12 is the greatest common factor.

Therefore 12 is the highest common factor or the HCF of 24 and 36.

Example 2: Find the HCF of 21 and 63.

Factors of 21 = 1, 3, 7, 21
Factors of 63 = 1, 3, 7, 9, 21, 63

Common factors are 1, 3, 7 and 21. Of these, 21 is the greatest common factor.

Thus, the HCF of 21 and 63 is 21.

Try this!
Find the HCF of 20 and 45.

Example 3: Find the HCF of 12 and 25.

Factors of 12 = 1, 2, 3, 4, 6 and 12

Factors of 25 = 1, 5 and 25

Common factor of 12 and 25 is 1

Here, 1 is the only common factor and hence the greatest common factor that divides 12 and 25 without leaving any remainder.

So, the HCF of 12 and 25 is 1.

If the HCF of two numbers is 1, then the numbers are called coprime numbers.

HCF by Prime Factorisation

Note that the HCF of two or more numbers is the product of their common prime factors. ⇒ Thus, we can find the HCF of two or more numbers by obtaining their prime factorisation.

Example 1: Find the HCF of 225 and 468.

By prime factorisation of 225 and 468, we get

3	225
3	75
5	25
5	5
	1

2	468
2	234
3	117
3	39
13	13
	1

Try this!
Find the HCF of 60 and 90 by prime factorisation.

Thus, 225 = (3) × (3) × 5 × 5

468 = 2 × 2 × (3) × (3) × 13

Thus the HCF of 225 and 468 = 3 × 3 = 9

Example 2: Find the HCF of 504 and 648.

By successive division of 504 and 648, we get

2	504
2	252
2	126
3	63
3	21
7	7
	1

2	648
2	324
2	162
3	81
3	27
3	9
3	3
	1

Try this!
Find the HCF of 84 and 105 by prime factorisation.

Now, encircle the common prime factors.

504 = (2) × (2) × (2) × (3) × (3) × 7

648 = (2) × (2) × (2) × (3) × (3) × 3 × 3

Thus, the HCF of 504 and 648 = 2 × 2 × 2 × 3 × 3 = 72

- *The HCF of two numbers is the greatest number that divides all the numbers without leaving any remainder.*
- *The numbers that have 1 as their HCF are called coprimes. The numbers themselves may or may not be prime numbers.*
- *The HCF is always smaller than or equal to the smaller number.*

Exercise 7.1

1. Find the HCF of the following numbers.

(a) 12 and 15	(b) 12 and 18	(c) 16 and 20	(d) 28 and 62

Do these sums in your notebook.

(e) 25 and 30 (f) 72 and 81 (g) 48 and 36 (h) 84 and 98

(i) 78 and 91 (j) 60 and 72 (k) 54 and 81 (l) 64 and 80

(m) 54 and 108 (n) 120 and 135

2. Find the HCF of the following numbers by prime factorisation.

(a) 15 and 30	(b) 36 and 54	(c) 63 and 49	(d) 75 and 165

Do these sums in your notebook

(e) 16 and 48 (f) 84 and 126 (g) 96 and 108 (h) 130 and 78

(i) 168 and 196 (j) 176 and 192 (k) 192 and 216 (l) 195 and 260

(m) 231 and 264 (n) 273 and 294

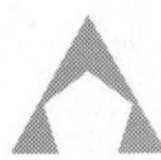

Lowest Common Multiple

When Rahul and Priya reached the ticket counter, two toy trains were waiting on either side of the narrow platform. Soon both trains left together for their round trips.

Observe the multiplication tables of the following numbers.

Multipliers →

Multiplicand ↓

×	1	2	3	4	5	6	7	8	9	10	11	12
2	2	4	6	8	10	12	14	16	18	20	22	24
3	3	6	9	12	15	18	21	24	27	30	33	36
5	5	10	15	20	25	30	35	40	45	50	55	60
7	7	14	21	28	35	42	49	56	63	70	77	84
10	10	20	30	40	50	60	70	80	90	100	110	120
15	15	30	45	60	75	90	105	120	135	150	165	180
20	20	40	60	80	100	120	140	160	180	200	220	240

The grid shows the first 12 multiples of the numbers 2, 3, 5, 7, 10, 15 and 20.

On comparison of these multiples, we find many common multiples.

For instance,
common multiples of 2 and 3 are 6, 12, 18, 24.
common multiples of 10 and 15 are 30, 60, 90, 120.

Notice that the first common multiple is the **least** among the **common multiples**

Of the common multiples of 2 and 3, 6 is the **lowest common multiple**

Of the common multiples of 10 and 15, 30 is the lowest common multiple.

Thus, the *lowest common multiple* or *LCM of two or more numbers is the smallest of their common multiples.*

Example 1: Find the LCM of 3 and 5 by recollecting their multiplication tables.

In the multiplication table of 3, 15 is the lowest multiple that is also divisible by 5.

So, 15 is the lowest common multiple (LCM) of 3 and 5.

Alternatively

Multiples of 3 are 3, 6, 9, 12, 15, 18, 21, 24, 27, 30, and so on.

Multiples of 5 are 5, 10, 15, 20, 25, 30, and so on.

So, common multiples of 3 and 5 are 15, 30, and so on.

Lowest among the common multiples of 3 and 5 is 15.

Therefore, 15 is the lowest common multiple (LCM) of 3 and 5.

Try this!
Find the LCM of 3 and 8.

Example 2: Find the LCM of 7 and 14.

Multiples of 7 are 7, 14, 21, 28, 35, 42, 49, 56, 63, 70, and so on.

Multiples of 14 are 14, 28, 42, 56, 70, and so on.

So, common multiples of 7 and 14 are 14, 28, 42, 56, 70, and so on.

Lowest among the common multiples of 7 and 14 is 14.

Therefore, 14 is the lowest common multiple (LCM) of 7 and 14.

Of two numbers, if one is a multiple of the other, the greater number is the LCM.

LCM as Product of Prime Factors

We can find the LCM of bigger numbers by finding the product of their prime factors.

Example: Find the LCM of 42 and 56.

Step 1: We first find the prime factors of the two numbers.

2	42
3	21
7	7
	1

2	56
2	28
2	14
7	7
	1

Step 2: We then find the common factors as well as the factors that are not common.

Mental maths

You know that of two numbers, if one is a multiple of the other, the greater number is the LCM.

Using this information, find the LCM of the following:

(a) LCM of 2 and 10 = ________

(b) LCM of 5 and 10 = ________

(c) LCM of 10 and 20 = ________

$42 = \textcircled{2} \times 3 \times \textcircled{7}$

$56 = \textcircled{2} \times 2 \times 2 \times \textcircled{7}$

Common factors are 2 and 7.

Product of common factors = 2 × 7 = 14

The factors that are not common are 3, 2 and 2 and their product is 3 × 2 × 2 = 12

Step 3: LCM = (Product of common factors) × (Product of factors that are not common)

= 14 × 12 = 168

Thus, LCM of 42 and 56 is 168.

LCM = Product of common factors × Product of factors that are not common

LCM by Prime Factorisation

A much easier method for finding the LCM of two or more numbers is to obtain the prime factorisation of the numbers.

Example: Find the LCM of 78 and 104 by the method of prime factorisation.

2	78,	104
2	39,	52
2	39,	26
3	39,	13
13	13,	13
	1,	1

Step 1: Arrange the numbers with commas in between. Start dividing by 2. 39 is brought down as it is not divisible by 2.

Step 2: Continue till none of the numbers is divisible by 2.

Step 3: Divide by the next prime divisor, 3, and so on.

Step 4: Stop when the quotient is 1.

LCM = product of all prime divisors = 2 × 2 × 2 × 3 × 13 = 312

The LCM of two numbers is the smallest number that will be divided by those numbers without leaving a remainder.

Exercise 7.2

1. **First find 8 multiples of each of these numbers, and then find 2 common multiples. Finally, find the LCM.**

Numbers		Multiples	Common Multiples	LCM
(a)	4			
	6			
(b)	5			
	10			
(c)	3			
	4			

2. **Find the LCM of the following numbers by recollecting their multiplication tables.**
(Do these sums in your notebook.)

(a) 3 and 4 (b) 6 and 8 (c) 5 and 11 (d) 5 and 6
(e) 5 and 7 (f) 6 and 10 (g) 12 and 14 (h) 10 and 14
(i) 10 and 12 (j) 12 and 15 (k) 8 and 16 (l) 16 and 18
(m) 4 and 5 (n) 5 and 20 (o) 8 and 12 (p) 71 and 13

3. **Find the LCM of the following numbers by prime factorisation.**

(a) 24 and 48	(b) 30 and 40	(c) 48 and 56	(d) 45 and 72
LCM =	LCM =	LCM =	LCM =

Do these sums in your notebook.

(e) 42 and 52 (f) 120 and 180 (g) 150 and 300 (h) 144 and 360
(i) 273 and 390 (j) 360 and 420 (k) 400 and 480 (l) 420 and 1,050

Revision Exercise

Do these sums in your notebook.

1 Write the prime factors and multiples of the following numbers and then find their HCF and LCM.

Prime factors	Numbers	Multiples
2, 2, **3**	12	12, 24, 36, 48, **60**, …
3, 5	15	15, 30, 45, **60**, 75, …
HCF = 3		LCM = 60
	7	
	3	
HCF =		LCM =
	39	
	52	
HCF =		LCM =
	40	
	50	
HCF =		LCM =
	42	
	63	
HCF =		LCM =
	72	
	108	
HCF =		LCM =

2 Find the HCF of the following pairs of numbers.

(a) 12 and 24 (b) 81 and 162 (c) 260 and 320 (d) 12 and 15

(e) 5 and 7 (f) 13 and 19 (g) 24 and 36 (h) 45 and 30

(i) 24 and 54 (j) 85 and 102 (k) 198 and 180 (l) 98 and 126

3 Find the LCM of the following numbers.

(a) 2 and 4 (b) 18 and 36 (c) 15 and 20 (d) 25 and 20

(e) 72 and 54 (f) 38 and 57 (g) 45 and 40 (h) 78 and 65

(i) 326 and 489 (j) 63 and 81 (k) 64 and 96 (l) 36 and 48

4 If 228 is a multiple of 19, is 19 a factor of 228?

5 If 29 is a factor of 261, is 29 a multiple of 261?

8 FRACTIONAL NUMBERS

Let's Recap

1. Shade the parts to show the given fractions.

(a) 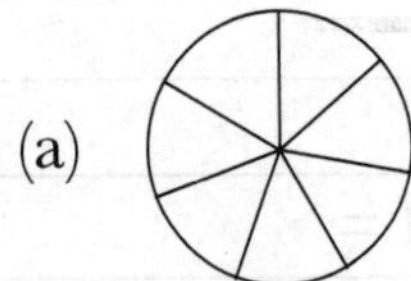 $\frac{3}{7}$

(b) 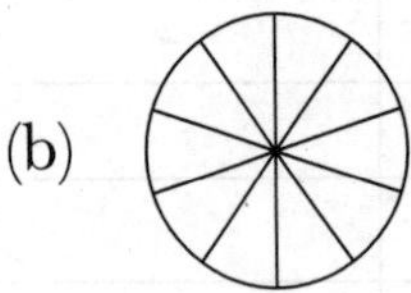 $\frac{3}{10}$

(c) 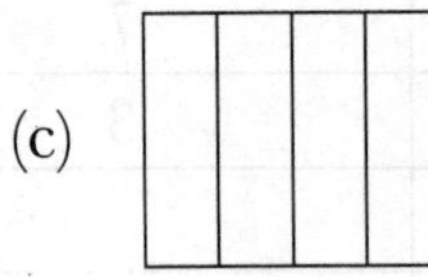 $\frac{3}{4}$

Do you remember?

2 → Numerator
— → Division line
5 → Denominator

2. Which of the following pairs are not equivalent fractions?

(a) 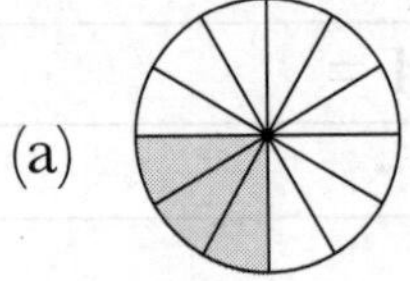 $\frac{3}{12}$ 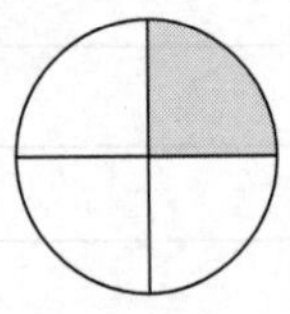 $\frac{1}{4}$

(b) 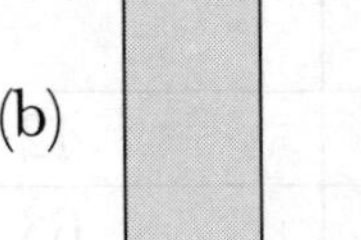 $\frac{1}{2}$ 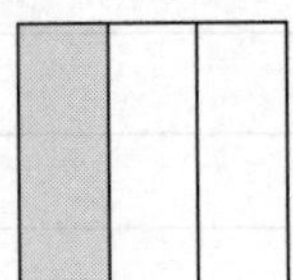 $\frac{1}{3}$

3. Write the numerator and the denominator in each of the following fractions?

(a) $\frac{2}{3}$, Numerator = ☐, Denominator = ☐

(b) $\frac{1}{4}$, Numerator = ☐, Denominator = ☐

(c) $\frac{4}{5}$, Numerator = ☐, Denominator = ☐

4. Write the fraction which is greater.

(a) $\frac{1}{3}$ or $\frac{2}{3}$, ☐

(b) $\frac{4}{7}$ or $\frac{5}{7}$, ☐

(c) $\frac{3}{5}$ or $\frac{3}{7}$, ☐

The three friends decided to share the chocolates they got from their homes. Priya broke her chocolate into 8 equal pieces and gave 4 pieces to Rahul. Rohan broke his chocolate into 6 equal pieces and gave 3 pieces to Rahul.

Fractions

When we divide a whole into smaller parts, the smaller parts are called fractions. The resultant numbers are called fractional numbers.

Parts of One Whole

When 1 whole is divided into parts, the resulting fractions that we get are called unit fractions. The numerator in all unit fractions is 1.

1 divided into 2 equal parts

$= 1 \div 2 = \frac{1}{2}$ **1 ← Numerator**, **2 ← Denominator**

Observe that $\frac{1}{2} + \frac{1}{2} = 1$ *or* $2 \times \frac{1}{2} = 1$

or 2 times $\frac{1}{2} = 1$

1 divided into 3 equal parts

$= 1 \div 3 = \mathbf{\frac{1}{3}}$

Observe that $\frac{1}{3} + \frac{1}{3} + \frac{1}{3} = 1$ *or* $3 \times \frac{1}{3} = 1$

or 3 times $\frac{1}{3} = 1$

1 divided into 8 equal parts

$= 1 \div 8 = \mathbf{\frac{1}{8}}$

Observe that $\frac{1}{8} + \frac{1}{8} + \frac{1}{8} + \frac{1}{8} + \frac{1}{8} + \frac{1}{8} + \frac{1}{8} + \frac{1}{8} = 1$ *or* $8 \times \frac{1}{8} = 1$ *or* 8 times $\frac{1}{8} = 1$

Parts of a Collection

A collection refers to a group of objects.

The chocolate shown is a collection of 24 equal pieces.

One-third

If the chocolate is divided into 3 equal parts, one part will have 8 pieces out of 24 equal pieces, which can be written as $\frac{8}{24}$.

This is same as $\frac{1}{3}$ of the total number of pieces or **one-third** of the chocolate.

Thus, $\frac{1}{3}$ of 24 is 8 [$24 \div 3 = 8$ and $8 \times 1 = 8$] and $\frac{8}{24} = \frac{1}{3}$.

Two-thirds

If the chocolate is divided into 3 equal parts, and 2 parts are taken together, the two parts will have 16 pieces altogether out of 24 equal pieces, which can be written as $\frac{16}{24}$.

This is same as $\frac{2}{3}$ of the total number of pieces or **two-thirds** of the chocolate.

Thus, $\frac{2}{3}$ of 24 is 16 [$24 \div 3 = 8$ and $8 \times 2 = 16$] and $\frac{16}{24} = \frac{2}{3}$.

Examples

$\frac{1}{3}$ of 18 is 6 [$18 \div 3 = 6$ and $6 \times 1 = 6$]

$\frac{1}{4}$ of 40 is 10 [$40 \div 4 = 10$ and $10 \times 1 = 10$]

$\frac{2}{3}$ of 30 is 20 [$30 \div 3 = 10$ and $10 \times 2 = 20$]

$\frac{2}{5}$ of 25 is 10 [$25 \div 5 = 5$ and $5 \times 2 = 10$]

Let us have a look at the following example.

There are 4 pieces of cake and little Johnny has nobody to share them with. How many pieces will Johnny get?

We know that $4 \div 1 = 4$ *or* $\frac{4}{1} = 4$

So, little Johnny will get all 4 pieces of the cake.

We see that 4 can be written as $\frac{4}{1}$.

Similarly,

$$1 = \frac{1}{1}, 2 = \frac{2}{1}, 3 = \frac{3}{1}, 7 = \frac{7}{1}, \text{ etc.}$$

***Example 1*:** 4 pieces of a pizza are divided equally among 2 girls. How many pieces will each girl get?

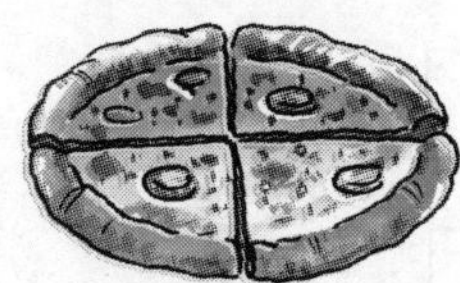

We know that $4 \div 2 = 2$

or $\frac{4}{2} = 2$

So, each girl will get 2 pieces of cake.

More Examples:

$$\frac{10}{2} = 10 \div 2 = 5$$

$$\frac{6}{2} = 6 \div 2 = 3$$

$$\frac{8}{4} = 8 \div 4 = 2$$

Try this!

Write the fraction for the following.

(a) 1 divided into 7 equal parts = ________

(b) 1 divided into 12 equal parts = ________

Shares of Zero

Suppose there are no pieces of cake. How many pieces will 2 boys get? As there are no pieces of cake to distribute, the boys will get nothing or 0 pieces.

So, $0 \div 2$ or $\frac{0}{2} = 0$. Similarly, $\frac{0}{1} = 0$, $\frac{0}{9} = 0$, etc.

Zero is not written as the denominator of any fraction.

Exercise 8.1

1. Write the fraction that describes the shaded portion in the following figures.

(a)

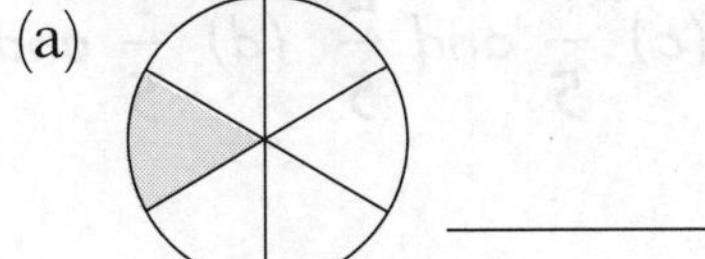

(b)

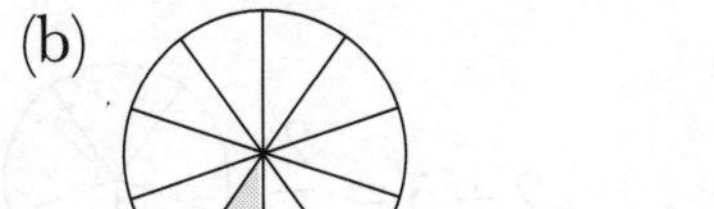

(c)

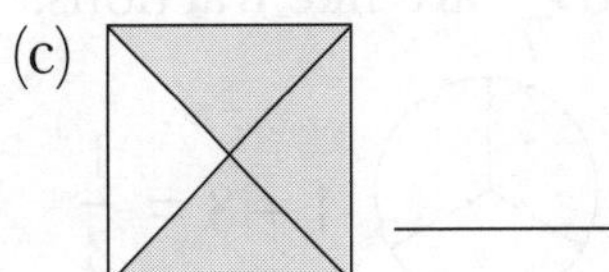

(d)

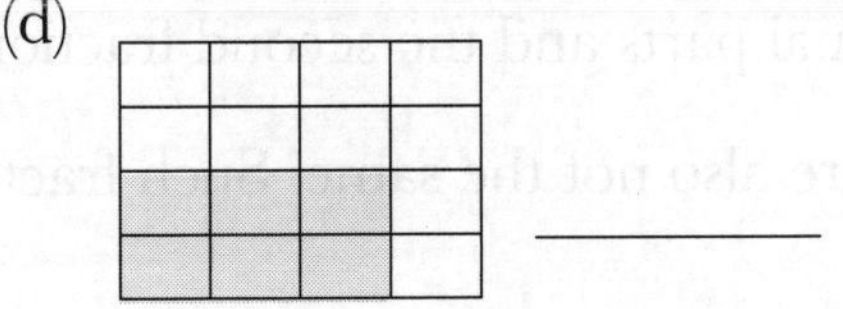

(e)

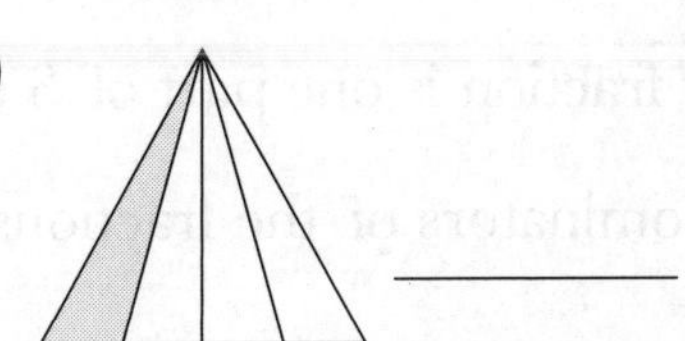

(f)

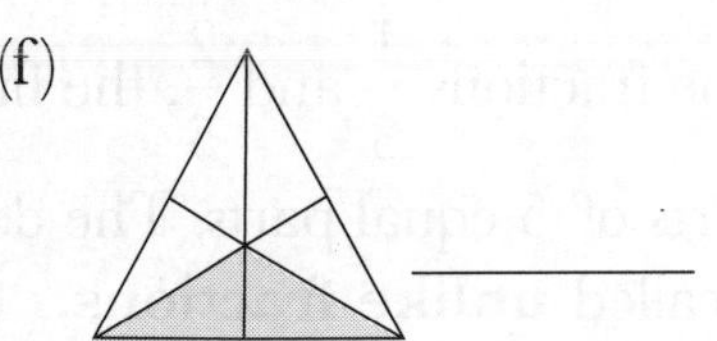

2. Fill in the boxes.

(a) $\frac{8}{2} = \boxed{4}$ (b) $\frac{6}{3} = \square$ (c) $\frac{16}{2} = \square$

(d) $\frac{27}{3} = \square$ (e) $\frac{18}{3} = \square$ (f) $\frac{14}{4} = \square$

3. Fill in the boxes provided for the parts of a collection.

(a) $\frac{1}{3}$ of 12 = 12 ÷ 3 = $\boxed{4} \times 1 = \boxed{4}$ (b) $\frac{1}{2}$ of 20 = $\square$

(c) $\frac{1}{4}$ of 16 = 16 ÷ 4 = $\square \times 1 = \square$ (d) $\frac{1}{5}$ of 25 = $\square$

(e) $\frac{1}{4}$ of 4 = 4 ÷ 4 = $\square \times 1 = \square$ (f) $\frac{2}{3}$ of 9 = $\square$

(g) $\frac{3}{5}$ of 15 = $\square$ (h) $\frac{1}{8}$ of 32 = $\square$

Types of Fractions

Let us learn the various types of fractions—like and unlike fractions, proper and improper fractions, equivalent fractions, etc.

Like and Unlike Fractions

$1 \div 4 = \frac{1}{4}$ $3 \div 4 = \frac{3}{4}$

Both these fractions, $\frac{1}{4}$ and $\frac{3}{4}$, are parts of 4 equal parts. The denominators of both the fractions are the same. Such fractions are called **like fractions.**

Fractions with the same denominator are called like fractions.

For example,

$\frac{1}{7}, \frac{3}{7}$ and $\frac{4}{7}$ are like fractions.

> **Try this!**
>
> Encircle the pair of like fractions.
>
> (a) $\frac{2}{3}$ and $\frac{3}{4}$ (b) $\frac{1}{3}$ and $\frac{1}{4}$
>
> (c) $\frac{1}{5}$ and $\frac{2}{5}$ (d) $\frac{1}{5}$ and $\frac{5}{7}$

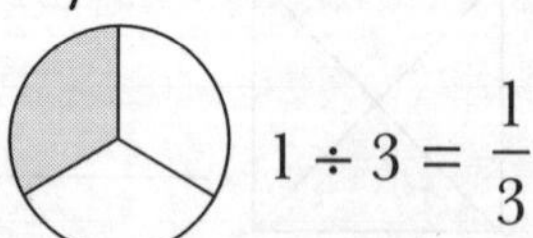

$1 \div 3 = \frac{1}{3}$ $2 \div 5 = \frac{2}{5}$

In the fractions $\frac{1}{3}$ and $\frac{2}{5}$, the first fraction is one part of 3 equal parts and the second fraction is 2 parts of 5 equal parts. The denominators of the fractions are also not the same. Such fractions are called **unlike fractions.**

Fractions with different denominators (numerators can be same or different) are called unlike fractions.

Examples: $\frac{1}{6}$ and $\frac{1}{5}$, $\frac{2}{7}$ and $\frac{2}{9}$, $\frac{3}{5}$ and $\frac{4}{7}$, etc., are pairs of unlike fractions.

Proper and Improper Fractions

Look at the fractions $\frac{1}{4}$, $\frac{4}{4}$ and $\frac{5}{4}$.

Pictorially,

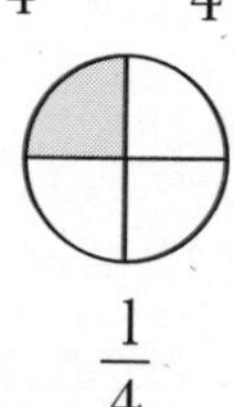

$\frac{1}{4}$

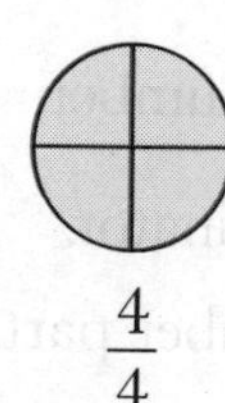

$\frac{4}{4}$

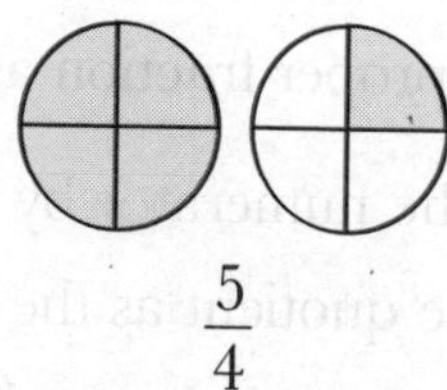

$\frac{5}{4}$

In the fraction $\frac{1}{4}$, the numerator is less than the denominator. This is known as a **proper fraction.**

A fraction where the numerator is less than the denominator is known as a proper fraction.

In $\frac{4}{4}$, the numerator is equal to the denominator. This is a **whole number** $\left(\frac{4}{4}=1\right)$.

In $\frac{5}{4}$, the numerator is greater than the denominator. This is known as an **improper fraction.**

A fraction where the numerator is greater than the denominator is known as an improper fraction.

Mixed Fractions

From the pictorial representation of $\frac{5}{4}$, we can see that $\frac{5}{4} = \frac{4}{4} + \frac{1}{4}$ or $1+\frac{1}{4}$ or 1 whole and $\frac{1}{4}$.

We can write this as $1\frac{1}{4}$, which is called as a mixed fraction. Thus, an improper fraction can be written as a **mixed fraction**

A mixed fraction has a whole number and a proper fraction.

Example 1: Write $\frac{7}{4}$ as a mixed fraction.

Step 1: Express the improper fraction as a division sum ⟶ 7 ÷ 4.

Step 2: Divide 7 by 4.

```
            1 ←— Quotient
Divisor ⟶ 4 ) 7
             −4
              3 ←— Remainder
```

We have, 7 ÷ 4 = 1 (quotient), 3 (remainder)

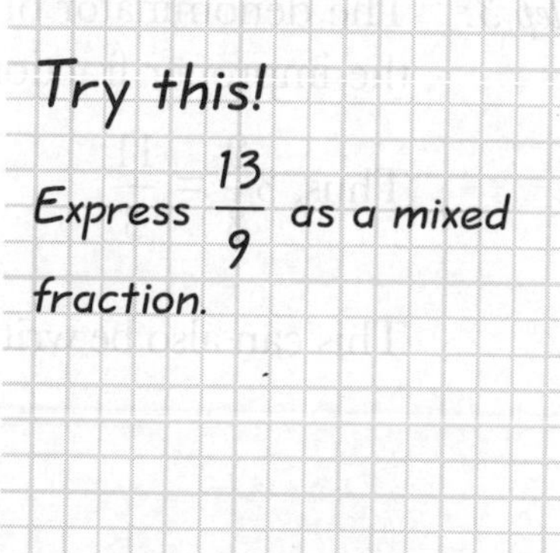

Try this!
Express $\frac{13}{9}$ as a mixed fraction.

This can be written as $1\frac{3}{4}$ → proper fraction (the $\frac{3}{4}$); ↓ 1 whole (the 1)

Thus, $\frac{7}{4} = 1\frac{3}{4}$

To express an improper fraction as a mixed number,

Step 1: Divide the numerator by the denominator.

Step 2: Write the quotient as the whole number part.

Step 3: Write the remainder as the numerator of the fractional part.

Step 4: Write the divisor as the denominator of the fractional part.

Example 2: Write $\frac{18}{3}$ as a mixed fraction.

$$\begin{array}{r|l} & 6 \\ \hline 3 & 18 \\ & -18 \\ \hline & \times \end{array}$$

Mixed fraction = Quotient $\frac{\text{Remainder}}{\text{Divisor}}$

Thus, $\frac{18}{3} = 6$ *(Here the result is a whole number as there is no remainder.)*

Example 3: Write $3\frac{2}{3}$ as an improper fraction.

Step 1: Multiply the denominator of the proper fractional part with the whole number.

$3 \times 3 = 9$

Step 2: Add the product to the numerator of the proper fractional part.

$9 + 2 = 11$

The result is the numerator of the improper fraction.

Step 3: The denominator of the proper fractional part remains the same as the denominator of the improper fraction.

Thus, $3\frac{2}{3} = \frac{11}{3}$

This can also be written as: $3\frac{\oplus 2}{\otimes 3} = \frac{(3 \times 3) + 2}{3} = \frac{9 + 2}{3} = \frac{11}{3}$

Example 4: Write $4\frac{3}{8}$ as an improper fraction.

$$4\frac{3}{8} = 4\frac{\oplus 3}{\otimes 8}$$

$$= \frac{8 \times 4 + 3}{8} = \frac{35}{8}$$

Thus, $4\frac{3}{8} = \frac{35}{8}$

Try this!

Express $2\frac{3}{4}$ as an improper fraction.

Equivalent Fractions

Look at the shaded parts of the following figures.

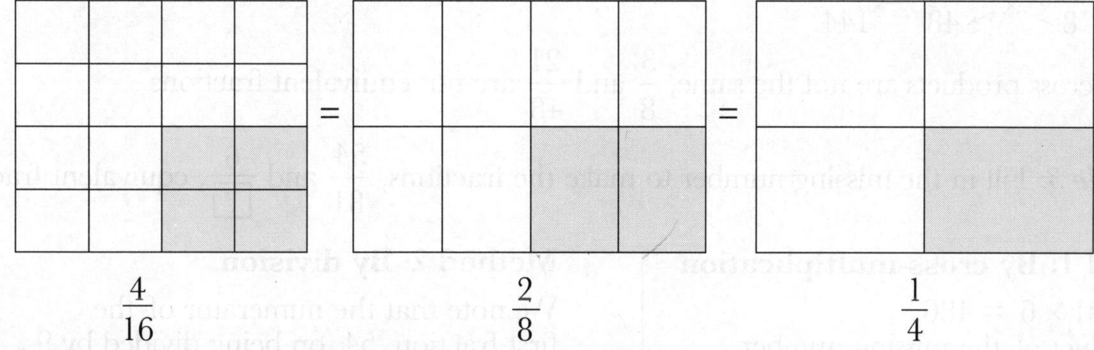

$\frac{4}{16}$ $\qquad$ $\frac{2}{8}$ $\qquad$ $\frac{1}{4}$

In all three figures, the shaded parts represent equal parts of the whole. Such fractions, called **equivalent fractions**, are derived by the **multiplication** of the numerator and denominator by the same number.

For example, $\frac{1 \times \boxed{2}}{4 \times \boxed{2}} = \frac{2}{8}$, $\frac{1 \times \boxed{4}}{4 \times \boxed{4}} = \frac{4}{16}$, $\frac{1 \times \boxed{3}}{4 \times \boxed{3}} = \frac{3}{12}$, $\frac{1 \times \boxed{5}}{4 \times \boxed{5}} = \frac{5}{20}$

If we write this process in reverse, equivalent fractions can again be derived by the **division** of the numerator and denominator by the same number.

For example, $\frac{5 \div \boxed{5}}{20 \div \boxed{5}} = \frac{1}{4}$, $\frac{3 \div \boxed{3}}{12 \div \boxed{3}} = \frac{1}{4}$, $\frac{4 \div \boxed{4}}{16 \div \boxed{4}} = \frac{1}{4}$, $\frac{2 \div \boxed{2}}{8 \div \boxed{2}} = \frac{1}{4}$

Equivalent fractions are obtained by multiplying or dividing the numerator and denominator of a fraction with a common number.

Cross-Multiplication (*To find out if two fractions are equivalent or not*)

Example 1: Is $\frac{4}{7}$ equivalent to $\frac{32}{56}$?

Step 1: Cross-multiply the denominator of the first fraction with the numerator of the second fraction. ⟶ $7 \times 32 = 224$

Step 2: Cross-multiply the numerator of the first fraction with the denominator of the second fraction. ⟶ $4 \times 56 = 224$

This can be written as: $\frac{4}{7} \times \frac{32}{56} = \frac{224}{224}$

If both cross products are the same, the fractions are equivalent fractions.

Thus, $\frac{4}{7}$ and $\frac{32}{56}$ are equivalent fractions.

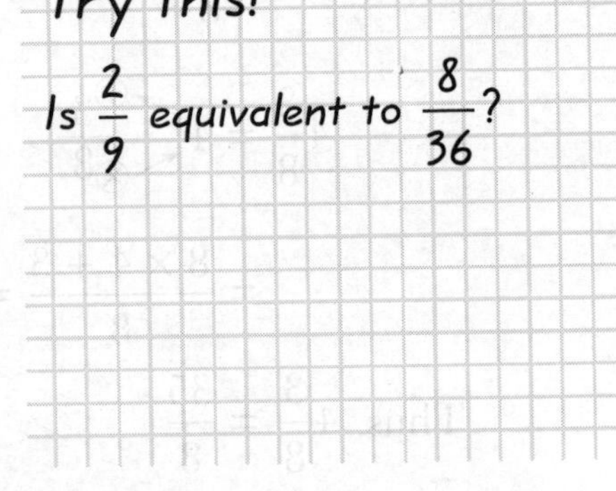

Example 2: Are $\frac{3}{8}$ and $\frac{21}{48}$ equivalent fractions?

We have $\frac{3}{8} \times \frac{21}{48} = \frac{168}{144}$

As both cross products are not the same, $\frac{3}{8}$ and $\frac{21}{48}$ are not equivalent fractions.

Example 3: Fill in the missing number to make the fractions, $\frac{54}{81}$ and $\frac{6}{\boxed{?}}$, equivalent fractions.

Method 1: By cross-multiplication

As $81 \times 6 = 486$,
the product of the missing number and 54 should also be equal to 486.
Thus, by reverse multiplication,

$486 \div 54 = 9$

Hence, the equivalent fractions are $\frac{54}{81}$ and $\frac{6}{9}$.

Method 2: By division

We note that the numerator of the first fraction, 54, on being divided by 9 gives the numerator of the second fraction.

$54 \div 9 = 6$

Therefore, the denominator also has to be divided by 9.

$81 \div 9 = 9$

Thus, the equivalent fractions are $\frac{54}{81}$ and $\frac{6}{9}$.

Exercise 8.2

1. Encircle the pairs that are like fractions.

(a) $\frac{3}{4}$ and $\frac{2}{4}$ (b) $\frac{1}{5}$ and $\frac{7}{5}$ (c) $\frac{6}{8}$ and $\frac{6}{10}$ (d) $\frac{5}{10}$ and $\frac{6}{10}$

(e) $\frac{7}{3}$ and $\frac{1}{3}$ (f) $\frac{8}{5}$ and $\frac{8}{6}$ (g) $\frac{1}{9}$ and $\frac{8}{9}$ (h) $\frac{6}{6}$ and $\frac{5}{6}$

(i) $\frac{3}{2}$ and $\frac{3}{3}$ (j) $\frac{7}{9}$ and $\frac{9}{7}$ (k) $\frac{5}{7}$ and $\frac{9}{7}$ (l) $\frac{7}{5}$ and $\frac{7}{9}$

2. Write one like fraction for each of the following fractions.

(a) $\frac{2}{3}$ and □ (b) $\frac{6}{10}$ and □ (c) $\frac{7}{13}$ and □ (d) $\frac{8}{5}$ and □

(e) $\frac{1}{9}$ and □ (f) $\frac{4}{5}$ and □ (g) $\frac{3}{7}$ and □ (h) $\frac{5}{9}$ and □

3. Write one unlike fraction for each of the following fractions.

(a) $\frac{2}{3}$ and □ (b) $\frac{6}{10}$ and □ (c) $\frac{7}{13}$ and □ (d) $\frac{8}{5}$ and □

(e) $\frac{1}{9}$ and □ (f) $\frac{4}{5}$ and □ (g) $\frac{6}{7}$ and □ (h) $\frac{2}{9}$ and □

Do these sums in your notebook.

4. Write the numerator (N) and denominator (D) of the following fractions and also write if they are proper or improper fractions.

(a) $\frac{3}{7}$ (b) $\frac{7}{3}$ (c) $\frac{56}{57}$ (d) $\frac{9}{11}$ (e) $\frac{12}{10}$

(f) $\frac{4}{40}$ (g) $\frac{39}{2}$ (h) $\frac{42}{41}$ (i) $\frac{3}{6}$ (j) $\frac{3}{3}$

5. Express the following improper fractions as mixed fractions.

(a) $\frac{5}{3}$ (b) $\frac{11}{10}$ (c) $\frac{14}{12}$ (d) $\frac{8}{7}$

(e) $\frac{9}{6}$ (f) $\frac{5}{2}$ (g) $\frac{8}{3}$ (h) $\frac{18}{4}$

(i) $\frac{23}{5}$ (j) $\frac{50}{6}$ (k) $\frac{25}{8}$ (l) $\frac{43}{7}$

6. Express the following mixed fractions as improper fractions.

(a) $1\frac{1}{3}$ (b) $1\frac{6}{9}$ (c) $3\frac{1}{3}$ (d) $8\frac{2}{3}$

(e) $6\frac{3}{5}$ (f) $10\frac{6}{10}$ (g) $3\frac{8}{12}$ (h) $5\frac{7}{15}$

(i) $8\frac{3}{12}$ (j) $20\frac{3}{14}$ (k) $15\frac{5}{4}$ (l) $24\frac{2}{3}$

7. Write three equivalent fractions for the following proper fractions.

(a) $\frac{1}{3}$ 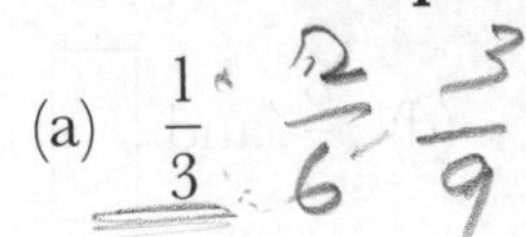 (b) $\frac{3}{5}$ 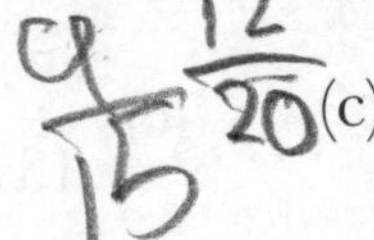 (c) $\frac{5}{7}$ (d) $\frac{4}{9}$

(e) $\frac{2}{10}$ (f) $\frac{3}{4}$ (g) $\frac{4}{7}$ (h) $\frac{1}{8}$

(i) $\frac{5}{9}$ (j) $\frac{7}{9}$ (k) $\frac{5}{8}$ (l) $\frac{7}{10}$

8. Write three equivalent fractions for the following improper fractions.

(a) $\frac{4}{3}$ (b) $\frac{5}{2}$ (c) $\frac{12}{5}$ (d) $\frac{9}{7}$

(e) $\frac{20}{11}$ (f) $\frac{7}{5}$ (g) $\frac{9}{5}$ (h) $\frac{10}{7}$

9. Find, using the cross-multiplication method, equivalent fractions among the following:

(a) $\frac{4}{5}$ and $\frac{24}{25}$ (b) $\frac{1}{6}$ and $\frac{8}{48}$ (c) $\frac{2}{7}$ and $\frac{14}{42}$ (d) $\frac{1}{3}$ and $\frac{3}{9}$

(e) $\frac{40}{72}$ and $\frac{5}{8}$ (f) $\frac{5}{55}$ and $\frac{1}{11}$ (g) $\frac{20}{14}$ and $\frac{5}{7}$ (h) $4\frac{2}{7}$ and $\frac{60}{14}$

(i) $2\frac{4}{5}$ and $2\frac{3}{6}$ (j) $3\frac{2}{5}$ and $1\frac{2}{5}$ (k) $1\frac{6}{7}$ and $1\frac{18}{21}$ (l) $10\frac{1}{2}$ and $3\frac{1}{2}$

Comparison of Fractions

Let us learn how to compare the different types of fractions.

Comparing Like Fractions (*Fractions with same denominator*)

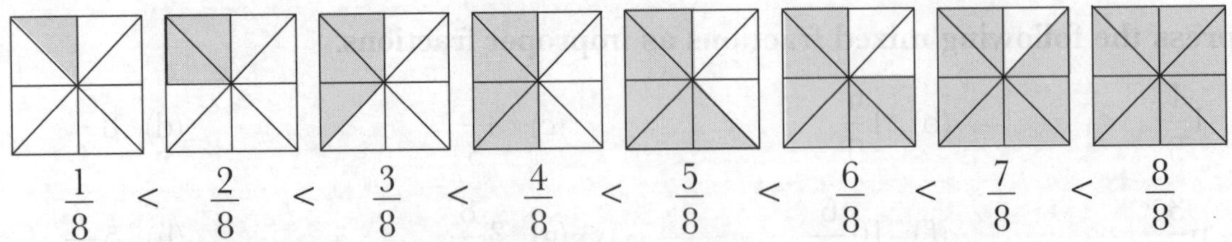

$$\frac{1}{8} < \frac{2}{8} < \frac{3}{8} < \frac{4}{8} < \frac{5}{8} < \frac{6}{8} < \frac{7}{8} < \frac{8}{8}$$

In case of like fractions, the fraction with the greater numerator is greater.

Example: Arrange the following fractions in descending order:

$$\frac{2}{7}, \frac{5}{7}, \frac{6}{7}, \frac{3}{7}$$

As the denominators of the given fractions are the same, the fraction with the greater numerator will be greater. Thus, starting with the greatest, the above fractions in descending order are:

$\frac{6}{7}, \frac{5}{7}, \frac{3}{7}$ and $\frac{2}{7}$.

Comparing Unlike Fractions

Let us now learn how to compare unlike fractions.

Mental maths

Encircle the fraction which is greater.

(a) $\frac{2}{5}, \frac{3}{5}, \frac{1}{5}$

(b) $\frac{4}{5}, \frac{4}{11}, \frac{4}{7}$

(c) $\frac{1}{6}, \frac{1}{8}, \frac{1}{3}$

Unlike Fractions with Same Numerator

$$\frac{2}{2} > \frac{2}{4} > \frac{2}{8} > \frac{2}{16}$$

In case of unlike fractions, when the numerator is the same, the fraction with the smaller denominator is greater.

Example 1: Arrange the following fractions in ascending order:

$$\frac{3}{16}, \frac{3}{4}, \frac{3}{10}, \frac{3}{9}$$

As the numerators of the given fractions are the same, the fraction with the smaller denominator will be greater. Thus, starting with the smallest, the above fractions in ascending order are:

$\frac{3}{16}, \frac{3}{10}, \frac{3}{9}$ and $\frac{3}{4}$.

Converting Unlike Fractions to Like Fractions

To compare unlike fractions with different numerators, we need to first convert them to like fractions. To change unlike fractions to like fractions, the denominators have to be made the same. This can be done by substituting the denominators by a common multiple. We substitute the denominators by the **LCM** of the denominators.

Example 2: Convert $\frac{1}{3}$ and $\frac{1}{4}$ into like fractions.

LCM of 3 and 4 is:

2	3, 4
2	3, 2
3	3, 1
	1, 1

LCM = 2 × 2 × 3 = 12

In the fraction $\frac{1}{3}$, both the denominator and the numerator are multiplied by 4.

So, $$\frac{1 \times 4}{3 \times 4} = \frac{4}{12}$$

This is done to convert $\frac{1}{3}$ to an equivalent fraction with denominator 12.

In the fraction $\frac{1}{4}$, both the denominator and the numerator are multiplied by 3. This is done to convert $\frac{1}{4}$ to an equivalent fraction with denominator 12.

So, $\frac{1\times 3}{4\times 3} = \frac{3}{12}$

Thus, we have $\frac{1}{3} = \frac{4}{12}$ and $\frac{1}{4} = \frac{3}{12}$

Unlike Fractions with Different Numerators

Example 3: Compare $\frac{4}{6}$ and $\frac{2}{4}$.

Method 1: We first **change the unlike fractions to like fractions** and then compare.

Step 1: LCM of 6 and 4 = 2 × 2 × 3 = 12

Step 2: Convert them to equivalent fractions.
Thus, the equivalent fractions are:

Since 12 ÷ 6 = **2**, $\frac{4}{6} = \frac{4\times \mathbf{2}}{6\times \mathbf{2}} = \frac{8}{12}$

Since 12 ÷ 4 = **3**, $\frac{2}{4} = \frac{2\times \mathbf{3}}{4\times \mathbf{3}} = \frac{6}{12}$

Rough Work
LCM
2 | 6, 4
2 | 3, 2
3 | 3, 1
1, 1

Step 3: Compare the two fractions.

Now, $\frac{8}{12}$ and $\frac{6}{12}$ are like fractions, where $\frac{8}{12} > \frac{6}{12}$

Thus, $\frac{4}{6} > \frac{2}{4}$

Method 2: Cross-multiplication method

$\frac{4}{6} \times \frac{2}{4} = \frac{12}{16}$ (Second numerator × first denominator) / (Second denominator × first numerator)

As the resultant fraction, $\frac{12}{16}$, is a proper fraction, the first fraction, $\frac{4}{6}$, is greater.

Thus, $\frac{4}{6} > \frac{2}{4}$

If the resultant fraction is a proper fraction, then the first fraction is greater. On the other hand, if the resultant fraction is an improper fraction, then the second fraction is greater.

Example 4: Arrange the following unlike fractions in descending order:

$\frac{2}{3}, \frac{4}{5}, \frac{6}{7}, \frac{1}{6}, \frac{3}{6}$

The LCM of all the denominators is 2 × 3 × 5 × 7 = 210

The equivalent fractions of the above fractions are:

$\frac{140}{210}\left[\frac{2\times70}{3\times70}\right], \frac{168}{210}\left[\frac{4\times42}{5\times42}\right], \frac{180}{210}\left[\frac{6\times30}{7\times30}\right], \frac{35}{210}\left[\frac{1\times35}{6\times35}\right], \frac{105}{210}\left[\frac{3\times35}{6\times35}\right]$, respectively.

Thus, the fractions in descending order are:

$\frac{180}{210} > \frac{168}{210} > \frac{140}{210} > \frac{105}{210} > \frac{35}{210}$ *or* $\frac{6}{7} > \frac{4}{5} > \frac{2}{3} > \frac{3}{6} > \frac{1}{6}$

Comparing Mixed Fractions with Improper Fractions

Example 1: Is $1\frac{1}{6} > \frac{10}{8}$?

We first change the mixed fraction to an improper fraction.

$$1\frac{1}{6} = \frac{6+1}{6} = \frac{7}{6}$$

Method 1: Convert the unlike fractions to like fractions.

Step 1: LCM of 6 and 8 = 2 × 2 × 2 × 3 = 24

Step 2: The equivalent fractions are $\frac{7}{6} = \frac{28}{24}$ and $\frac{10}{8} = \frac{30}{24}$

As $\frac{28}{24} < \frac{30}{24}$, $\frac{7}{6} < \frac{10}{8}$ *or* $1\frac{1}{6} < \frac{10}{8}$

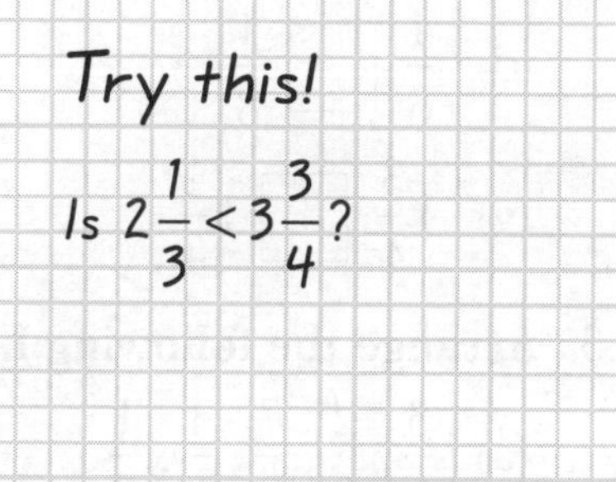

Method 2: By cross-multiplication.

By cross-multiplying $\frac{7}{6}$ and $\frac{10}{8}$, we get $\frac{7}{6} \times \frac{10}{8} = \frac{60}{56}$

As the resultant fraction, $\frac{60}{56}$, is an improper fraction, the second fraction, $\frac{10}{8}$, is greater.

Thus, $\frac{7}{6} < \frac{10}{8}$ *or* $1\frac{1}{6} < \frac{10}{8}$

Comparing Mixed Fractions

Example 2: Is $2\frac{3}{8} < 3\frac{3}{5}$?

We first convert mixed fractions to improper fractions and then compare the two.

Step 1: $2\frac{3}{8} = \frac{16+3}{8} = \frac{19}{8}$ and $3\frac{3}{5} = \frac{15+3}{5} = \frac{18}{5}$

Step 2: By cross-multiplication, $\frac{19}{8} \times \frac{18}{5} = \frac{144}{95}$

As the resultant fraction, $\frac{144}{95}$, is an improper fraction, the second fraction, $\frac{18}{5}$, is greater.

Thus, $\frac{19}{8} < \frac{18}{5}$ *or* $2\frac{3}{8} < 3\frac{3}{5}$

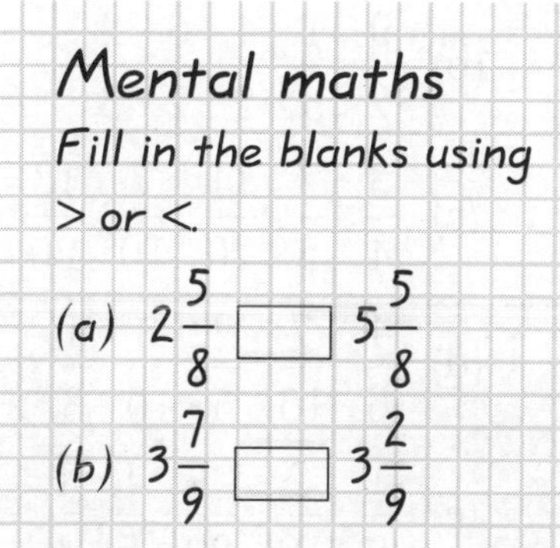

Mental maths
Fill in the blanks using > or <.
(a) $2\frac{5}{8}$ ☐ $5\frac{5}{8}$
(b) $3\frac{7}{9}$ ☐ $3\frac{2}{9}$

Exercise 8.3

1. Fill in the missing number to make the following fractions equivalent.

(a) $\frac{1}{5} = \frac{6}{\square}$ (b) $\frac{2}{3} = \frac{\square}{36}$ (c) $\frac{3}{5} = \frac{\square}{15}$

(d) $\frac{\square}{7} = \frac{45}{63}$ (e) $\frac{6}{\square} = \frac{48}{64}$ (f) $\frac{\square}{6} = \frac{42}{36}$

(g) $\frac{5}{2} = \frac{\square}{10}$ (h) $1\frac{2}{3} = \frac{\square}{9}$ (i) $\frac{\square}{6} = 7\frac{1}{2}$

2. Put > or < signs to compare the following fractions.

(a) $\frac{3}{7} \square \frac{6}{7}$ (b) $\frac{11}{12} \square \frac{1}{12}$ (c) $\frac{6}{8} \square \frac{7}{8}$

(d) $\frac{4}{6} \square \frac{4}{8}$ (e) $\frac{6}{9} \square \frac{6}{7}$ (f) $\frac{5}{10} \square \frac{5}{12}$

(g) $1\frac{3}{4} \square 1\frac{1}{4}$ (h) $1\frac{5}{7} \square 3\frac{1}{7}$ (i) $3\frac{1}{5} \square 5\frac{1}{3}$

3. Arrange the following like fractions in descending order.

(a) $\frac{3}{8}, \frac{2}{8}, \frac{7}{8}, \frac{4}{8}, \frac{1}{8}$ ____________________

(b) $\frac{4}{5}, \frac{1}{5}, \frac{2}{5}, \frac{3}{5}, \frac{5}{5}$ ____________________

(c) $\frac{6}{16}, \frac{24}{16}, \frac{17}{16}, \frac{15}{16}, \frac{10}{16}$ ____________________

(d) $\frac{9}{10}, \frac{7}{10}, \frac{13}{10}, \frac{21}{10}, \frac{2}{10}$ ____________________

(e) $\frac{1}{4}, 2\frac{2}{4}, \frac{3}{4}, 1\frac{1}{4}, \frac{4}{4}$ ____________________

4. Arrange the following unlike fractions in ascending order.

(a) $\frac{6}{10}, \frac{6}{7}, \frac{6}{13}, \frac{6}{8}, \frac{6}{9}$ ____________________

(b) $\frac{9}{2}, \frac{1}{3}, \frac{4}{2}, \frac{6}{2}, \frac{2}{3}$ ____________________

(c) $\frac{3}{4}, \frac{2}{5}, \frac{11}{20}, \frac{7}{10}, \frac{13}{20}$ ____________________

(d) $\frac{4}{6}, \frac{7}{15}, \frac{2}{5}, \frac{8}{10}, \frac{1}{3}$ ____________________

(e) $\frac{1}{8}, \frac{2}{10}, \frac{3}{20}, \frac{1}{5}, \frac{1}{4}$ ____________________

5. **Compare the following mixed fractions using the > or < signs.**

(a) $1\frac{4}{6}$ ☐ $\frac{11}{7}$ (b) $1\frac{5}{9}$ ☐ $\frac{14}{8}$ (c) $2\frac{1}{3}$ ☐ $1\frac{3}{4}$

(d) $3\frac{6}{7}$ ☐ $4\frac{2}{5}$ (e) $5\frac{1}{3}$ ☐ $6\frac{1}{2}$ (f) $7\frac{3}{5}$ ☐ $5\frac{3}{6}$

Converting a Fraction to its Simplest Form

  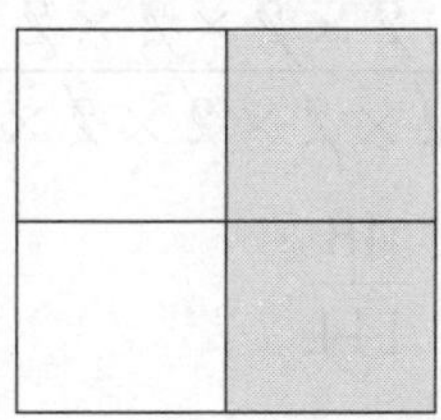 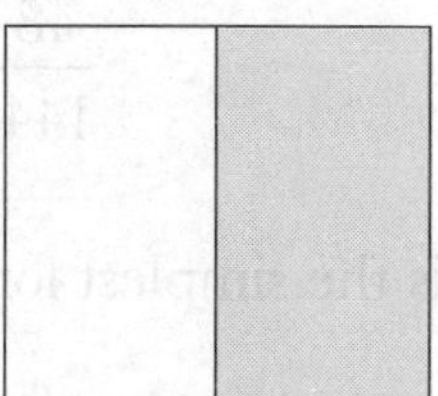

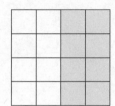

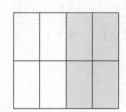

The equivalent fractions in the above figures are:

$$\frac{8}{16} = \frac{4}{8} = \frac{2}{4} = \frac{1}{2}$$

$\frac{4}{8}$ can be derived from $\frac{8}{16}$ by dividing the numerator and denominator by 2.

Similarly, $\frac{2}{4}$ and $\frac{1}{2}$ can be derived from $\frac{4}{8}$ and $\frac{2}{4}$ by dividing the numerator and denominator by 2, respectively. However, $\frac{1}{2}$ cannot be reduced any further.

Thus, $\frac{1}{2}$ is the simplest form of all its equivalent fractions $\frac{2}{4}, \frac{4}{8}, \frac{8}{16}$, etc.

Similarly, $\frac{2}{3}$ is the simplest form of all its equivalent fractions $\frac{6}{9}, \frac{4}{6}, \frac{8}{12}$, etc.

Notice that in both cases, the HCF of the numerator and denominator of the simplest form is 1.

A fraction is in its simplest form only if the HCF of its numerator and denominator is 1.

Example 1: Is $\frac{21}{28}$ in its simplest form?

Factorising the numerator and denominator, we find:

$$\frac{21}{28} = \frac{7\times3\times1}{7\times2\times2\times1}$$

As the HCF of the numerator and denominator is $7 \times 1 = 7$, the fraction $\frac{21}{28}$ is not in its simplest form.

Example 2: Reduce $\frac{48}{144}$ to its simplest form.

Factorising the numerator and denominator we find:

$$\frac{48}{144} = \frac{2\times2\times2\times2\times3\times1}{2\times2\times2\times2\times3\times3\times1}$$

Cancelling all the common factors, except 1, between the numerator and the denominator we get:

$$\frac{48}{144} = \frac{\cancel{2}\times\cancel{2}\times\cancel{2}\times\cancel{2}\times\cancel{3}\times1}{\cancel{2}\times\cancel{2}\times\cancel{2}\times\cancel{2}\times\cancel{3}\times3\times1} = \frac{1}{3\times1} = \frac{1}{3}$$

Thus $\frac{1}{3}$ is the simplest form of $\frac{48}{144}$.

Try this!

Reduce $\frac{18}{24}$ to its simplest form.

Exercise 8.4

Do these sums in your notebook.

1. Reduce the following fractions to their simplest forms.

(a) $\frac{14\ (\div 2)}{26\ (\div 2)}$ (b) $\frac{9\ (\div 3)}{12\ (\div 3)}$ (c) $\frac{15\ (\div 5)}{20\ (\div 5)}$ (d) $\frac{18\ (\div 6)}{30\ (\div 6)}$

2. Reduce the following fractions to their simplest forms.

(a) $\frac{2}{6}$ (b) $\frac{8}{10}$ (c) $\frac{6}{12}$ (d) $\frac{10}{12}$

(e) $\frac{9}{18}$ (f) $\frac{16}{24}$ (g) $\frac{5}{20}$ (h) $\frac{6}{18}$

(i) $\frac{14}{28}$ (j) $\frac{11}{33}$

3. Which of the following fractions are in their simplest forms? Reduce the ones which are not.

(a) $\frac{1}{4}$ (b) $\frac{2}{6}$ (c) $\frac{4}{5}$ (d) $\frac{5}{6}$

(e) $\frac{6}{18}$ (f) $\frac{8}{20}$

Word Problems

Example 1: During the games period 36 boys went down to the field. $\frac{1}{2}$ of the boys played football. How many boys played football?

Number of boys who went down to the field = 36

$\frac{1}{2}$ of them played football

∴ Number of boys who played football

$\frac{1}{2}$ of 36 = 18

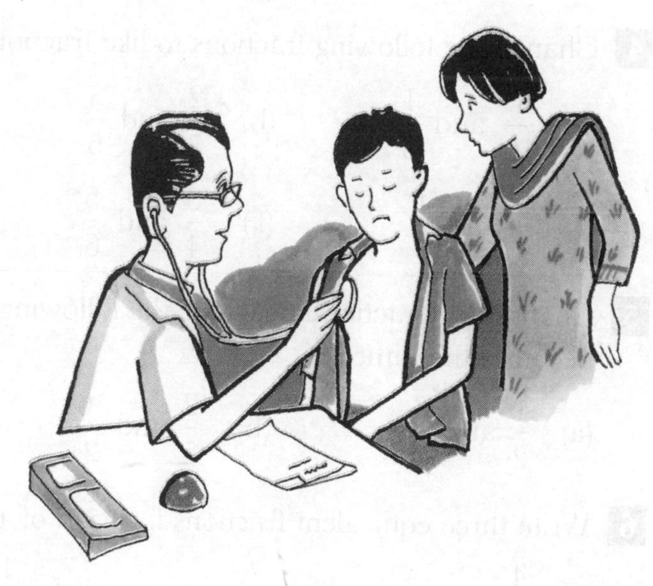

Example 2: Doctor Ram examined 45 patients. $\frac{1}{5}$ of the patients had fever. How many patients had fever?

Number of patients = 45

$\frac{1}{5}$ of patients had fever

∴ Number of patients who had fever

$\frac{1}{5}$ of 45 = 9

Exercise 8.5

1. There were 46 vehicles on the road. If $\frac{1}{2}$ of them were buses, how many buses were there on the road?	Number of vehicles on the road = ________ Fraction of the buses = ________ Number of buses on the road = ________
2. Suneeta bought 68 apples. She found $\frac{1}{4}$ of them bad, so threw them away. How many were thrown away?	Number of apples Suneeta bought = ________ Fraction of apples thrown away = ________ Number of apples thrown away = ________

Revision Exercise

Do these sums in your notebook.

1 Express the following improper fractions as mixed fractions.

(a) $\frac{10}{7}$ (b) $\frac{13}{11}$ (c) $\frac{23}{15}$ (d) $\frac{18}{5}$ (e) $\frac{45}{14}$

2 Express the following mixed fractions as improper fractions.

(a) $2\frac{2}{3}$ (b) $3\frac{4}{5}$ (c) $1\frac{6}{11}$ (d) $7\frac{1}{3}$ (e) $11\frac{4}{5}$

(f) $8\frac{1}{4}$ (g) $3\frac{1}{4}$ (h) $5\frac{3}{5}$ (i) $12\frac{3}{4}$ (j) $15\frac{1}{3}$

3 Fill in the missing numbers to make the following fractions equivalent.

(a) $\frac{1}{?} = \frac{8}{72}$ (b) $\frac{?}{36} = \frac{4}{3}$ (c) $1\frac{1}{2} = \frac{?}{26}$ (d) $?\frac{6}{9} = \frac{14}{3}$ (e) $?\frac{?}{8} = \frac{34}{16}$

4 Change the following fractions to like fractions.

(a) $\frac{1}{10}$ and $\frac{1}{3}$ (b) $\frac{2}{7}$ and $\frac{3}{5}$ (c) $1\frac{1}{4}$ and $3\frac{1}{3}$ (d) $1\frac{1}{5}$ and $1\frac{1}{2}$

(e) $\frac{3}{9}$ and $\frac{4}{6}$ (f) $\frac{3}{4}$ and $\frac{5}{6}$ (g) $\frac{2}{5}$ and $\frac{3}{4}$ (h) $1\frac{1}{3}$ and $2\frac{3}{5}$

5 Change one fraction in each of the following pairs such that the numerator in each pair becomes the same.

(a) $\frac{1}{2}$ and $\frac{3}{9}$ (b) $\frac{2}{5}$ and $\frac{6}{21}$ (c) $\frac{8}{9}$ and $\frac{16}{22}$ (d) $\frac{28}{40}$ and $\frac{7}{9}$

6 Write three equivalent fractions for each of the following fractions.

(a) $\frac{4}{5}$ (b) $\frac{7}{8}$ (c) $\frac{11}{9}$ (d) $2\frac{1}{2}$ (e) $1\frac{3}{8}$

7 Reduce the following fractions to their simplest forms.

(a) $\frac{6}{10}$ (b) $\frac{15}{35}$ (c) $\frac{36}{54}$ (d) $\frac{42}{126}$ (e) $\frac{114}{133}$

(f) $\frac{50}{200}$ (g) $\frac{81}{729}$ (h) $\frac{100}{200}$ (i) $\frac{125}{250}$ (j) $\frac{200}{450}$

8 There are 50 flowers in a garden. If $\frac{2}{5}$ of them are roses, how many roses are there in the garden?

9 There are 54 children playing in a park. If $\frac{5}{9}$ of them are boys, how many boys are there in the park?

ADDITION AND SUBTRACTION OF FRACTIONS

Let's Recap

1. Add the following.

(a) $\frac{1}{5} + \frac{2}{5}$ = ☐ = ☐

(b) $\frac{3}{7} + \frac{2}{7}$ = ☐ = ☐

(c) $\frac{2}{9} + \frac{5}{9}$ = ☐ = ☐

(d) $\frac{4}{11} + \frac{3}{11}$ = ☐ = ☐

(e) $\frac{3}{13} + \frac{5}{13}$ = ☐ = ☐

(f) $\frac{7}{16} + \frac{2}{16}$ = ☐ = ☐

Do you remember?
While adding fractions with same denominators, add the numerators and keep the denominator as it is.

2. Subtract the following.

(a) $\frac{2}{3} - \frac{1}{3}$ = ☐ = ☐

(b) $\frac{4}{5} - \frac{1}{5}$ = ☐ = ☐

(c) $\frac{5}{7} - \frac{2}{7}$ = ☐ = ☐

(d) $\frac{5}{9} - \frac{3}{9}$ = ☐ = ☐

(e) $\frac{10}{11} - \frac{9}{11}$ = ☐ = ☐

(f) $\frac{15}{17} - \frac{5}{17}$ = ☐ = ☐

Do you remember?
While subtracting fractions with same denominators, subtract the numerators and keep the denominator as it is.

The three friends went to a snack bar to have their lunch. Hungrily the two boys bought a cake and ate half each. Seeing Priya, they bought another cake and the three friends had one-third of the cake each.

Addition of Fractions

You have learnt that fractions can be of different types—like fractions, unlike fractions, mixed fractions, etc. Let us learn how the different types of fractions are added.

Addition of Like Fractions

In Class III we have learnt addition of two like fractions. Let us learn the addition of more than two like fractions.

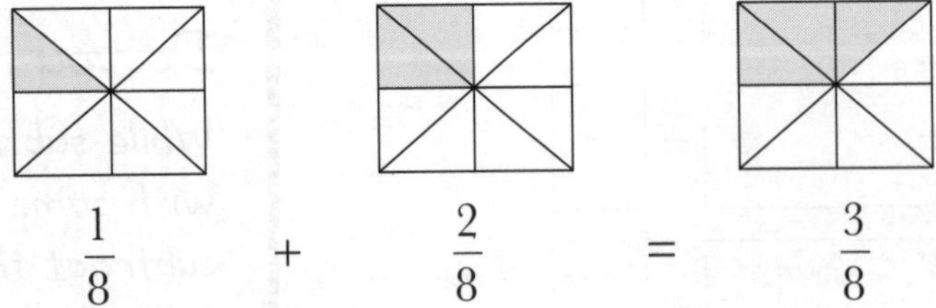

$$\frac{1}{8} + \frac{2}{8} = \frac{3}{8}$$

The sum of two or more like fractions is a fraction where the denominator is the same as that of the addends and the numerator is the sum of all the numerators of the addends.

$$\textbf{Sum of like fractions} = \frac{\textbf{Sum of numerators}}{\textbf{Common denominator}}$$

Example 1: Add: $\frac{3}{13}+\frac{2}{13}+\frac{5}{13}$

$$\frac{3}{13}+\frac{2}{13}+\frac{5}{13}=\frac{3+2+5}{13}=\frac{10}{13}$$

Thus, $$\frac{3}{13}+\frac{2}{13}+\frac{5}{13}=\frac{10}{13}$$

Example 2: Add: $\frac{3}{20}+\frac{1}{20}+\frac{2}{20}+\frac{4}{20}$

$$\frac{3}{20}+\frac{1}{20}+\frac{2}{20}+\frac{4}{20}=\frac{3+1+2+4}{20}$$

$$=\frac{10}{20}=\frac{\cancel{2}\times\cancel{5}\times1}{\cancel{2}\times2\times\cancel{5}\times1}=\frac{1}{2}$$

Try this!

Add the following

$\frac{2}{9}+\frac{1}{9}+\frac{4}{9}$

Addition of Unlike Fractions

In order to add unlike fractions, we convert them into like fractions. This is done by finding the LCM and taking it as the common denominator of all the given fractions.

Example 1: Add: $\frac{1}{2}+\frac{1}{3}$

Step 1: Find the LCM of 2 and 3. LCM of 2 and 3 is 6.

Step 2: Convert both like fractions into equivalent fractions with the common denominator, 6.

Step 3: Now, as the fractions are like fractions, we get $\frac{1}{2}=\frac{3}{6}$ and $\frac{1}{3}=\frac{2}{6}$

Now, $$\frac{3}{6}+\frac{2}{6}=\frac{3+2}{6}=\frac{5}{6}$$

Thus, $$\frac{1}{2}+\frac{1}{3}=\frac{5}{6}$$

Example 2: Add: $\frac{1}{10}+\frac{7}{15}+\frac{2}{5}$

Step 1: Write the LCM as the common denominator. LCM of 10, 15 and 5 = 30

Step 2: Divide the common denominator, 30, by each denominator.

$$\frac{30}{10}=3;\quad \frac{30}{15}=2;\quad \frac{30}{5}=6$$

Step 3: Multiply the numerator with the respective quotients to obtain like fractions.

We have, $$\frac{1\times3}{30}+\frac{7\times2}{30}+\frac{2\times6}{30}$$

Step 4: Add the like fractions.

$$\frac{3}{30}+\frac{14}{30}+\frac{12}{30}=\frac{3+14+12}{30}=\frac{29}{30}$$

Try this!
Add the following

$\frac{2}{3}+\frac{3}{5}$

Addition of Mixed Fractions

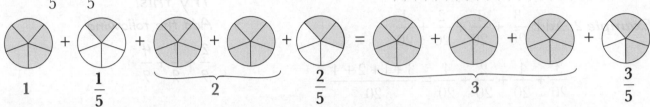

Add: $1\frac{1}{5}+2\frac{2}{5}$

$1 + \frac{1}{5} + 2 + \frac{2}{5} = 3 + \frac{3}{5}$

From the above figures, it can be seen that *the sum of the integral parts (whole numbers) and the sum of the fractional parts give the sum of mixed fractions.*

Example 1: Add: $3\frac{3}{7}+2\frac{2}{7}$

Step 1: Add the fractional parts.

$$\frac{3}{7}+\frac{2}{7}=\frac{3+2}{7}=\frac{5}{7}$$

Step 2: Add the integral parts.

$3+2=5$

Step 3: We get: $3\frac{3}{7}+2\frac{2}{7}=5\frac{5}{7}$

Example 3: Add: $2\frac{1}{2}+3\frac{1}{3}+5\frac{3}{4}+4\frac{5}{6}$

Step 1: Add the fractional parts.
LCM of 2, 3, 4 and 6 is 12.

$$\frac{1}{2}+\frac{1}{3}+\frac{3}{4}+\frac{5}{6}$$

$$=\frac{1\times6+1\times4+3\times3+5\times2}{12}$$

$$=\frac{6+4+9+10}{12}=\frac{29}{12}=2\frac{5}{12}$$

Step 2: Add the integral parts.

$2+3+5+4=14$

Step 3: We get:

$$2\frac{1}{2}+3\frac{1}{3}+5\frac{3}{4}+4\frac{5}{6}=14+2\frac{5}{12}=16\frac{5}{12}$$

Example 2: Add: $6\frac{3}{10}+4\frac{1}{5}$

Step 1: Add the fractional parts.

$$\frac{3}{10}+\frac{1}{5}=\frac{3\times1+1\times2}{10}=\frac{3+2}{10}=\frac{5}{10}=\frac{1}{2}$$

Step 2: Add the integral parts.

$6+4=10$

Step 3: We get: $6\frac{3}{10}+4\frac{1}{5}=10\frac{1}{2}$

Example 4: Add: $\frac{11}{7}+3\frac{2}{14}+14+\frac{1}{7}$

Step 1: Simplify by adding the like fractions.

$$\frac{12}{7}+3\frac{2}{14}+14 \qquad \left(\frac{11}{7}+\frac{1}{7}=\frac{12}{7}\right)$$

Step 2: Add the fractional parts.
LCM of 7 and 14 is 14.

So, $\frac{12}{7}+\frac{2}{14}=\frac{12\times2+2\times1}{14}=\frac{24+2}{14}=\frac{26}{14}$

$$=\frac{\not{2}\times13\times1}{\not{2}\times7\times1}=1\frac{6}{7}$$

Step 3: Add the integral parts.

$3+14=17$

Step 4: We get: $\frac{11}{7}+3\frac{2}{14}+14+\frac{1}{7}$

$$=17+1\frac{6}{7}=18\frac{6}{7}$$

Exercise 9.1

Do these sums in your notebook.

1. Add the following like fractions.

(a) $\frac{4}{9}+\frac{3}{9}+\frac{1}{9}$ (b) $\frac{1}{13}+\frac{3}{13}+\frac{5}{13}$ (c) $\frac{3}{15}+\frac{3}{15}+\frac{2}{15}$

(d) $\frac{4}{17}+\frac{6}{17}+\frac{5}{17}$ (e) $\frac{10}{19}+\frac{2}{19}+\frac{7}{19}$ (f) $\frac{1}{21}+\frac{2}{21}+\frac{4}{21}$

(g) $\frac{1}{22}+\frac{4}{22}+\frac{6}{22}$ (h) $\frac{8}{23}+\frac{9}{23}+\frac{3}{23}$ (i) $\frac{20}{40}+\frac{9}{40}+\frac{1}{40}$

2. Add the following unlike fractions.

(a) $\frac{1}{4}+\frac{1}{6}$ (b) $\frac{3}{15}+\frac{2}{10}$ (c) $\frac{1}{3}+\frac{2}{7}$

(d) $\frac{2}{3}+\frac{2}{5}$ (e) $\frac{1}{16}+\frac{1}{8}+\frac{1}{4}$ (f) $\frac{2}{9}+\frac{6}{27}+\frac{1}{3}$

(g) $\frac{4}{18}+\frac{1}{4}+\frac{3}{12}$ (h) $\frac{2}{9}+\frac{1}{6}+\frac{1}{2}$ (i) $\frac{2}{8}+\frac{1}{9}+\frac{3}{36}+\frac{5}{18}$

(j) $\frac{1}{2}+\frac{2}{3}+\frac{4}{7}+\frac{3}{14}$ (k) $\frac{2}{5}+\frac{4}{15}+\frac{4}{9}+\frac{14}{30}$ (l) $\frac{2}{6}+\frac{3}{13}+\frac{1}{3}+\frac{1}{2}$

3. Add the following fractions.

(a) $1+\frac{1}{2}$ (b) $3+\frac{2}{3}$ (c) $7+\frac{6}{9}$

(d) $1\frac{1}{2}+\frac{1}{2}$ (e) $6\frac{2}{8}+\frac{2}{8}$ (f) $10\frac{5}{12}+\frac{1}{12}$

(g) $6\frac{1}{7}+2\frac{3}{7}$ (h) $3\frac{1}{9}+2\frac{3}{9}+1\frac{2}{9}$ (i) $2\frac{1}{11}+4\frac{3}{11}+3\frac{4}{11}$

4. Add the following fractions.

(a) $2\frac{1}{2}+3\frac{1}{3}$ (b) $6\frac{4}{6}+2\frac{1}{4}$ (c) $3\frac{2}{5}+2\frac{1}{3}$

(d) $3\frac{1}{6}+2\frac{3}{8}$ (e) $5\frac{2}{7}+6\frac{1}{4}$ (f) $12\frac{4}{6}+10\frac{2}{5}$

(g) $4\frac{5}{21}+3\frac{1}{15}$ (h) $5\frac{12}{27}+3\frac{2}{36}$ (i) $3\frac{1}{5}+4+\frac{2}{15}$

(j) $3+\frac{6}{14}+4\frac{1}{4}$ (k) $3\frac{3}{5}+\frac{1}{5}+\frac{4}{6}$ (l) $5\frac{1}{6}+\frac{2}{15}+\frac{2}{6}+\frac{1}{15}$

Subtraction of Fractions

Let us now learn how the different types of fractions—like fractions, unlike fractions and mixed fractions—are subtracted.

Subtraction of Like Fractions

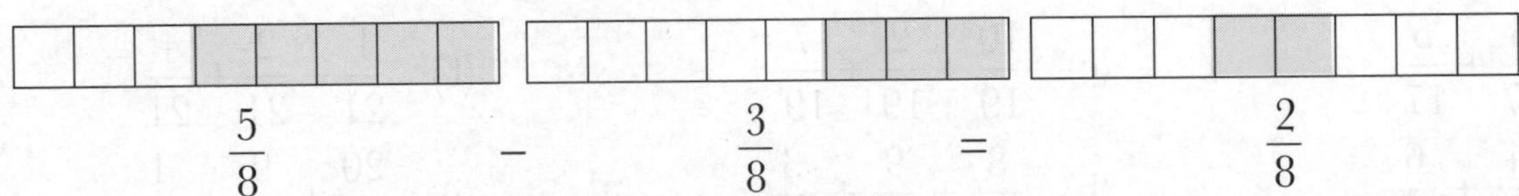

$$\frac{5}{8} - \frac{3}{8} = \frac{2}{8}$$

Thus, *the difference of like fractions is a fraction in which the denominator is the same as that of the given fractions and the numerator is the difference of their numerators.*

$$\textbf{Difference of like fractions} = \frac{\textbf{Difference of numerators}}{\textbf{Common denominator}}$$

Example: Subtract: $\frac{15}{20} - \frac{3}{20} - \frac{2}{20}$

$\frac{15}{20} - \frac{3}{20} - \frac{2}{20}$

$= \frac{15-3-2}{20} = \frac{10}{20} = \frac{\cancel{2}\times\cancel{5}\times 1}{2\times\cancel{2}\times\cancel{5}\times 1} = \frac{1}{2}$

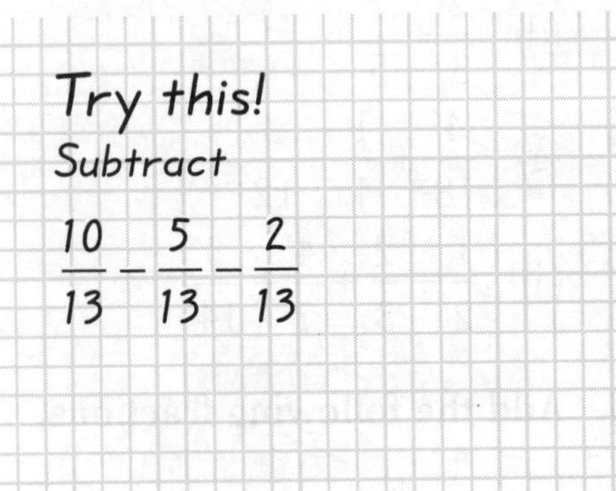

Try this!
Subtract
10/13 − 5/13 − 2/13

Subtraction of Unlike Fractions

Here, we convert the fractions into like fractions by finding a common denominator for all the fractions.

Example 1: Subtract: $\frac{5}{6} - \frac{1}{3}$

Step 1: Find the LCM of the denominators. The LCM of 6 and 3 is 6, which will be the common denominator of both the fractions.

Step 2: The denominator of $\frac{5}{6}$ is 6. So, we leave it as it is.

Step 3: The equivalent fraction of $\frac{1}{3}$ with denominator 6 is $\frac{1\times 2}{3\times 2} = \frac{2}{6}$

Step 4: Now, subtract the like fractions: $\frac{5}{6} - \frac{2}{6} = \frac{5-2}{6} = \frac{3}{6} = \frac{\cancel{3}\times 1}{2\times\cancel{3}\times 1} = \frac{1}{2}$

Thus, $\frac{5}{6} - \frac{1}{3} = \frac{1}{2}$

Example 2: Subtract: $\frac{3}{4}-\frac{1}{8}-\frac{4}{16}$

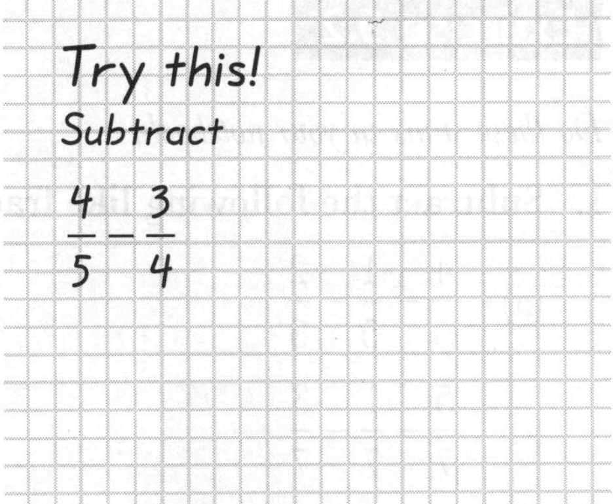

LCM of 4, 8 and 16 is 16.

$$\frac{3\times4-1\times2-4\times1}{16}=\frac{12-2-4}{16}=\frac{6}{16}=\frac{3}{8}$$

Thus, $\frac{3}{4}-\frac{1}{8}-\frac{4}{16}=\frac{3}{8}$

Subtraction of Like Mixed Fractions

Example: Subtract: $5\frac{4}{5}-3\frac{2}{5}$

Step 1: Subtract the integral parts. $5-3=2$

Step 2: Subtract the fractional parts.

$$\frac{4}{5}-\frac{2}{5}=\frac{4-2}{5}=\frac{2}{5}$$

Step 3: We write the differences from *Step 1* and *Step 2* as $2\frac{2}{5}$

Thus, $5\frac{4}{5}-3\frac{2}{5}=2\frac{2}{5}$

Try this!
Subtract
$6\frac{5}{7}-4\frac{1}{7}$

Subtraction of Unlike Mixed Fractions

Example 1: Subtract: $3\frac{4}{7}-2\frac{1}{2}$

Step 1: Subtract the integral parts.

$3-2=1$

Step 2: Subtract the fractional parts.

$$\frac{4}{7}-\frac{1}{2}=\frac{4\times2-1\times7}{14}=\frac{8-7}{14}=\frac{1}{14}$$

Thus, $3\frac{4}{7}-2\frac{1}{2}=1\frac{1}{14}$

Example 2: Subtract: $5\frac{6}{8}-2\frac{1}{6}-1\frac{1}{8}$

Step 1: Subtract the integral parts.

$5-2-1=2$

Step 2: Subtract the like fractional parts.

$$\frac{6}{8}-\frac{1}{8}=\frac{6-1}{8}=\frac{5}{8}$$

Step 3: Subtract the unlike fractional parts.

$$\frac{5}{8}-\frac{1}{6}=\frac{5\times3-1\times4}{24}=\frac{15-4}{24}=\frac{11}{24}$$

Thus, $5\frac{6}{8}-2\frac{1}{6}-1\frac{1}{8}=2\frac{11}{24}$

Exercise 9.2

Do these sums in your notebook.

1. Subtract the following like fractions.

(a) $\frac{4}{5}-\frac{1}{5}-\frac{2}{5}$ (b) $\frac{5}{9}-\frac{3}{9}-\frac{1}{9}$ (c) $\frac{6}{7}-\frac{1}{7}-\frac{1}{7}$

(d) $\frac{5}{7}-\frac{1}{7}-\frac{3}{7}$ (e) $\frac{9}{11}-\frac{4}{11}-\frac{2}{11}$ (f) $\frac{8}{12}-\frac{1}{12}-\frac{1}{12}$

(g) $\frac{15}{17}-\frac{5}{17}-\frac{7}{17}$ (h) $\frac{20}{17}-\frac{3}{17}-\frac{8}{17}$ (i) $\frac{16}{20}-\frac{5}{20}-\frac{1}{20}$

2. Subtract the following unlike fractions.

(a) $\frac{5}{6}-\frac{1}{4}$ (b) $\frac{1}{2}-\frac{1}{3}$ (c) $\frac{1}{3}-\frac{1}{4}$

(d) $\frac{3}{4}-\frac{3}{5}$ (e) $\frac{6}{7}-\frac{6}{14}$ (f) $\frac{1}{6}-\frac{1}{10}$

(g) $\frac{6}{10}-\frac{7}{15}$ (h) $\frac{9}{12}-\frac{5}{8}$ (i) $\frac{2}{3}-\frac{1}{5}$

(j) $\frac{1}{2}-\frac{1}{12}-\frac{1}{3}$ (k) $\frac{10}{15}-\frac{1}{5}-\frac{1}{10}$ (l) $\frac{7}{9}-\frac{2}{6}-\frac{1}{3}$

3. Subtract the following fractions.

(a) $2\frac{1}{2}-\frac{1}{2}$ (b) $3\frac{1}{3}-\frac{1}{3}$ (c) $7\frac{3}{8}-\frac{3}{8}$

(d) $8\frac{4}{9}-\frac{4}{9}$ (e) $2\frac{1}{2}-1\frac{1}{2}$ (f) $4\frac{3}{5}-2\frac{2}{5}$

(g) $3\frac{4}{11}-1\frac{1}{11}$ (h) $6\frac{5}{13}-2\frac{3}{13}$ (i) $7\frac{5}{7}-2\frac{1}{7}-2\frac{2}{7}$

(j) $9\frac{7}{9}-3\frac{3}{9}-1\frac{1}{9}$ (k) $5\frac{3}{12}-2\frac{1}{12}-1$ (l) $10\frac{7}{10}-3-2\frac{2}{10}$

4. Subtract the following fractions.

(a) $3\frac{1}{3}-1\frac{1}{5}$ (b) $6\frac{1}{2}-4\frac{1}{4}$ (c) $7\frac{1}{5}-2\frac{1}{6}$

(d) $4\frac{3}{4}-2\frac{3}{5}$ (e) $5\frac{3}{5}-2\frac{1}{2}$ (f) $4\frac{5}{7}-1\frac{1}{2}$

(g) $3\frac{30}{45}-1\frac{5}{30}$ (h) $3\frac{3}{8}-1\frac{2}{9}$ (i) $7\frac{9}{12}-3\frac{2}{12}-2\frac{1}{8}$

(j) $5\frac{9}{15}-1\frac{1}{10}-2\frac{2}{10}$ (k) $7\frac{4}{6}-2\frac{2}{15}-3$ (l) $4\frac{10}{21}-1-1\frac{2}{15}$

Word Problems

Example 1: A basket had $2\frac{3}{5}$ kg of potatoes. Another $1\frac{1}{2}$ kg of potatoes was put in the basket. What is the mass of the potatoes in the bag now?

Basket had $2\frac{3}{5}$ kg $= \frac{13}{5}$ kg of potatoes

Mass of potatoes added $1\frac{1}{2}$ kg $= \frac{3}{2}$ kg

Mass of potatoes in the bag $\frac{13}{5} + \frac{3}{2}$ kg

$= \frac{26+15}{10}$ kg

$= \frac{41}{10}$ kg $= 4\frac{1}{10}$ kg

Thus the bag now has $4\frac{1}{10}$ kg of potatoes.

Example 2: A class has 52 students of which $\frac{6}{13}$ are girls. How many boys study in the class?

Fraction of girls in the class $= \frac{6}{13}$

Fraction of boys in the class $= 1 - \frac{6}{13}$

$= \frac{13-6}{13} = \frac{7}{13}$

Number of boys in the class $= \frac{7}{13}$ of 52

$= \frac{7 \times 52}{13} = \frac{7 \times 2 \times 2 \times \cancel{13}}{\cancel{13}} = 28$ boys

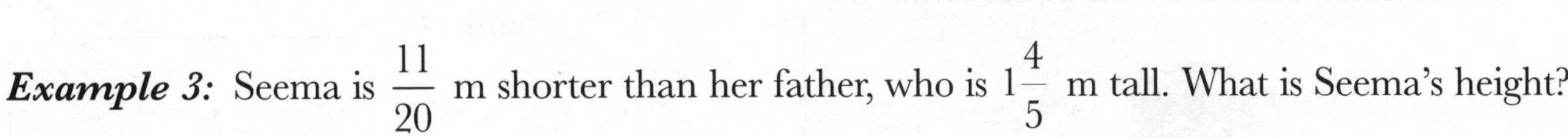

Example 3: Seema is $\frac{11}{20}$ m shorter than her father, who is $1\frac{4}{5}$ m tall. What is Seema's height?

Father's height $1\frac{4}{5}$ m $= \frac{9}{5}$ m

Seema is shorter by $\frac{11}{20}$ m

Seema's height $\frac{9}{5} - \frac{11}{20} = \frac{36-11}{20}$ m

$= \frac{25}{20}$ m $= \frac{5}{4}$ m $= 1\frac{1}{4}$ m

Thus Seema's height is $1\frac{1}{4}$ m.

Exercise 9.3

1. A rope of length $3\frac{1}{3}$ m is tied with another rope of length $4\frac{1}{6}$ m. What is the length of the new rope?	Length of one rope = ________ m Length of the other rope = ________ m Total length of the new rope = ________ m
2. Anirban travelled $\frac{1}{2}$ km on foot and $4\frac{2}{5}$ km by bus to reach his school. How far did he travel to reach his school?	Distance travelled on foot = ________ km Distance travelled by bus = ________ km Total distance travelled to reach the school = ________ km
3. Seema ate $\frac{3}{7}$ of a chocolate and Ritu ate $\frac{2}{7}$. How much did they eat altogether?	Fraction of chocolate Seema ate = ________ Fraction of chocolate Ritu ate = ________ Fraction of chocolate they ate together = ________
4. A cricket ball costs Rs $23\frac{1}{2}$ while a tennis ball costs Rs $16\frac{3}{4}$. How much more does a cricket ball cost?	Cost of cricket ball = Rs ________ Cost of tennis ball = Rs ________ Cost of cricket ball is more by = Rs ________
5. There is 120 ℓ of water in a tank. $\frac{5}{8}$ of the water is used for washing clothes. How much water remains in the tank?	Amount of water in the tank = ________ ℓ Water used for washing clothes = ________ Amount of water remaining in the tank = ________ ℓ
6. Anita had Rs $22\frac{1}{2}$. She spent Rs $15\frac{1}{4}$ to buy a notebook. What is the amount of money left with her?	Amount of money Anita had = Rs ________ Amount she spent = Rs ________ Amount of money left with her = Rs ________

Revision Exercise

Do these sums in your notebook.

1 Add the following fractions.

(a) $\frac{4}{13}+\frac{6}{13}$ (b) $\frac{2}{19}+\frac{17}{19}$ (c) $\frac{1}{7}+\frac{2}{5}$

(d) $\frac{3}{2}+\frac{7}{4}$ (e) $1\frac{1}{7}+2\frac{2}{7}$ (f) $3\frac{1}{2}+4\frac{3}{5}$

(g) $\frac{5}{12}+\frac{7}{12}$ (h) $\frac{6}{7}+\frac{1}{2}$ (i) $\frac{3}{4}+\frac{1}{8}$

(j) $\frac{2}{3}+\frac{3}{4}+\frac{3}{8}$ (k) $\frac{4}{5}+\frac{6}{7}+\frac{1}{2}$ (l) $\frac{1}{7}+\frac{1}{2}+\frac{3}{14}$

2 Subtract the following fractions.

(a) $\frac{6}{7}-\frac{3}{7}$ (b) $\frac{13}{23}-\frac{11}{23}$ (c) $\frac{6}{10}-\frac{1}{4}$

(d) $\frac{1}{2}-\frac{3}{11}$ (e) $\frac{7}{2}-\frac{2}{7}$ (f) $2\frac{2}{5}-1\frac{1}{5}$

(g) $\frac{9}{16}-\frac{1}{16}$ (h) $\frac{7}{9}-\frac{2}{3}$ (i) $\frac{5}{8}-\frac{1}{2}$

(j) $\frac{5}{6}-\frac{3}{4}$ (k) $1\frac{3}{5}-1\frac{2}{7}$ (l) $2\frac{5}{8}-1\frac{1}{6}$

3 Rajeev spent $\frac{2}{3}$ of his pocket money to buy a book and $\frac{1}{5}$ to watch a movie. What fraction of the pocket money did he spend?

4 Four friends tie four lengths of rope to make a long rope. Roshan brings a $3\frac{1}{3}$ m rope, Atul, a $2\frac{2}{6}$ m rope, Ashutosh, a $4\frac{1}{4}$ m rope and Anirban brings a $3\frac{1}{2}$ m rope. What is the length of the long rope?

5 There are 28 plants in a garden, of which $\frac{2}{7}$ have thorns in their stems. How many plants do not have thorns in their stems?

10 DECIMALS

The friends came to a cage where they saw a panda.

Decimal Fractions

Now that you are familiar with fractional numbers, let us learn about another way of writing fractions—decimal fractions.

One-Tenths

The number 1,000 is written in the place-value chart as:

Thousands	Hundreds	Tens	Ones
1	0	0	0

When we divide 1,000 by 10, we get 1,000 ÷ 10 = 100

The number 100 is written in the place-value chart as:

Thousands	Hundreds	Tens	Ones
	1	0	0

We observe that *on being divided by 10, the digit 1 has shifted one step to its right and one 0 on the extreme right has been taken away.*

When we divide 100 by 10, we get 100 ÷ 10 = 10

The number 10 is written in the place-value chart as:

Thousands	Hundreds	Tens	Ones
		1	0

Again, *the digit 1 has shifted one step to its right and one 0 on the extreme right has been taken away.*

When we divide 10 by 10, we get 10 ÷ 10 = 1, which is written in the place-value chart as:

Thousands	Hundreds	Tens	Ones
			1

Notice that *the digit 1 has again shifted one place to its right and the remaining digit, 0, has been taken away.*

What do we get when 1 is divided by 10?

We get $1 \div 10 = 1 \times \frac{1}{10} = \mathbf{\frac{1}{10}}$

$\frac{1}{10}$, also known as a vulgar fraction, is read as *one by ten*. This is the common way of writing fractions. A **decimal fraction** is a simpler way of writing a fraction when the denominator is 10 or 100; 1,000; etc.

In decimal fractions, $\mathbf{\frac{1}{10}}$ is written as **0.1** and read as **point one**

It represents the **one-tenth** part and, compared to 1, is written in the place-value chart as shown below:

Thousands	Hundreds	Tens	Ones	Decimal Point	Tenths	
			1	•	0	= 1
			0	•	1	= 0.1

We observe that on being divided by 10, the digit 1 has again shifted one place to its right but not before crossing a decimal point. We add one more column in the place-value chart. This column is called the **tenths**.

By convention, if there is no digit to the left of a decimal point we write one 0. This does not change the value of the decimal and moreover, it prevents us from making mistakes while reading decimal fractions. Thus, if a circle is divided into ten equals parts, one part can be written as 0.1, which is one part of ten equal parts or one-tenths.

Common Fractions	Decimal Fractions	Depiction	Read as:
$\frac{1}{10}$	0.1		One-tenth or point one
$\frac{2}{10}$ or $\frac{1}{5}$	0.2		Two-tenths or point two
$\frac{3}{10}$	0.3		Three-tenths or point three
$\frac{5}{10}$ or $\frac{1}{2}$	0.5		Five-tenths or point five
$\frac{7}{10}$	0.7		Seven-tenths or point seven
$\frac{8}{10}$ or $\frac{4}{5}$	0.8		Eight-tenths or point eight
$\frac{10}{10}$ or 1	1.0		Ten-tenths or one

One-hundredths

The fraction $\frac{1}{10}$ that represents 1 part of 10 equal parts can be written as 0.1 and read as one-tenths or point one.

The fraction $\frac{1}{100}$ represents 1 part of 100 equal parts. It can be written as **0.01** and read as **one-hundredths** or **point zero one**.

Hundreds	Tens	Ones	Decimal Point	Tenths	Hundredths
		0	·	0	1

Thus $1 \div 10 = 0.1$ and $0.1 \div 10 = 0.01$

We observe that the digit 1 has again shifted one place to the right and one zero has been placed after the decimal point. We add another column to the right of the tenths column, the **hundredths** column.

Example 1: $\frac{5}{100} = 0.05$

= Five parts of hundred equal parts

(read as: point zero five)

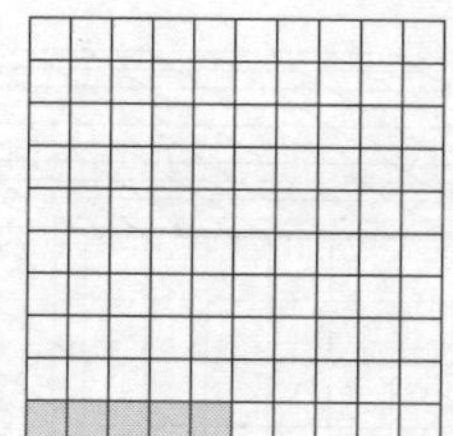

Example 2: $\frac{10}{100} = 0.10$

= Ten parts of hundred equal parts

(read as: point one zero)

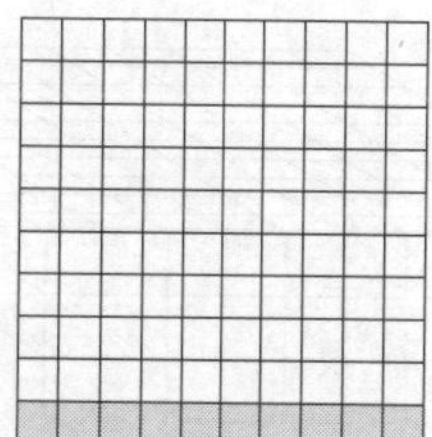

We see that $0.10 = \frac{1\not{0}}{10\not{0}} = 0.1$ or point one. So, adding zeroes to the right of a digit after the decimal point does not change the value of the decimal fraction. Similarly, 0.1 = 0.10 = 0.100 = 0.1000 = ..., and so on.

Example 3: $\frac{50}{100} = 0.50$

= 50 parts of 100 equal parts (read as: point five)

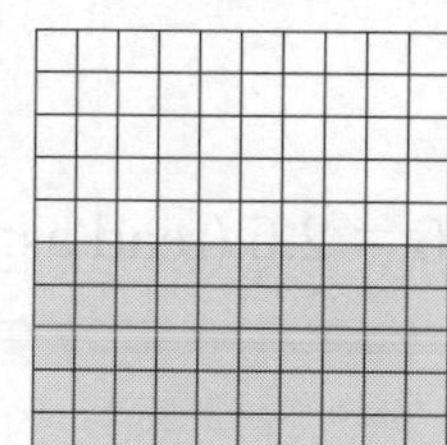

$0.5 = 0.50 = 0.500 = 0.5000 = \frac{1}{2}$

Example 4: $\frac{78}{100} = 0.78$

= 78 parts of 100 equal parts (read as: point seven eight)

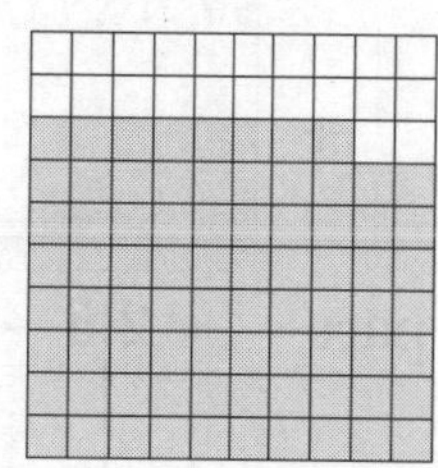

One-Thousandths

What do we get when 0.01 is divided by 10?

The fraction $\frac{1}{1000}$ represents 1 part of 1000 equal parts. It can be written as **0.001** and read as **one-thousandths** *or* **point zero zero one.**

Hundreds	Tens	Ones	Decimal Point	Tenths	Hundredths	Thousandths
		0	.	0	0	1

Thus $1 \div 10 = 0.1$, $0.1 \div 10 = 0.01$ and $0.01 \div 10 = 0.001$

We observe that the digit 1 has again shifted one place to the right and two zeroes have been placed after the decimal point. We add another column to the right of the hundredths column, the **thousandths** column.

Example 1: $\frac{111}{1000} = 0.111$

= 111 parts of 1000 equal parts

(read as: point one one one)

Example 2: $\frac{500}{1000} = 0.500$

= 500 parts of 1000 equal parts

(read as: point five)

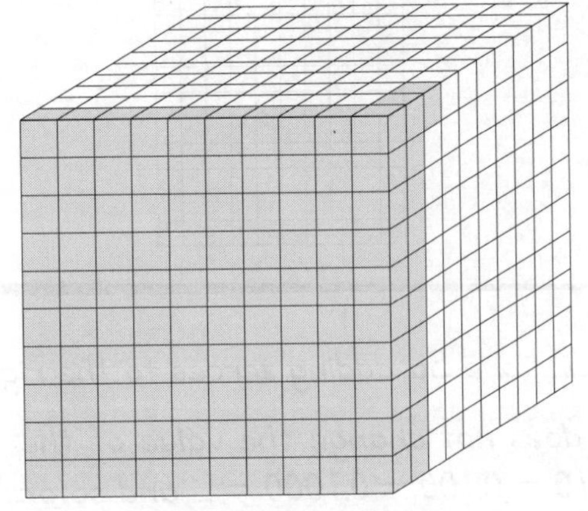

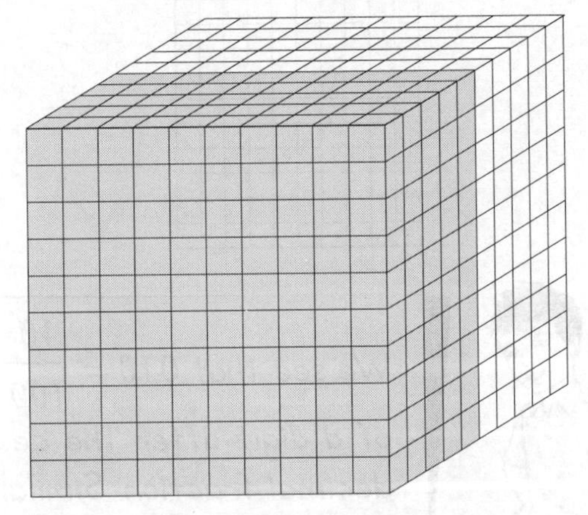

$0.5 = 0.50 = 0.500 = 0.5000 = \frac{1}{2}$

Combining Whole Numbers and Decimal Parts

Whole numbers and decimal parts are combined like this:

+ + = 2 wholes + 0.6 = 2.6 (read as: two point six)

Whole number part ⟶ **2.6** ⟵ Decimal part

↑

Decimal point

Exercise 10.1

1. Complete the following table.

	In Tenths *or* Hundredths	In Fractions	In Decimals
(a)	One-tenths	$\frac{1}{10}$	0.10
(b)			
(c)			
(d)			
(e)			
(f)			

Do these sums in your notebook.

2. Write the following in numeral form.

(a) Three point six

(b) Seven point eight four

(c) Zero point zero one

(d) Fifty-one point zero one five

(e) Four point one two

(f) Nine point zero five

3. **Write the following decimal fractions in words.**

(a) 2.7 (b) 3.18 (c) 46.015 (d) 0.001

(e) 7.101 (f) 82.151 (g) 41.08 (h) 14.35

(i) 6.83 (j) 5.26 (k) 57.06 (l) 28.06

Conversion between Common Fractions and Decimal Fractions

Common fractions can be converted to decimal fractions and *vice versa*. Let us learn the rules for these conversions.

Writing Common Fractions as Decimal Fractions

1. When the denominator is **10,** put the decimal point to the **left of one digit** from the extreme right of the numerator.

Examples: $\frac{3}{10}$ = 0.3 (read as: point three)

$\frac{33}{10}$ = 3.3 (read as: three point three)

$\frac{333}{10}$ = 33.3 (read as: thirty-three point three)

$\frac{3333}{10}$ = 333.3 (read as: three hundred thirty-three point three)

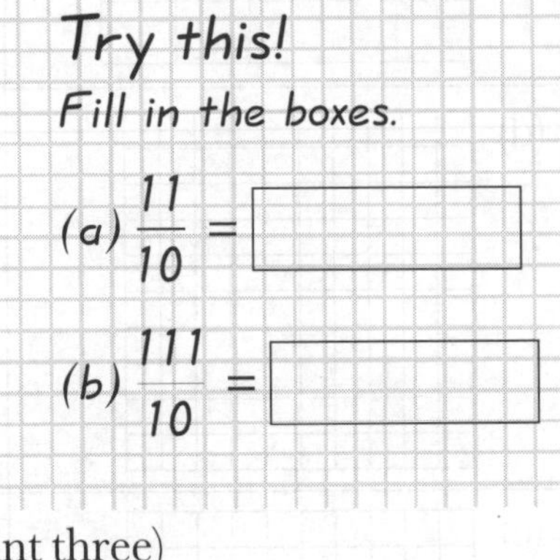

Try this!
Fill in the boxes.
(a) 11/10 =
(b) 111/10 =

2. When the denominator is **100,** put the decimal point to the left of two digits from the extreme right of the numerator.

Examples: $\frac{5}{100}$ = 0.05 (read as: point zero five)

$\frac{55}{100}$ = 0.55 (read as: zero point five five)

$\frac{555}{100}$ = 5.55 (read as: five point five five)

$\frac{5555}{100}$ = 55.55 (read as: fifty-five point five five)

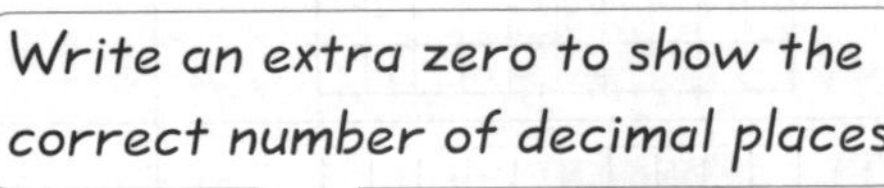

Write an extra zero to show the
correct number of decimal places

3. When the denominator is **1000,** put the decimal point to the **left of three digits** from the extreme right of the numerator.

Examples: $\frac{7}{1000}$ = 0.007 (read as: point zero zero seven)

$\frac{77}{1000}$ = 0.077 (read as: point zero seven seven)

$\frac{777}{1000}$ = 0.777 (read as: point seven seven seven)

$\frac{7777}{1000}$ = 7.777 (read as: seven point seven seven seven)

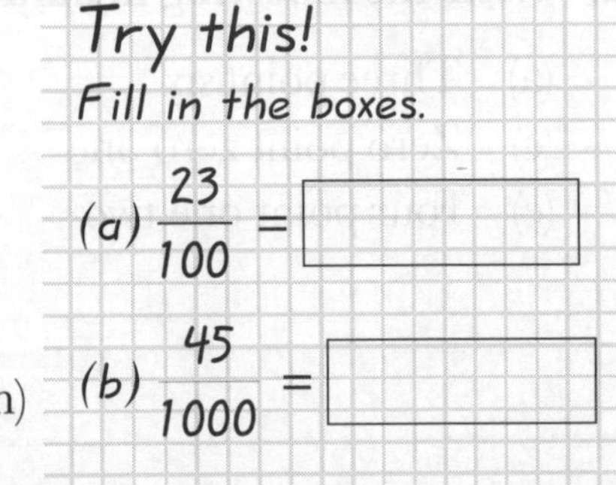

Try this!
Fill in the boxes.
(a) 23/100 =
(b) 45/1000 =

Writing Decimal Fractions as Common Fractions

To express a decimal fraction as a common fraction,
Step 1: Write the given decimal fraction as the numerator and remove the decimal point.
Step 2: Write 1 in the denominator and as many zeroes next to it as the number of digits after the decimal point (in the decimal fraction).

Example 1: Express 1.3 as a common fraction.

Step 1: Write the decimal fraction as the numerator, but remove the decimal point → 13

Step 2: Count the number of digits to the right of the decimal point in the decimal fraction.

Now write the digit 1 in the denominator and write that many zeroes to the right. → $\frac{13}{10}$

(In this case the number of digits to the right of the decimal point is 1, so we write 10 in the denominator)

Thus, $1.3 = \frac{13}{10}$

Example 2: Express 4.76 as a common fraction.

We observe that there are two digits to the right of the decimal point.

So, $4.76 = \frac{476}{100}$

Example 3: Express 7.801 as a common fraction.

We observe that there are three digits to the right of the decimal point.

So, $7.801 = \frac{7801}{1000}$

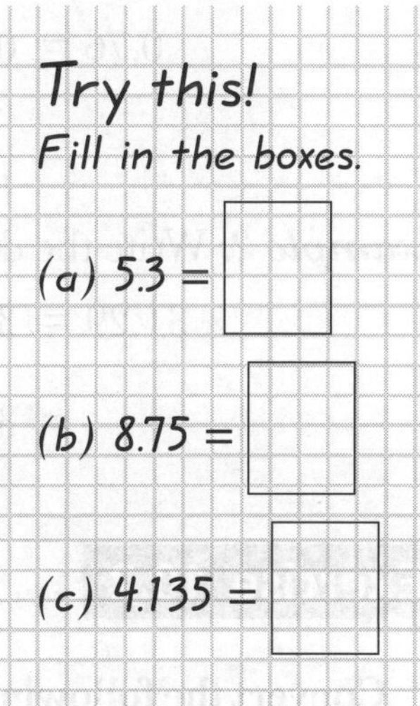

Try this!
Fill in the boxes.
(a) 5.3 =
(b) 8.75 =
(c) 4.135 =

More Examples:

$2.8 = \frac{28}{10}$ $6.87 = \frac{687}{100}$ $8.954 = \frac{8954}{1000}$

$3.7 = \frac{37}{10}$ $5.75 = \frac{575}{100}$ $7.453 = \frac{7453}{1000}$

$6.9 = \frac{69}{10}$ $4.86 = \frac{486}{100}$ $6.321 = \frac{6321}{1000}$

Expanded Form of Decimals

Consider the number 642.873.

Let us expand each of the digits in this number using the place-value chart.

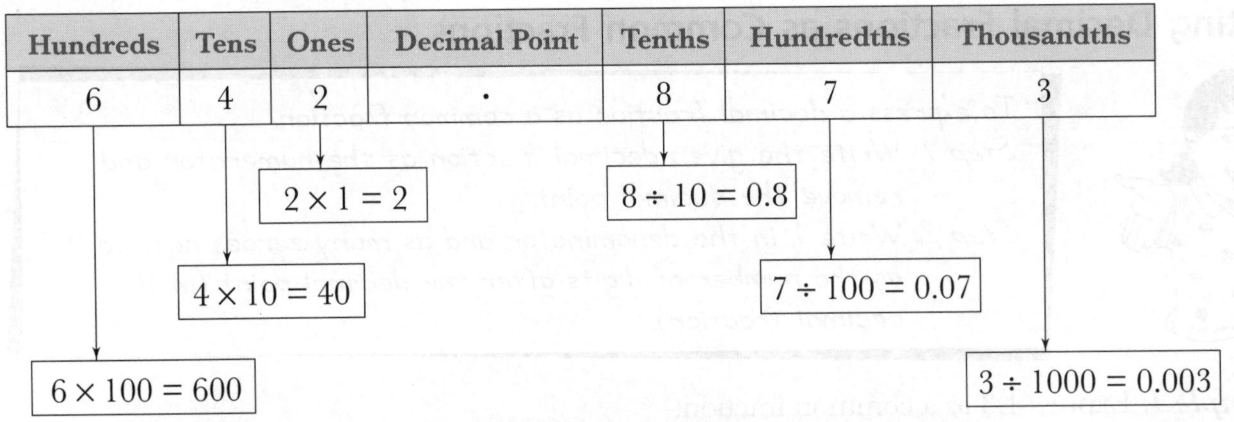

Hundreds	Tens	Ones	Decimal Point	Tenths	Hundredths	Thousandths
6	4	2	·	8	7	3

Thus, $642.873 = 6$ hundreds + 4 tens + 2 ones + 8 tenths + 7 hundredths + 3 thousandths

$= 600 + 40 + 2 + 0.8 + 0.07 + 0.003$ (decimal expansion)

$= 600 + 40 + 2 + \frac{8}{10} + \frac{7}{100} + \frac{3}{1000}$ (fractional expansion)

Example 1: Write the decimal and fractional expansion of 0.76

$0.76 = 0.7 + 0.06$ (decimal expansion)

$= \frac{7}{10} + \frac{6}{100}$ (fractional expansion)

Example 2: Write the decimal and fractional expansion of 31.29

$31.29 = 30 + 1 + 0.2 + 0.09$ (decimal expansion)

$= 30 + 1 + \frac{2}{10} + \frac{9}{100}$ (fractional expansion)

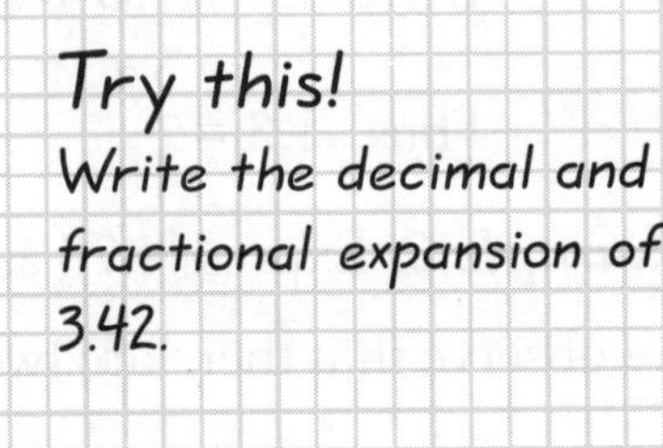

Try this!
Write the decimal and fractional expansion of 3.42.

Exercise 10.2

1. Convert the following common fractions into decimal fractions.

(a) $\frac{2}{10} =$ ____________ (b) $\frac{22}{10} =$ ____________ (c) $\frac{222}{10} =$ ____________

(d) $\frac{634}{10} =$ ____________ (e) $\frac{62}{100} =$ ____________ (f) $\frac{261}{100} =$ ____________

(g) $\frac{3941}{100} =$ ____________ (h) $\frac{3}{100} =$ ____________ (i) $\frac{4263}{1000} =$ ____________

(j) $\frac{718}{1000} =$ ____________ (k) $\frac{5}{1000} =$ ____________ (l) $\frac{5}{50} =$ ____________

2. Convert the following decimal fractions into common fractions.

(a) 3.6 = ____________ (b) 23.1 = ____________ (c) 4.5 = ____________

(d) 0.7 = ____________ (e) 18.26 = ____________ (f) 21.03 = ____________

(g) 0.02 = ____________ (h) 1.01 = ____________ (i) 2.371 = ____________

(j) 38.492 = ____________ (k) 11.001 = ____________ (l) 0.006 = ____________

3. **Write the decimal and fractional expansion of the following.** *(Do these sums in your notebook.)*

(a) 36.234 (b) 6.4 (c) 2.61 (d) 1.05 (e) 0.203
(f) 0.307 (g) 63.718 (h) 9.6 (i) 21.37 (j) 432.231

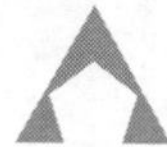

Comparison of Decimals

We know that a decimal has two parts—a **whole part** and a **decimal part.**

For example, 793 . 56

793 → Whole part or (integral part)
56 → Decimal part

Rule 1: When comparing decimal fractions, the fraction with the greater **integral part** is greater.

Example 1: Compare 11.1 and 1.1

Pictorially,

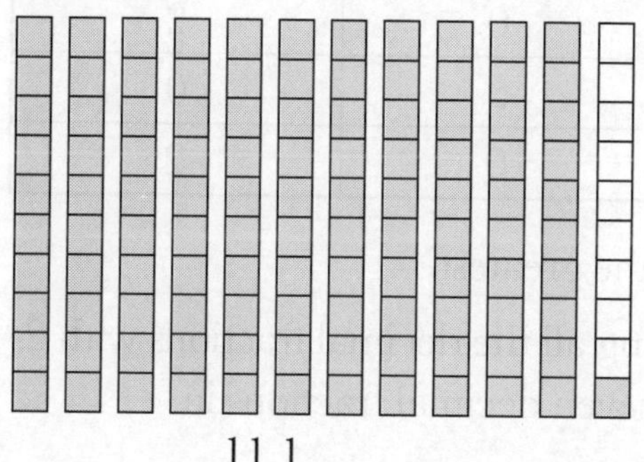

11.1 1.1

We can see from these figures that 11.1 is greater than 1.1.

The decimal parts in both the fractions are the same. The integral part in 11.1 is 11 and in 1.1 is 1. So, 11.1 > 1.1

Rule 2: If the integral parts of two decimal fractions are the same, the decimal fraction with the greater digit in the **tenths** place is greater.

Example 2: Compare 2.14 and 2.65

The integral part of both decimal fractions is 2. The digits in the tenths places are 1 and 6, respectively. As 1 < 6, 2.14 < 2.65

Rule 3: If the integral parts as well as the digits in the tenths place are the same in two decimal fractions, the decimal fraction with the greater digit in the **hundredths** place is greater.

Example 3: Compare 0.17 and 0.15

The integral part of both decimal fractions is 0.
The digit in the tenths place in both decimal fractions is 1.
The digits in the hundredths places are 7 and 5, respectively. As 7 > 5, 0.17 > 0.15.

Rule 4: If the integral parts, and digits in the tenths as well as the hundredths place are the same, the decimal fraction with the greater digit in the **thousandths** place is greater.

Example 4: Compare 32.308 and 32.305

The integral part of both decimal fractions is 32

The digit in the tenths place of both decimal fractions is 3
The digit in the hundredths place of both decimal fractions is 0
The digits in the thousandths places are 8 and 5, respectively.
As 8 > 5, 32.308 > 32.305

Ascending and Descending Orders of Decimal Fractions

Let us arrange the following decimal fractions in descending and ascending order:

2.02, 20.2, 22.202, 2.22, 0.202, 0.22, 2.002

First, write the decimal fractions in a place-value chart.

Decimal fraction	Tens	Ones	Decimal Point	Tenths	Hundredths	Thousandths
2.02		2	.	0	2	0
20.2	2	0		2	0	0
22.202	2	2	.	2	0	2
2.22		2	.	2	2	0
0.202		0	.	2	0	2
0.22		0	.	2	2	0
2.002		2	.	0	0	2

To arrange the decimal fractions in descending order, start from the greatest.

The greatest integral part is 22, followed by 20 and then 2. Among all the decimal fractions with 2 as the integral part, 2.22 is greater than 2.02 and 2.002. So, the seven decimal fractions in descending order are:

22.202, 20.2, 2.22, 2.02, 2.002, 0.22, 0.202

Similarly, the above decimal fractions can be written in ascending order as:

0.202, 0.22, 2.002, 2.02, 2.22, 20.2, 22.202

Exercise 10.3

1. Compare the following decimal fractions and fill in the boxes using a '>' or '<' sign.

(a) 3.4 ☐ 6.5 (b) 11.02 ☐ 1.30 (c) 2.632 ☐ 2.723
(d) 1.2 ☐ 1.02 (e) 10.13 ☐ 10.17 (f) 3.676 ☐ 3.667
(g) 0.9 ☐ 0.1 (h) 2.87 ☐ 2.88 (i) 0.23 ☐ 1.32

2. Arrange the following decimal fractions in descending order.

(a) 34.3, 344.34, 4.34, 4.43, 3.44, 3.43 ______________
(b) 2.282, 2.822, 2.228, 8.228, 8.282 ______________

(c) 0.01, 1.1, 1.001, 1101, 0.011, 0.101 ____________________

(d) 555.55, 55.555, 5.555, 5.55, 5.5, 55.5 ____________________

3. Arrange the following decimal fractions in ascending order.

(a) 281.39, 461.38, 3.961, 2.638, 2.579 ____________________

(b) 7.777, 77.77, 7.77, 777.77, 777.7 ____________________

(c) 69.96, 96.69, 9.696, 9.969, 9.699 ____________________

(d) 1.01, 10.01, 11.1, 10.1, 1.101, 1.001 ____________________

Addition and Subtraction of Decimal Fractions

Addition and subtraction of decimal fractions are the same as addition and subtraction of numbers, but we need to be careful about the decimal point.

Tenths

To represent tenths on the number line, the distance between two whole numbers is divided into ten equal parts.

Let us **add** 1.1 and 0.2.

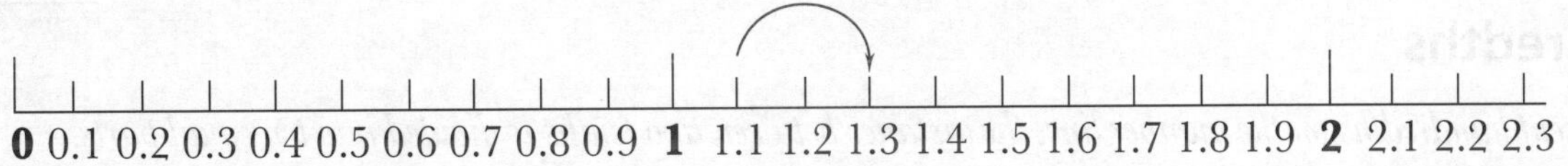

or

```
  1 . 1
+ 0 . 2
-------
  1 . 3
```

Example 1: Add 6.3 and 2.5

```
  6 . 3
+ 2 . 5
-------
  8 . 8
```

So, 6.3 + 2.5 = 8.8

Example 2: Add 3.8 and 2.7

Adding 0.8 and 0.7, we get 15 tenths.

Now, 15 tenths = 1 one and 5 tenths. **Carrying over** 1 one, we get

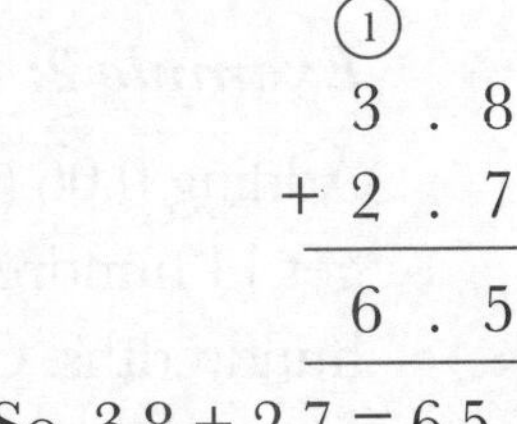

So, 3.8 + 2.7 = 6.5

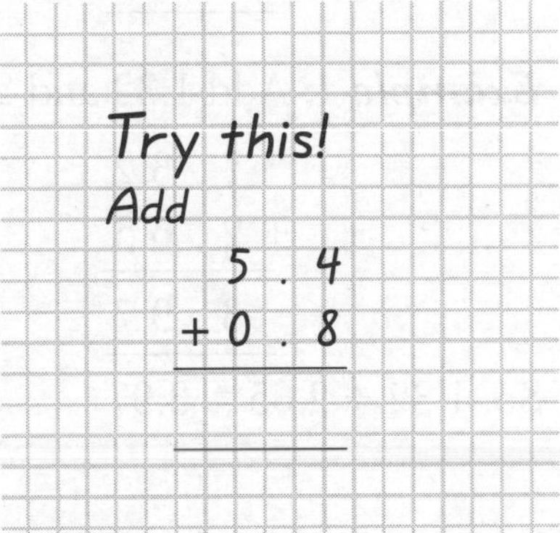

Let us now **subtract** 0.3 from 0.8.

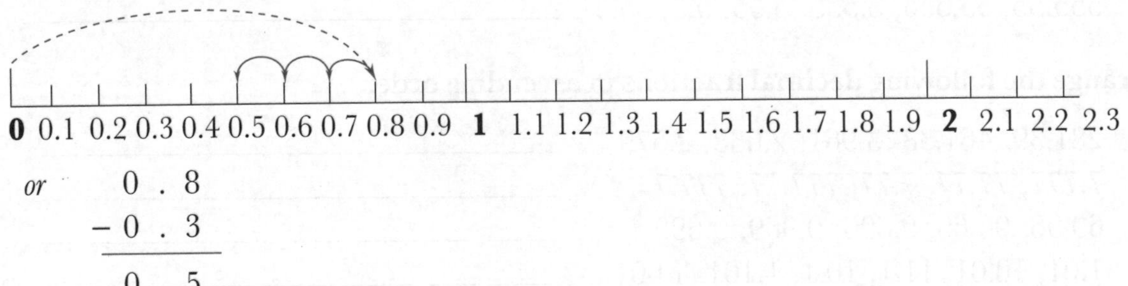

or

$$\begin{array}{r} 0\,.\,8 \\ -\,0\,.\,3 \\ \hline 0\,.\,5 \end{array}$$

Example 3: Subtract 1.4 from 2.7

or

$$\begin{array}{r} 2\,.\,7 \\ -\,1\,.\,4 \\ \hline 1\,.\,3 \end{array}$$

So, 2.7 – 1.4 = 1.3

Example 4: Subtract 1.8 from 3.1

Borrowing ten-tenths from 3 ones, we get 11 tenths and are left with 2 ones in the minuend.

$$\begin{array}{r} ②\;\;⑪ \\ \not{3}\,.\,\not{1} \\ -\,1\,.\,8 \\ \hline 1\,.\,3 \end{array}$$

So, 3.1 – 1.8 = 1.3

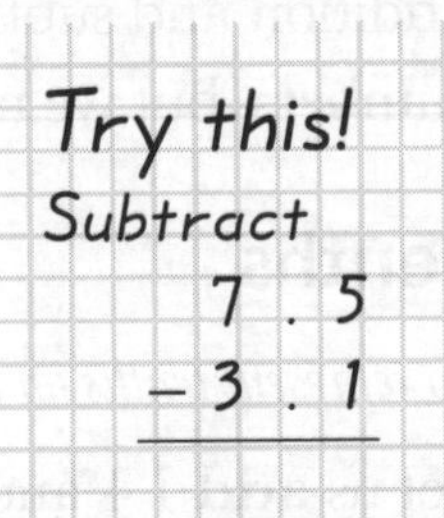

Hundredths

To represent hundredths on the number line, the distance between two tenths is divided into ten equal parts.

Let us **add** 0.03 and 0.06.

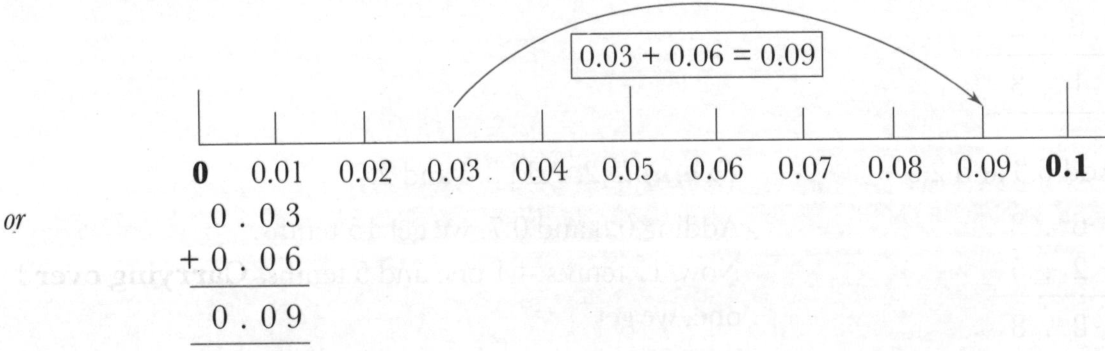

or

$$\begin{array}{r} 0\,.\,03 \\ +\,0\,.\,06 \\ \hline 0\,.\,09 \end{array}$$

Example 1: Add 1.32 and 2.65

$$\begin{array}{r} 1\,.\,32 \\ +\,2\,.\,65 \\ \hline 3\,.\,97 \end{array}$$

So, 1.32 + 2.65 = 3.97

Example 2: Add 3.76 and 2.18

Adding 0.06 (6 hundredths) and 0.08 (8 hundredths) we get 14 hundredths. Now, 14 hundredths = 1 tenth and 4 hundredths. Carrying over 1 tenth we get

$$\begin{array}{r} ①\;\; \\ 3\,.\,76 \\ +\,2\,.\,18 \\ \hline 5\,.\,94 \end{array}$$

So, 3.76 + 2.18 = 5.94

Try this!
Add

$$\begin{array}{r} 6\,.\,64 \\ +\,2\,.\,28 \\ \hline \end{array}$$

Let us now **subtract** 0.05 from 0.08.

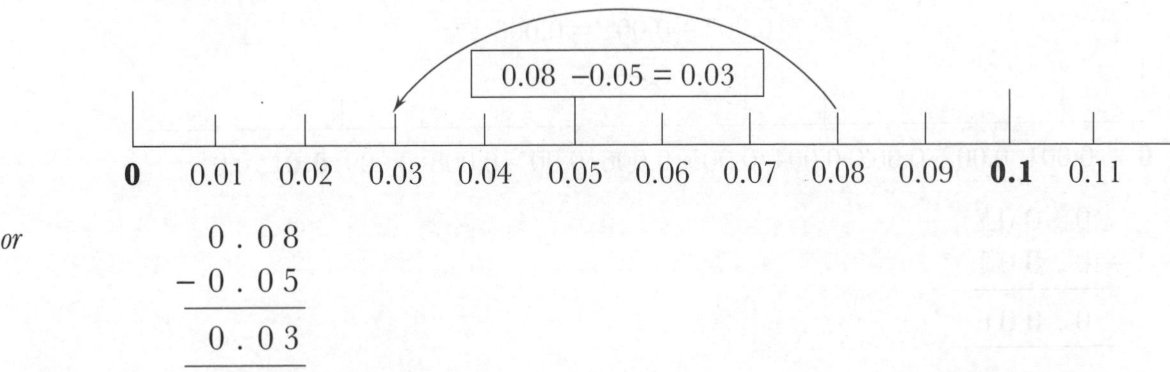

or

$$\begin{array}{r} 0.08 \\ -\,0.05 \\ \hline 0.03 \end{array}$$

Example 3: Subtract 1.24 from 3.75

$$\begin{array}{r} 3.75 \\ -\,1.24 \\ \hline 2.51 \end{array}$$

So, 3.75 – 1.24 = 2.51

Example 4: Subtract 5.38 from 9.52

Borrowing ten hundredths from 5 tenths (or 50 hundredths), we get 12 hundredths and are left with 4 tenths in the minuend.

$$\begin{array}{r} \scriptstyle 4\ 12 \\ 9.\not{5}\,\not{2} \\ -\,5.38 \\ \hline 4.14 \end{array}$$

So, 9.52 – 5.38 = 4.14

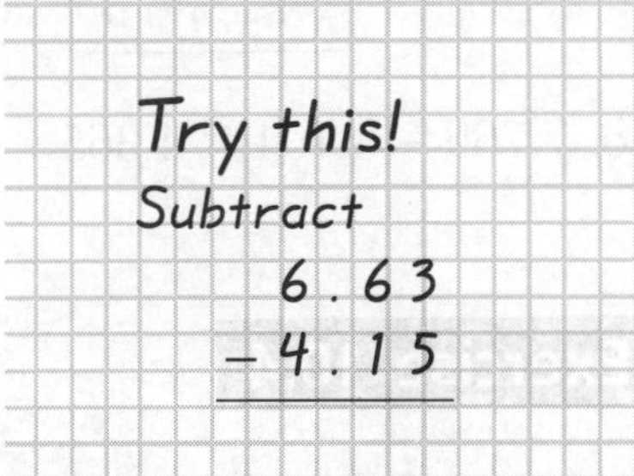

Thousandths

To represent thousandths on the number line, the distance between two hundredths is divided into ten equal parts.

Let us **add** 0.002 and 0.006

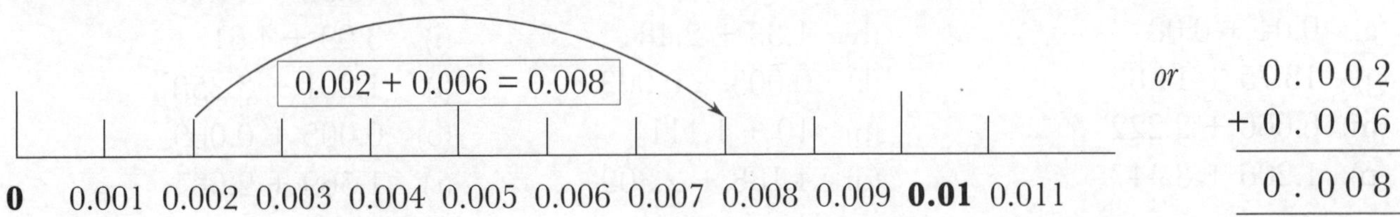

or

$$\begin{array}{r} 0.002 \\ +\,0.006 \\ \hline 0.008 \end{array}$$

Example 1: Add 6.425 and 2.302

$$\begin{array}{r} 6.425 \\ +\,2.302 \\ \hline 8.727 \end{array}$$

So, 6.425 + 2.302 = 8.727

Example 2: Add 2.037 and 2.307

Adding 0.007 (7 thousandths) and 0.007 (7 thousandths), we get 14 thousandths. Now, 14 thousandths = 1 hundredth and 4 thousandths. Carrying over 1 hundredth, we get

$$\begin{array}{r} \scriptstyle 1\ \ \\ 2.037 \\ +\,2.307 \\ \hline 4.344 \end{array}$$

So, 2.037 + 2.307 = 4.344

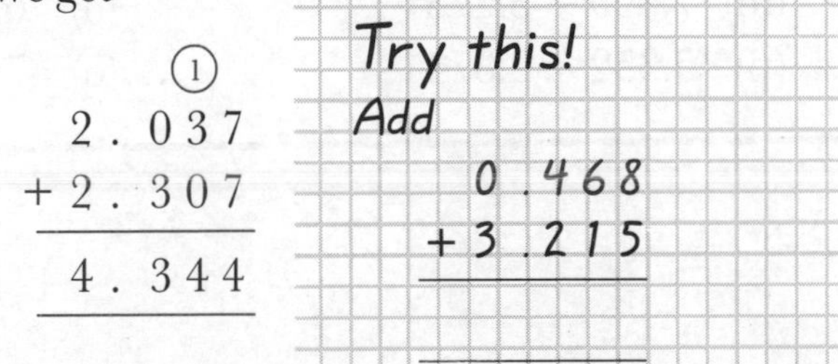

Let us now **subtract** 0.001 from 0.007

0.007 – 0.001 = 0.006

0 0.001 0.002 0.003 0.004 0.005 0.006 0.007 0.008 0.009 **0.01** 0.01

or

$$\begin{array}{r} 0.007 \\ -\,0.001 \\ \hline 0.006 \\ \hline \end{array}$$

Example 3: Subtract 3.404 from 7.769

$$\begin{array}{r} 7.769 \\ -\,3.404 \\ \hline 4.365 \\ \hline \end{array}$$

So, 7.769 – 3.404 = 4.365

Example 4: Subtract 2.449 from 6.773

$$\begin{array}{r} \scriptsize{6\ 12} \\ 6.7\not{7}\not{3} \\ -\,2.449 \\ \hline 4.324 \\ \hline \end{array}$$

So, 6.773 – 2.449 = 4.324

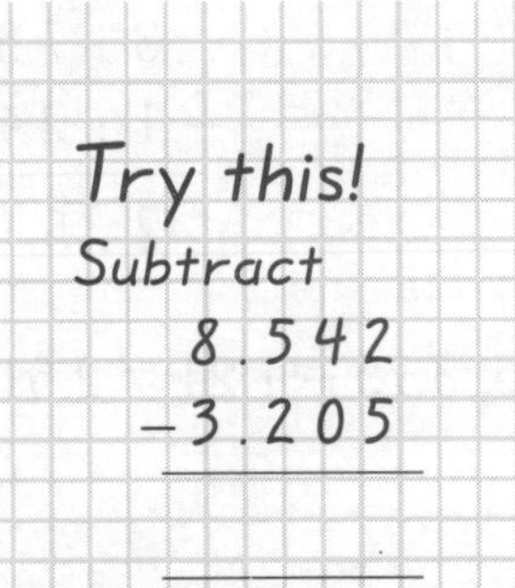

Exercise 10.4

Do these sums in your notebook.

1. **Add the following decimal fractions.**

(a) 0.01 + 0.01	(b) 1.11 + 2.22	(c) 3.35 + 2.51
(d) 6 + 2.06	(e) 34.5 + 21.6	(f) 13.56 + 14.78
(g) 0.04 + 0.08	(h) 1.33 + 2.48	(i) 3.99 + 4.61
(j) 18.75 + 14.88	(k) 0.005 + 0.003	(l) 1.201 + 3.358
(m) 6.666 + 2.222	(n) 10 + 1.111	(o) 0.005 + 0.009
(p) 1.206 + 3.447	(q) 4.188 + 2.309	(r) 1.569 + 2.684

2. **Subtract the following decimal fractions.**

(a) 25.5 – 12.2	(b) 0.09 – 0.08	(c) 3.75 – 1.51
(d) 8.98 – 3.03	(e) 34.73 – 12.21	(f) 25.4 – 18.7
(g) 1.02 – 0.98	(h) 6.33 – 2.44	(i) 3 – 1.33
(j) 0.006 – 0.003	(k) 1.009 – 0.001	(l) 6.535 – 2.103
(m) 7.999 – 3.273	(n) 0.018 – 0.009	(o) 3.121 – 1.107
(p) 5.352 – 2.874	(q) 7 – 5.555	(r) 10 – 2.693

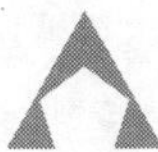

Use of Decimals in Money

You know that fifteen rupees and fifty paise is written as Rs 15.50, where the dot separates the rupee part from the paise part. This dot is nothing but the decimal point.

+ + = Rs 15.50

+ + = Rs 25.20

+

+ = Rs 150.50

We know that 1 Rupee (Re) = 100 paise (p) *or* Rs $\frac{1}{100}$ = 1 p *or* Rs 0.01 = 1 p

Similarly, Rs $\frac{1}{2} = \frac{1}{2} \times 100$ p = 50 p

or, Rs $\frac{1}{2} \times \frac{50}{50} = \frac{50}{100}$ = Rs 0.50 = 50 paise

> *Rupees and paise are written as decimal fractions with the rupees to the left and paise to the right of the decimal point.*

Some examples are:

Rs 8.60 = 8 rupees and 60 paise
Rs 1.50 = 1 rupee and 50 paise
Rs 3.05 = 3 rupees and 5 paise

Note the difference between the tenths place and the hundredths place.

3 paise is written as **Rs 0.03** and not as **Rs 0.3**.

because, Rs 0.3 = Rs $\frac{3}{100}$ = Rs 0.30 or **30 paise**

Similarly,	9 rupees and 9 paise = Rs 9.09	1 rupee and 10 paise = Rs 1.10
	9 rupees and 90 paise = Rs 9.90	1 rupee and 1 paise = Rs 1.01

Use of Decimals in Measurements

Let us now learn about the use of decimals in the measurement of length, mass and capacity.

Measurement of Length

1 kilometre (km) = 1,000 metres *or* $\frac{1}{1000}$ km = 1 metre *or* 0.001 km = 1 metre

Thus, 5 m = 0.005 km 555 m = 0.555 km

55 m = 0.055 km 5555 m = 5.555 km

To convert from m to km, shift the decimal point three places to the left.

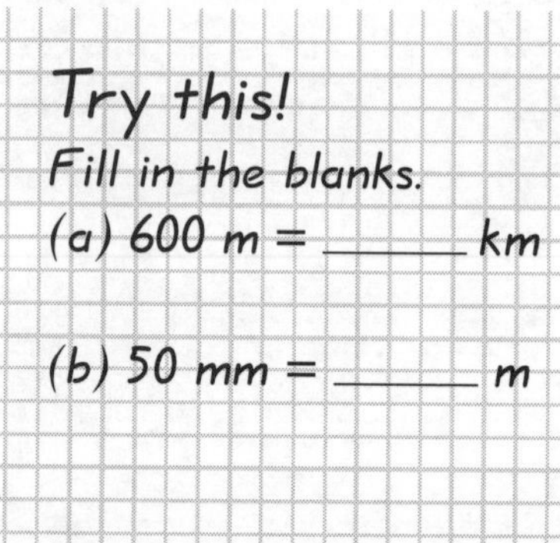

Try this!
Fill in the blanks.
(a) 600 m = ______ km
(b) 50 mm = ______ m

1 metre (m) = 1,000 millimetres (mm) or $\frac{1}{1000}$ m = 1 mm

or 0.001 m = 1 mm

Thus, 2 mm = 0.002 m 200 mm = 0.2 m

20 mm = 0.02 m 2002 mm = 2.002 m

To convert from mm to m, shift the decimal point three places to the left.

Measurement of Mass

1 kilogram (kg) = 1,000 grams (g)

or $\frac{1}{1000}$ kg = 1 g *or* 0.001 kg = 1 g

Thus, 3 g = 0.003 kg 175 g = 0.175 kg

24 g = 0.024 kg 4369 g = 4.369 kg

To convert from g to kg, shift the decimal point three places to the left.

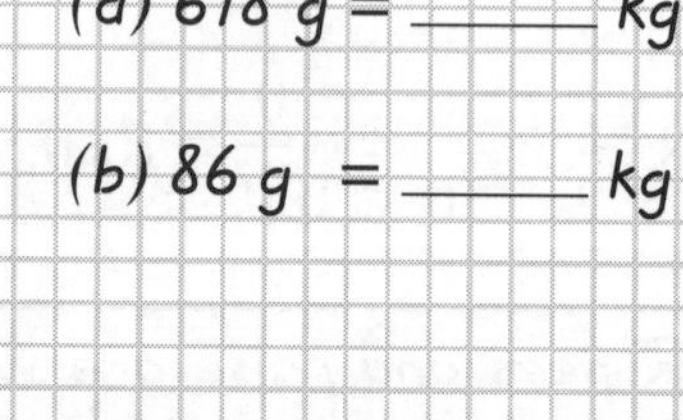

Measurement of Capacity

1 litre (ℓ) = 1,000 millilitres (mℓ)

or $\frac{1}{1000}$ ℓ = 1 mℓ *or* 0.001 ℓ = 1 mℓ

Thus, 6 mℓ = 0.006 ℓ 72 mℓ = 0.072 ℓ

500 mℓ = 0.5 ℓ 4028 mℓ = 4.028 ℓ

To convert from mℓ to ℓ, shift the decimal point three places to the left.

Try this!

Fill in the blanks.

(a) 725 mℓ = ______ ℓ

(b) 52 mℓ = ______ ℓ

Exercise 10.5

1. Write the following as decimal fractions.

(a) 3 rupees 25 paise ________ (b) 10 rupees 10 paise ________
(c) Four rupees forty-five paise ________ (d) 10 rupees 1 paise ________
(e) Thirty rupees and three paise ________
(f) Ninety-nine rupees and nine paise ________
(g) Ninety-nine rupees and ninety paise ________
(h) Seventy-five rupees and sixty-four paise ________

2. Write the following in kilometres.

(a) 500 m = ________ (b) 514 m = ________
(c) 612 m = ________ (d) 264 m = ________
(e) 100 m = ________ (f) 10 m = ________
(g) 21 m = ________ (h) 3 m = ________
(i) 2 m = ________ (j) 6,003 m = ________

3. Write the following in metres.

(a) 400 mm = ________ (b) 360 mm = ________
(c) 137 mm = ________ (d) 240 mm = ________
(e) 24 mm = ________ (f) 30 mm = ________
(g) 3 mm = ________ (h) 5,691 mm = ________
(i) 2,302 mm = ________ (j) 1,001 mm = ________

4. Write the following in kilograms.

(a) 250 g = ________ (b) 500 g = ________
(c) 750 g = ________ (d) 333 g = ________
(e) 50 g = ________ (f) 10 g = ________
(g) 3 g = ________ (h) 1 g = ________
(i) 7,125 g = ________ (j) 10,900 g = ________

5. Write the following in litres.

(a) 200 $m\ell$ = ________ (b) 500 $m\ell$ = ________
(c) 785 $m\ell$ = ________ (d) 250 $m\ell$ = ________
(e) 50 $m\ell$ = ________ (f) 5 $m\ell$ = ________
(g) 2 $m\ell$ = ________ (h) 2,002 $m\ell$ = ________
(i) 5,000 $m\ell$ = ________ (j) 7,008 $m\ell$ = ________

Revision Exercise

Do these sums in your notebook.

1 Write the following decimal fractions in words.

(a) 3.7 (b) 2. 58 (c) 0.012 (d) 1.203 (e) 22.046

2 Write the following in numeral form.

(a) Zero point zero zero five
(b) Three point five four
(c) Six point zero three two
(d) Thirty-five point one zero three

3 Write the following decimal fractions in expanded form.

(a) 2.67 (b) 40.314 (c) 6.003 (d) 88.108 (e) 170.01

4 Arrange the following decimal fractions in ascending order.

(a) 493.64, 78.963, 78.638, 493.963, 493.638
(b) 6.34, 3.64, 4.36, 4.63, 3.46, 6.43
(c) 0.23, 2.3, 2.03, 0.32, 3.2, 3.02

5 Add the following decimal fractions.

(a) 3.42 + 5.03 (b) 8.76 + 1.23 (c) 21.56 + 16.35
(d) 26.12 + 3.24 + 6.17 (e) 2.08 + 1.6 + 11.1 (f) 3.4 + 5.004 + 2.04

6 Subtract the following decimal fractions.

(a) 7.82 – 3.01 (b) 17.52 – 11.37 (c) 24.65 – 12.38
(d) 28.68 – 14.34 (e) 28.34 – 14.68 (f) 7.8 – 5.013

7 Express the following common fractions as decimal fractions.

(a) $\frac{22}{10}$ (b) $\frac{335}{100}$ (c) $\frac{4356}{1000}$ (d) $\frac{6431}{100}$

8 Express the following decimal fractions as common fractions.

(a) 18.91 (b) 35.43 (c) 45.231 (d) 61.237

9 Write the decimal and fractional expansion of the following.

(a) 35.8 (b) 61.23 (c) 5.123 (d) 1.854

10 Express the decimal fractions as required.

(a) 5 rupees 5 paise = Rs ☐ (b) 62 rupees 50 paise = Rs ☐
(c) 7 kg 500 g = ☐ kg (d) 83 ℓ 83 mℓ = ☐ ℓ
(e) 6 km 750 m = ☐ km (f) 74 m = ☐ km
(g) 3,100 mℓ = ☐ ℓ (h) 15,500 mℓ = ☐ ℓ

MEASUREMENT OF LENGTH, MASS AND CAPACITY

Let's Rècap

1. Convert the following into the required units of measurement.

   (a) 3 km = ________ m (b) 8 m 50 cm = ________ cm

   (c) 3 kg = ________ g (d) 1 kg 500 g = ________ g

   (e) 1 ℓ 800 mℓ = ________ mℓ (f) 7 ℓ 400 mℓ = ________ mℓ

2. Add or subtract as required.

   (a) 5 kg 870 g = ________ g
   + 1 kg 575 g = ________ g
   ________ g
   = ____ kg ____ g

   (b) 8 kg 400 g = ________ g
   − 2 kg 425 g = ________ g
   ________ g
   = ____ kg ____ g

   (c) 15 m 95 cm = ________ cm
   + 5 m 55 cm = ________ cm
   ________ cm
   = ____ m ____ cm

   (d) 4 km 322 m = ________ m
   − 2 km 276 m = ________ m
   ________ m
   = ____ km ____ m

   (e) 6 ℓ 335 mℓ = ________ mℓ
   + 2 ℓ 895 mℓ = ________ mℓ
   ________ mℓ
   = ____ ℓ ____ mℓ

   (f) 10 ℓ 300 mℓ = ________ mℓ
   − 7 ℓ 650 mℓ = ________ mℓ
   ________ mℓ
   ____ ℓ ____ mℓ

3. Multiply the following.

   (a) 3 m 11 cm × 4 = ________
   (b) 2 km 234 m × 3 = ________
   (c) 2 kg 140 g × 5 = ________
   (d) 4 ℓ 108 mℓ × 6 = ________

4. Divide the following.

(a) 447 m ÷ 3	(b) 820 g ÷ 5	(c) 760 mℓ ÷ 8	(d) 2 ℓ 106 mℓ ÷ 9
$3\overline{)447}$			

The three kids reached the reptile section of the zoo, where they saw the Indian python.

 Units of Measurement

The standard units of measurement are:

metre (m) for length
gram (g) for mass
litre (ℓ) for capacity

Very often, the need arises to measure quantities bigger or smaller than the standard units. We have seen how greater lengths are measured in kilometres and smaller capacities are measured in millilitres. We also know that,

1 km = 1000 m
1 kg = 1000 g
1 ℓ = 1000 mℓ

In this chapter we will learn more about the various units of measurement.

Just as there are place values between thousands and thousandths, there are units between *kilo* and *milli*. Thus, in addition to *kilo* and *milli*, prefixes like *hecto*, *deca*, *deci* and *centi* are used to relate to the basic unit. The following chart shows the place values of these prefixes:

Place value	Thousands	Hundreds	Tens	Ones	Tenths	Hundredths	Thousandths
Prefix	kilo	hecto	deca	Basic unit metre, gram, litre	deci	centi	milli

Measurement of Length

The basic unit of length is metre. Let us see how the basic unit and the other units are related to each other.

Relating the Basic Unit to Other Units

The basic unit, metre, can be related to other units using the following flow chart:

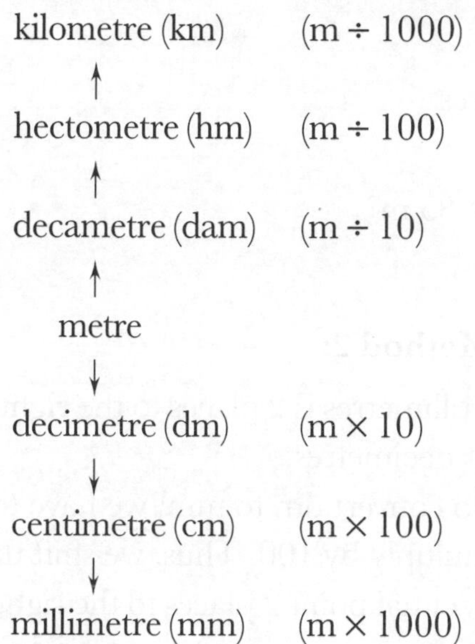

10 millimetres (mm) = 1 centimetre
10 centimetres (cm) = 1 decimetre
10 decimetres (dm) = 1 metre
10 metres (m) = 1 decametre
10 decametres (dam) = 1 hectometre
10 hectometres (hm) = 1 kilometre

For better understanding
7 m = (7 ÷ 1000) km = 0.007 km
7 m = (7 × 100) cm = 700 cm

Thus, we have

1000 m = 1 km		1000 mm = 1 m
100 m = 1 hm	and	100 cm = 1 m
10 m = 1 dam		10 dm = 1 m

The flow chart given for measurement of length can be used for measurement of mass and capacity after replacing metre with gram and litre, respectively.

Let us now relate all the units of length to each other.

Rule 1: To convert a bigger unit into a smaller unit, **multiply by 10 for every move to the right**.

Rule 2: To convert a smaller unit into a bigger unit, **divide by 10 for every move to the left**

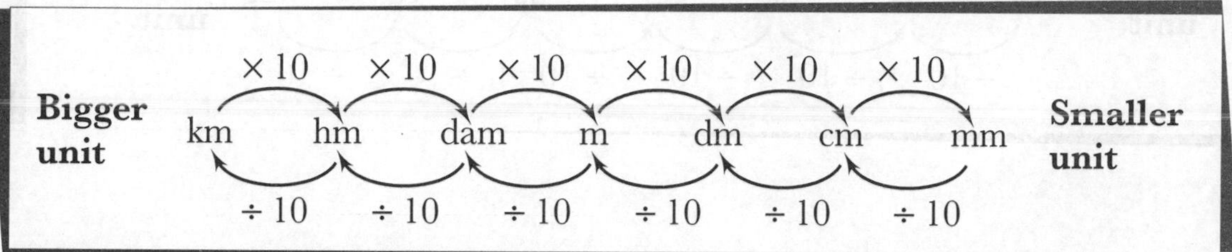

Example 1: Convert 7 hectometres into centimetres.

Centimetres is four places to the right of hectometres. To convert hm to cm, we have to multiply by 10,000.

7 hm = 7 × 10,000 = 70,000 cm

Example 2: Convert 365 metres into kilometres.

Kilometres is 3 places to the left of metre. So to convert m to km, we have to divide by 1,000.

365 m = 365 ÷ 1000 = 0.365 km

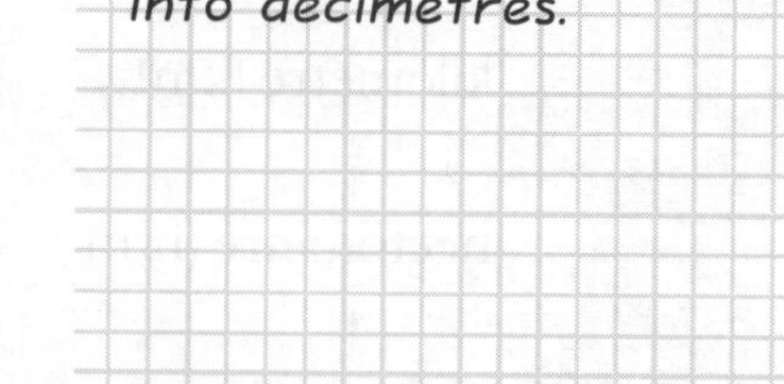

Example 3: Convert 5 decametres 35 metres into metres.

5 dam 35 m = 5 dam + 35 m
= (5 × 10) m + 35 m = 50 m + 35 m = 85 m

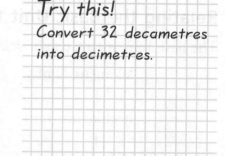

Example 4: Convert 2.65 decimetres into millimetres.

Method 1:

2.65 dm = 2 dm + 0.6 dm + 0.05 dm
= (2 × 100) mm + (0.6 × 100) mm + (0.05 × 100) mm
= 200 mm + 60 mm + 5 mm
= 265 mm

Method 2:

Millimetres is 2 places to the right of decimetres.
To convert dm to mm, we have to multiply by 100. Thus, we shift the decimal point 2 places to the right.
So, 2.65 dm = 265 mm (2 . 6 5)

Measurement of Mass

Gram is the basic unit of mass.

Let us now relate all the units of mass to each other.

Rule 1: To convert a bigger unit into a smaller one, we **multiply**.

Rule 2: To convert a smaller unit into a bigger one, we **divide**.

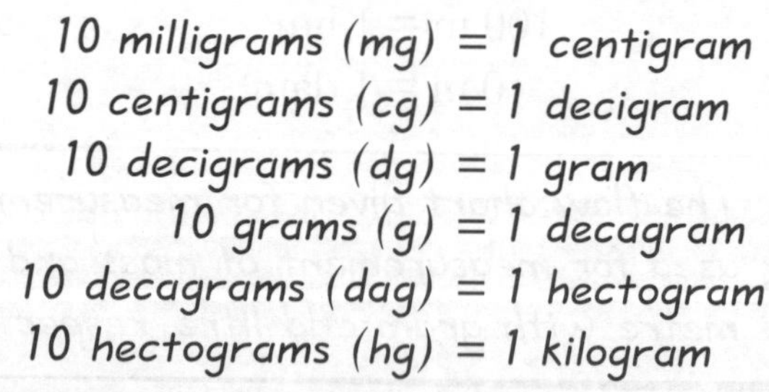

10 milligrams (mg) = 1 centigram
10 centigrams (cg) = 1 decigram
10 decigrams (dg) = 1 gram
10 grams (g) = 1 decagram
10 decagrams (dag) = 1 hectogram
10 hectograms (hg) = 1 kilogram

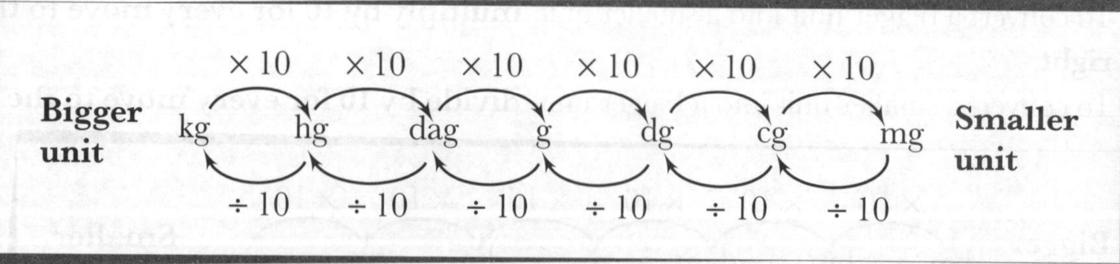

Example 1: Convert 24 decagrams into milligrams.

Milligrams is four places to the right of decagrams. To convert dag to mg, we have to multiply by 10,000.

24 dag = 24 × 10,000 = 2,40,000 mg

Example 2: Convert 21.6 decigrams into decagrams.

Decagrams is two places to the left of decigrams. To convert decigrams into decagrams, we have to divide by 100. Thus, we shift the decimal point two places to the left.

So, 21.6 dg = 21.6 ÷ 100 = 0.216 dag (2 1 .6)

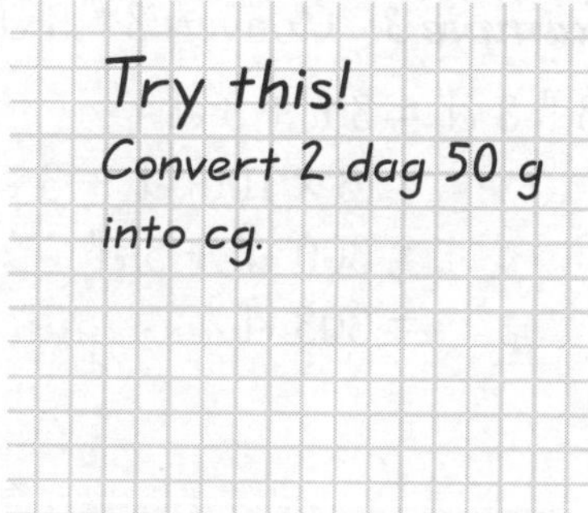

Try this!
Convert 2 dag 50 g into cg.

Example 3: Convert 5 kg 8 dag into grams.

5 kg 8 dag = 5 kg + 8 dag
= (5 × 1000) g + (8 × 10) g
= 5000 g + 80 g
= 5,080 g

Example 4: Convert 64,380 g into kilograms.

Kilograms is three places to the right of grams. So we divide by 1,000 or shift the decimal point three places to the left.

64,380 g = 64380 g ÷ 1000
= 64.380 kg (64 3 8 0.)

Measurement of Capacity

Litre is the basic unit of capacity.

Let us now relate all the units of capacity to each other. To relate the other units of capacity to each other, we apply same rules as we did for measurement of length and mass.

10 millilitres (ml) = 1 centilitre
10 centilitres (cl) = 1 decilitre
10 decilitres (dl) = 1 litre
10 litres (l) = 1 decalitre
10 decalitres (dal) = 1 hectolitre
10 hectolitres (hl) = 1 kilolitre

Rule 1: To convert a bigger unit to a smaller one, we **multiply**.

Rule 2: To convert a smaller unit to a bigger one, we **divide**.

Bigger unit kl → hl → dal → l → dl → cl → ml **Smaller unit**

× 10 × 10 × 10 × 10 × 10 × 10

÷ 10 ÷ 10 ÷ 10 ÷ 10 ÷ 10 ÷ 10

Example 1: Convert 3.54 kℓ into cℓ.

Centilitres is five places to the right of kilolitres. To convert kℓ to cℓ, we have to multiply by 1,00,000. Thus, we shift the decimal point five places to the right.

Thus, 3.54 kℓ = 354000 cℓ

(3.5 4 0 0 0)

Example 2: Convert 247 cℓ into kℓ.

Kilolitres is five places to the left of centilitres. To convert cℓ to kℓ, we have to divide by 1,00,000. Thus, we shift the decimal point five places to the left.

Thus, 247 cℓ = 0.00247 kℓ

(0 0 2 4 7.)

Example 3: Convert 3 ℓ 3 cℓ into centilitres.

3 ℓ 3 cℓ = 3 ℓ + 3 cℓ
= (3 × 100) cℓ + 3 cℓ
= 300 cℓ + 3 cℓ
= 303 cℓ

Example 4: Convert 23.65 litres into litres, decilitres and centilitres.

23.65 ℓ = 23 ℓ + 0.6 ℓ + 0.05 ℓ
= 23 ℓ + (6 × 0.1) ℓ + (5 × 0.01) ℓ
= 23 ℓ + (6 × 1 dℓ) + (5 × 1 cℓ)
(because 1 ℓ = 10 dℓ and 1 ℓ = 100 cℓ)
Thus, 23.65 ℓ = 23 ℓ 6 dℓ 5 cℓ

The following conversion table will help you check if you have got the relationships right.

To change	From milli	From centi	From deci	From m, g, ℓ	From deca	From hecto	From kilo
To milli		×10	×100	×1000	×10000	×100000	×1000000
To centi	÷10		×10	×100	×1000	×10000	×100000
To deci	÷100	÷10		×10	×100	×1000	×10000
To m, g, ℓ	÷1000	÷100	÷10		×10	×100	×1000
To deca	÷10000	÷1000	÷100	÷10		×10	×100
To hecto	÷100000	÷10000	÷1000	÷100	÷10		×10
To kilo	÷1000000	÷100000	÷10000	÷1000	÷100	÷10	

Exercise 11.1

1. Fill in the blanks.

(a) 1 km = ______ cm
(b) 1 dm = ______ m
(c) 3 dam = ______ dm
(d) 4 cm = ______ m
(e) 718 mm = ______ dm
(f) 64,931 mm = ______ m
(g) 1 kg = ______ dag
(h) 1 dg = ______ hg
(i) 63 g = ______ cg
(j) 4.6 kg = ______ hg
(k) 492 g = ______ mg
(l) 234.96 cg = ______ dag
(m) 1 ℓ = ______ dℓ
(n) 1 ℓ = ______ kℓ
(o) 74 hℓ = ______ ℓ
(p) 36 cℓ = ______ hℓ
(q) 6.43 daℓ = ______ cℓ
(r) 234.96 cℓ = ______ daℓ

Do these sums in your notebook.

2. Convert the following.

(a) 6 hm 4 m into m (b) 10 hm 10 cm into cm (c) 3 dam 7 m into m
(d) 1.386 km into m (e) 3.49 hm into m (f) 215 cm into m

3. Convert the following.

(a) 16 g 16 cg into mg (b) 8 kg 8 g into dg (c) 84 hg 3 g into cg
(d) 1.480 kg into g (e) 3.25 dg into g (f) 720 cg into g

4. Convert the following.

(a) 4.34 ℓ into cℓ (b) 6122 mℓ into ℓ (c) 6 kℓ 3 daℓ into ℓ
(d) 319 dℓ into ℓ (e) 8100 mℓ into ℓ (f) 3.10 kℓ into ℓ

5. Convert the following.

(a) 304 cm into m and cm (b) 364 m into hm and m
(c) 364 m into dam and m (d) 67.4 hm into km and hm
(e) 3479 g into kg and g (f) 8009 cg into dg and cg
(g) 468.3 g into dag, g and dg (h) 4312 mℓ into ℓ and mℓ
(i) 6398 dℓ into daℓ, ℓ and dℓ (j) 398 mℓ into dℓ, cℓ and mℓ

Mathematical Operations with Units of Measurements

The process for addition, subtraction, multiplication and division of units of measurement is the same as that for numbers, but we have to be careful about the units that represent the lengths, masses and capacities.

Addition

Example 1: Add 4 ℓ 33 cℓ 6 mℓ and 2 ℓ 81 cℓ 5 mℓ.

	ℓ	dℓ	cℓ	mℓ
	①		①	
	4	3	3	6
+	2	8	1	5
	7	1	5	1

Thus, 4 ℓ 33 cℓ 6 mℓ + 2 ℓ 81 cℓ 5 mℓ = 7 ℓ 15 cℓ 1 mℓ

Example 2: Add 3 kg 500 g and 2 kg 53 g + 1 kg 650 g

	kg	g
	①	①
	3	500
+	2	53
+	1	650
	7	203

Thus, 3 kg 500 g + 2 kg 53 g + 1 kg 650 g = 7 kg 203 g

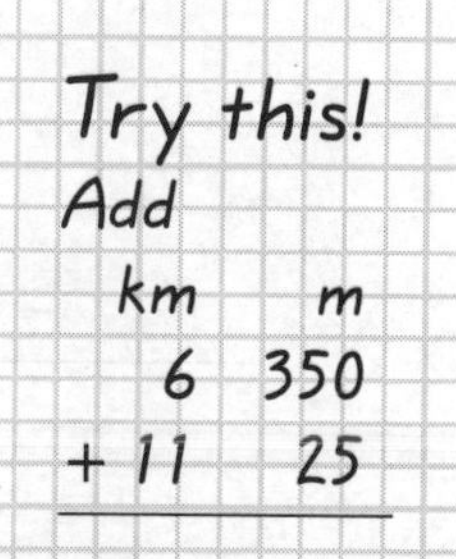

Subtraction

Example 1: Subtract 1 hℓ 39 ℓ from 4 hℓ 28 ℓ.

	hℓ	daℓ	ℓ
	4	2	8
−	1	3	9
	2	8	9

Thus, 4 hℓ 28 ℓ − 1 hℓ 39 ℓ = 2 hℓ 89 ℓ

Example 2: Subtract 428 dg from 1 kg.

First, convert 1 kg into dg.

1 kg = 10,000 dg

	kg	hg	dag	g	dg
	1	0	0	0	0
−			4	2	8
		9	5	7	2

Thus, 1 kg − 428 dg = 9 hg 572 dg

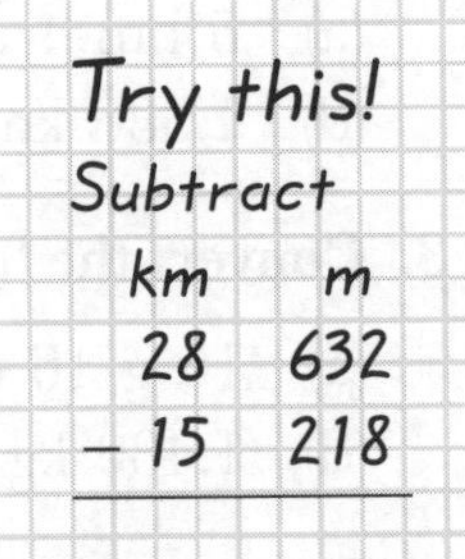

You can remember the order km, hm, dam, m, dm, cm, mm as:
Karan Had Drawn Many Different Colourful Masks.

Multiplication

Example 1: Multiply 6 ℓ 235 mℓ by 9.

	ℓ	dℓ	cℓ	mℓ
	6	2	3	5
	×			9
5	6	1	1	5

Thus, 6 ℓ 235 mℓ × 9 = 56 ℓ 115 mℓ

Example 2: Multiply 28 dg 7 cg by 7.

		dg	cg
	2	8	7
	×		7
2	0	.0	9

Thus, 28 dg 7 cg × 7 = 200 dg 9 cg

Try this!
Multiply

hm	m
4	23
×	5

Division

Example 1: Divide 4 km 936 m by 4.

```
      km  hm  dam  m
       1   2   3   4
  4 |  4   9   3   6
      -4
      ----
           9
          -8
          ----
           1   3
          -1   2
          --------
               1   6
              -1   6
              --------
                   ×
```

Thus, 4 km 936 m ÷ 4 = 1 km 234 m

Example 2: Divide 13 ℓ 5 cℓ by 3.

```
          ℓ  dℓ  cℓ
          4   3   5
  3 | 1   3   0   5
     -1   2
     --------
          1   0
            -9
          ------
              1   5
             -1   5
             -------
                  ×
```

Thus, 13 ℓ 5 cℓ ÷ 3 = 4 ℓ 35 cℓ

Example 3: Divide 14 hg 45 g by 5.

```
        hg  dag  g
         2   8   9
5 |  1   4   4   5
    -1   0
    ---------------
         4   4
        -4   0
    ---------------
             4   5
           - 4   5
    ---------------
                 ×
```

Thus, 14 hg 45 g ÷ 5 = 2 hg 89 g

Try this!

Divide

```
     kg   hg   dag
4 | 24    5    2
```

Watch out for the units!

Exercise 11.2

Do these sums in your notebook.

1. Add the following.

(a) 3 g 4 cg + 6 g 5 cg (b) 5 ℓ 23 mℓ + 2 ℓ 45 mℓ
(c) 2 km 300 m + 3 km 250 m (d) 7 hℓ 22 ℓ + 3 hℓ 66 ℓ
(e) 21 dag 96 dg + 32 dag 35 dg (f) 13 m 47 mm + 28 m 65 mm
(g) 7 dg 88 mg + 3 dg 66 mg (h) 22 daℓ 99 mℓ + 87 daℓ 63 mℓ
(i) 3 kg 150 g + 6 kg 750 g + 8 kg 500 g + 1 kg 250 g
(j) 1 m 80 mm + 2 m 320 mm + 3 m 150 mm + 5 m 450 mm

2. Subtract the following.

(a) 3 kg 700 g – 1 kg 300 g (b) 8 hℓ 9 ℓ – 3 hℓ 3 ℓ
(c) 8 cm 5 mm – 5 cm 3 cm (d) 9 kg 4 hg – 4 kg 9 hg
(e) 4 ℓ – 1 ℓ 400 mℓ (f) 10 g – 5 g 555 mg
(g) 800 dm – 540 dm 22 mm (h) 3 ℓ 46 cℓ – 1 ℓ 54 cℓ
(i) 30 dag 20 dg – 15 dag 15 dg (j) 1 kℓ – 34 ℓ 25 cℓ

3. Multiply the following.

(a) 2 km 300 m × 3 (b) 8 ℓ 202 mℓ × 2 (c) 4 g 110 mg × 3
(d) 3 hm 14 m × 8 (e) 5 dℓ 23 mℓ × 7 (f) 7 dag 17 dg × 10
(g) 31 ℓ 58 mℓ × 6 (h) 4 kg 650 g × 9 (i) 6 km 874 m × 5
(j) 28 kℓ 28 daℓ × 8

4. Divide the following.

(a) 4 kg 44 g ÷ 4 (b) 14 ℓ 770 mℓ ÷ 7 (c) 24 km 600 m ÷ 3
(d) 8 dag 4 g ÷ 2 (e) 10 hg 505 dg ÷ 5 (f) 9 dℓ 78 mℓ ÷ 3
(g) 8 dg 20 mg ÷ 5 (h) 1 km 668 m ÷ 6
(i) 1 kℓ 668 ℓ ÷ 6 (j) 3 kg 3 g ÷ 7

Word Problems

Example 1: A vegetable vendor has 5 kg 650 g of potatoes, 4 kg 800 g of onions and 3 kg 500 g of carrots on his cart. What is the total mass of the vegetables on his cart?

	kg	g
Potatoes	5 kg	650 g
Onions	+ 4 kg	800 g
Carrots	+ 3 kg	500 g
Total mass	13 kg	950 g

Example 2: Anuradha's sister weighs 51 kg 200 g. Anuradha weighs 16 kg 700 g less than her sister. How much does Anuradha weigh?

	kg	g
Sister's weight	51 kg	200 g
Less	– 16 kg	700 g
Anuradha's weight	34 kg	500 g

Example 3. A car runs 13 km 350 m on 1 litre of petrol. How far will the car run on 7 litres of petrol?

	13 km	350 m
×		7
	93 km	450 m

Thus, the car will run 93 km 450 m on 7 litres of petrol.

Example 4. 2 ℓ 800 *m*ℓ of milk is shared equally by 8 boys. How much milk does each boy get to drink?

```
    ℓ  dℓ  cℓ  mℓ
        3   5   0
 8 | 2  8   0   0
   –2   4
   ----------
        4   0
       –4   0
   ----------
        ×   0
           –0
   ----------
            ×
   ----------
```

Thus, each boy gets 350 *m*ℓ of milk.

Exercise 11.3

1. A man travels 3 km 500 m by rickshaw, 7 km 850 m by bus and 54 km by suburban train to reach his office. What is the total distance covered by him?	Distance travelled by rickshaw = _____ km _____ m Distance travelled by bus = _____ km _____ m Distance travelled by suburban train = _____ km Total distance travelled = _____ km _____ m
2. Rakesh weighs 35 kg 400 g and Pramod weighs 34 kg 650 g. How much do the both boys weigh? 	Weight of Rakesh = _____ kg _____ g Weight of Pramod = _____ kg _____ g Total weight of both the boys = _____ kg _____ g
3. An empty 5 litre can is filled with 2 ℓ 150 *m*ℓ of cold water and 1 ℓ 900 *m*ℓ of warm water. How much water is there in the can now?	Amount of cold water filled in the can = _____ ℓ _____ *m*ℓ Amount of warm water filled in the can = _____ ℓ _____ *m*ℓ Total amount of water in the can = _____ ℓ _____ *m*ℓ
4. A milkman adds water to 8 ℓ 350 *m*ℓ of milk to fill his 10 litre can. How much water did the milkman add? 	Capacity of the can = ℓ Amount of milk in the can = _____ ℓ _____ *m*ℓ Amount of water added = _____ ℓ _____ *m*ℓ

Revision Exercise

Do these sums in your notebook.

1 Convert the following.

(a) 3 km 4 m into m (b) 27.6 dal into cl (c) 674 mm into m
(d) 5.6 hg into g (e) 4784 cm into m (f) 21 dl into dal
(g) 800 ml into dl (h) 6.71 hm into cm (i) 0.03 kg into g

2 Add the following.

(a) 14 m 28 cm + 4 m 15 cm (b) 4 km 225 m + 800 m
(c) 4 dag 20 dg + 2 dag 15 dg (d) 1g 32 mg + 672 mg
(e) 3 dl 3 ℓ + 42 ml (f) 28 ℓ 25 ml + 10 ℓ 352 ml

3 Subtract the following.

(a) 3 m 42 cm – 1 m 6 cm (b) 7 dam – 7 m
(c) 67 g 50 mg – 25 g 15 mg (d) 25 kg 620 g – 11 kg 50 g
(e) 7 ℓ 55 ml – 2 ℓ 27 ml (f) 4 ℓ 56 cl – 1 ℓ 28 cl

4 Multiply the following.

(a) 4 m 72 cm × 3 (b) 28 kg 5 hg × 4 (c) 42 km 4 hm × 5
(d) 2 dag 15 dg × 2 (e) 8 dl 18 ml × 5 (f) 32 ℓ 200 ml × 8

5 Divide the following.

(a) 69 kg 336 g ÷ 3 (b) 44 km 64 dam ÷ 4 (c) 50 ℓ 65 ml ÷ 5

6 A milkman adds 2 ℓ 650 ml of milk in a can which already contains 2 ℓ 300 ml of milk. If he sells 3 ℓ 750 ml of milk, how much milk remains in his can?

7 From a rope of 2 dam 34 cm long, 900 cm is cut off. What is the length of the rope now?

8 A man drove at a constant speed to cover 367 km 500 m in 7 hours. How much distance did the man cover every hour?

9 12 hg of cherries is distributed equally among 8 boys. What mass of cherries does each boy get?

10 A tap fills 5 litres of water in a tank every minute. If the capacity of the tank is 150 litres, how much time will it take to fill the tank?

11 An empty water tank was filled with 35 ℓ 750 ml of water in the morning and 28 ℓ 580 ml of water in the afternoon. During the day, 39 ℓ 330 ml of water was taken out and used. How much water remained in the tank? How many 5 ℓ buckets can be filled with the remaining water?

12 A cook uses 2 cl 4 ml of cooking oil everyday. How much oil does the cook use in a week?

13 A leaking water tank loses 3 ℓ 45 ml of water every hour. How much water will run out of the water tank in 5 hours?

12 TIME

Let's Recap

1. Fill in the blanks.

(a) 2 months 12 days = ________ days
(b) 1 week 3 days = ________ days
(c) 4 weeks 2 days = ________ days
(d) 3 days = ________ hours
(e) 2 days 2 hours = ________ hours
(f) 6 days 16 hours = ________ hours
(g) 7 hours = ________ min
(h) 3 hours 20 min = ________ min
(i) 10 min = ________ s
(j) 6 min 40 s = ________ s

2. Write the correct time with a.m. or p.m.

(a) 7 hours after midnight = ____________
(b) 7 hours before midnight = ____________
(c) 5 hours after noon = ____________
(d) 5 hours before noon = ____________
(e) 2 hours 20 min after 7 p.m. = ____________
(f) 3 hours 30 min after 10 a.m. = ____________
(g) 4 hours 20 min after 2:40 p.m. = ____________
(h) 1 hour 30 min after 11:30 p.m. = ____________

3. Add the following.

(a)

h
14
+ 5

(b)

min
24
+ 18

(c)

h	min
2	15
+ 5	35

(d)

h	min
7	28
+ 1	12

4. Subtract the following.

(a)

h
28
− 18

(b)

min
56
− 25

(c)

h	min
14	37
− 6	13

(d)

h	min
32	45
− 6	36

The three friends reached the final section of the zoo.

Reading Time

You must have seen clock faces with Hindu–Arabic numerals. Similarly, we can also have clock faces marked in Roman numerals.

This clock face has Hindu–Arabic numerals.

The hour hand is between 1 and 2.

The minute hand is on 6.

We know that there are 5 minutes between any two hour digits.

So, $6 \times 5 = 30$ minutes.

The time is **1:30**.

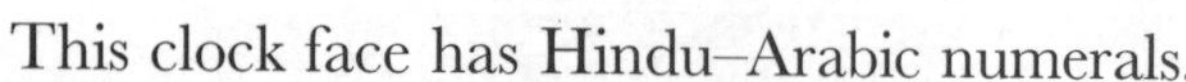

This clock face has Roman numerals.

The hour hand is between 10 and 11.

The minute hand is at 2 marks past the 2 hour digit.

$2 \times 5 = 10$ minutes

10 minutes + 2 minutes = 12 minutes

The time is **10:12**.

An hour has 60 minutes. 15 minutes out of 60 minutes is $\frac{15}{60} = \frac{\cancel{3} \times \cancel{5} \times 1}{2 \times 2 \times \cancel{3} \times \cancel{5} \times 1} = \frac{1}{4}$

So, **15 minutes = quarter hour**. So, 12:15 is also read as **quarter-past 12**.

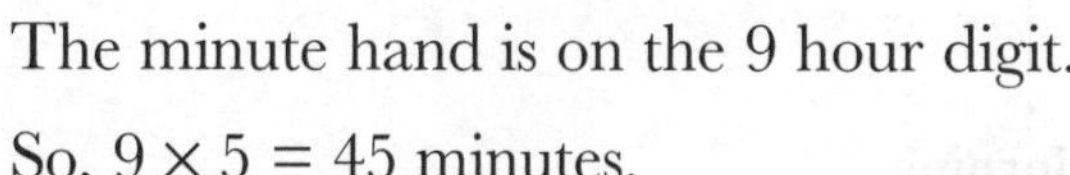

The minute hand is on the 9 hour digit.

So, $9 \times 5 = 45$ minutes.

$$\frac{45}{60} = \frac{3 \times \cancel{3} \times \cancel{5} \times 1}{2 \times 2 \times \cancel{3} \times \cancel{5} \times 1} = \frac{3}{4} \text{ or } 3 \times \frac{1}{4}$$

So, **45 minutes = three-quarters**

But, $1 - \frac{1}{4} = \frac{3}{4}$ *or* $\frac{3}{4} + \frac{1}{4} = 1$, i.e., add another quarter to make $\frac{3}{4}$ one whole.

So, **6:45** is also read as **quarter to 7**.

The minute hand is on the 6 hour digit.

So, $6 \times 5 = 30$ minutes

$$\frac{30}{60} = \frac{\cancel{2} \times \cancel{3} \times \cancel{5} \times 1}{2 \times \cancel{2} \times \cancel{3} \times \cancel{5} \times 1} = \frac{1}{2}$$

So, **30 minutes = half-hour**

8:30 is also read as **half-past 8**.

By convention we do not read 8:30 as half to 9 although it is mathematically correct.

A.M., P.M. and 24-Hour Clocks

If we read 10:30 on a clock how do we know if the time is 10:30 a.m. or 10:30 p.m.?

Simply by looking around us. If it is morning and there is all the daytime activity going on around us, it is 10:30 a.m. If it is dark outside and people are preparing to go to bed, it must be 10:30 p.m.

Morning
(a.m.)

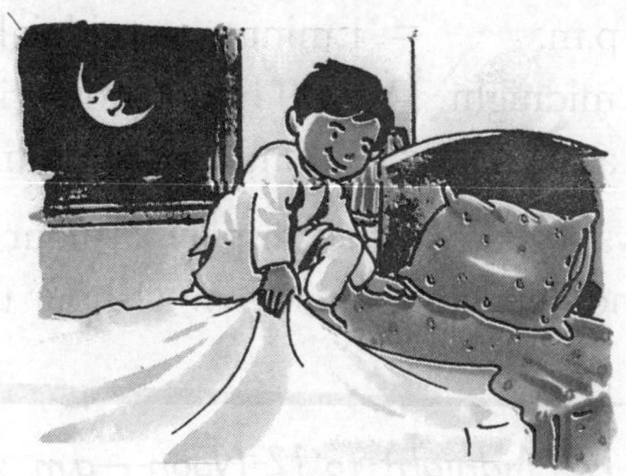

Night
(p.m.)

Now, suppose you set an alarm clock at 3 to remind you to get out to play the next afternoon, but the clock rings out loudly in the middle of the night at 3 to wake up everybody, then what do you do?

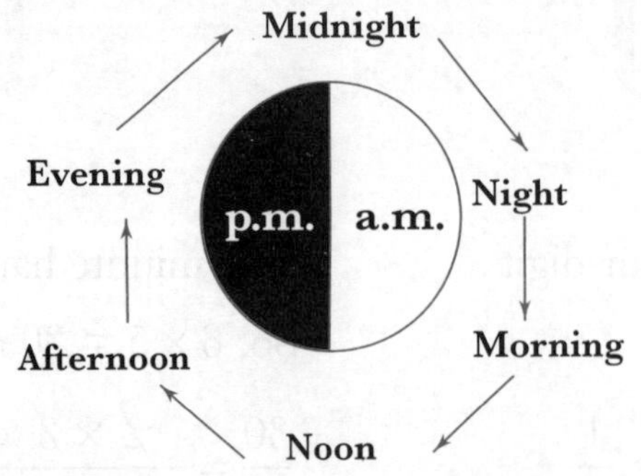

To avoid mistakes in the communication of time, 24 hours are written as follows:

12-Hour Time		24-Hour Time		12-Hour Time		24-Hour Time	
12	Midnight	0000	hours	12	Noon	1200	hours
1:00	a.m.	0100	hours	1:00	p.m.	1300	hours
2:00	a.m.	0200	hours	2:00	p.m.	1400	hours
3:00	a.m.	0300	hours	3:00	p.m.	1500	hours
4:00	a.m.	0400	hours	4:00	p.m.	1600	hours
5:00	a.m.	0500	hours	5:00	p.m.	1700	hours
6:00	a.m.	0600	hours	6:00	p.m.	1800	hours
7:00	a.m.	0700	hours	7:00	p.m.	1900	hours
8:00	a.m.	0800	hours	8:00	p.m.	2000	hours
9:00	a.m.	0900	hours	9:00	p.m.	2100	hours
10:00	a.m.	1000	hours	10:00	p.m.	2200	hours
11:00	a.m.	1100	hours	11:00	p.m.	2300	hours

The minutes are written after the hours as follows:

7:30 a.m. = 0730 hours   5:46 a.m. = _____ hours
7:15 p.m. = 1915 hours   6:38 p.m. = _____ hours
11:59 p.m. = 1 minute to midnight = 2359 hours
12:00 midnight = 0000 hours (not written as 2400 hours)
12:01 a.m. = 1 minute past midnight = 0001 hours

Nowadays digital watches display 24-hour time. Bus, Railway and Airline timetables also list arrival and departure timings in 24-hour time.

- ➤ *12 Midnight to 12 Noon—a.m.*
- ➤ *12 Noon to 12 Midnight—p.m.*

Try this!

Fill in the blanks using 24-hour clock.

(a) 1 : 20 a.m. = ___________ hours

(b) 3 : 15 p.m. = ___________ hours

1. **Write the time shown on the following clock faces.**

(a)

(b)

(c)

(d)

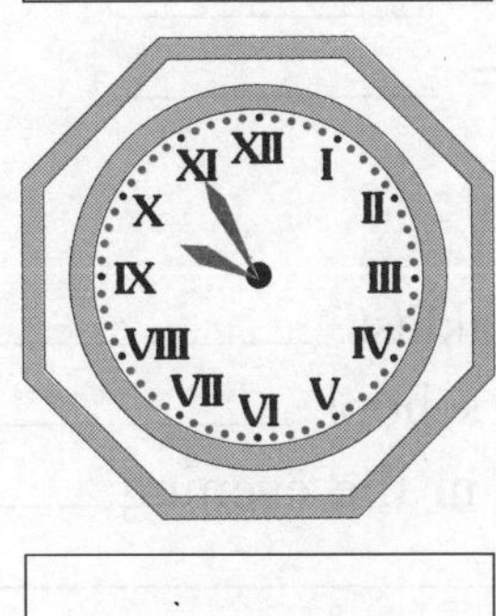

(e)

(f)

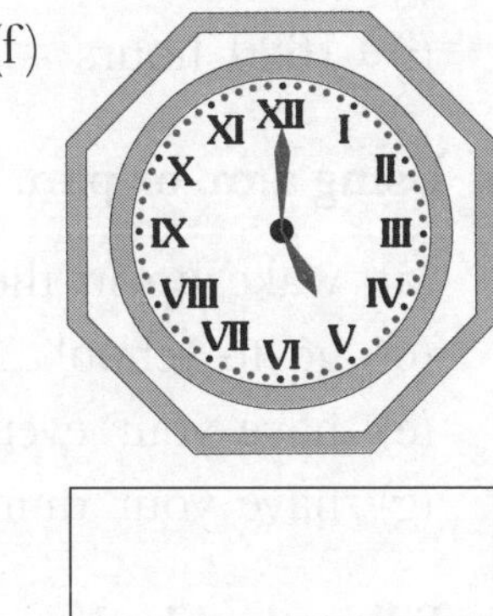

2. **Draw the hands on the following clock faces.**

(a)

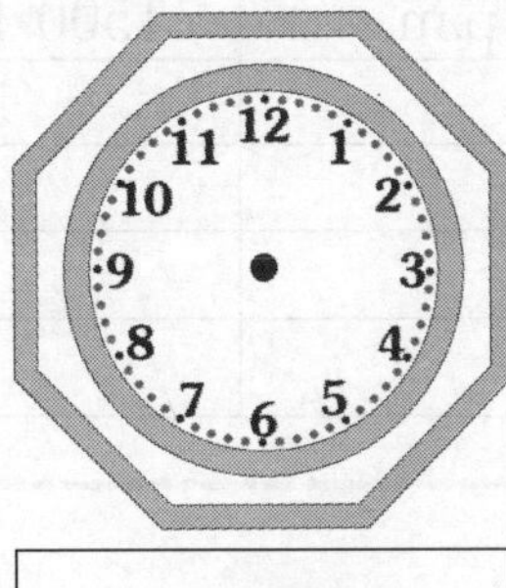

5:30

(b)

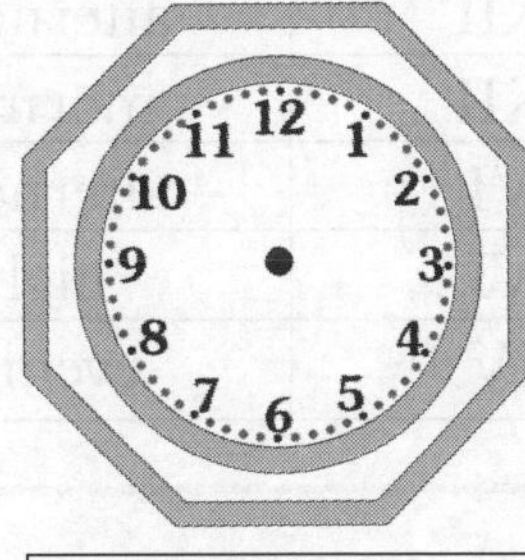

6:40

(c)

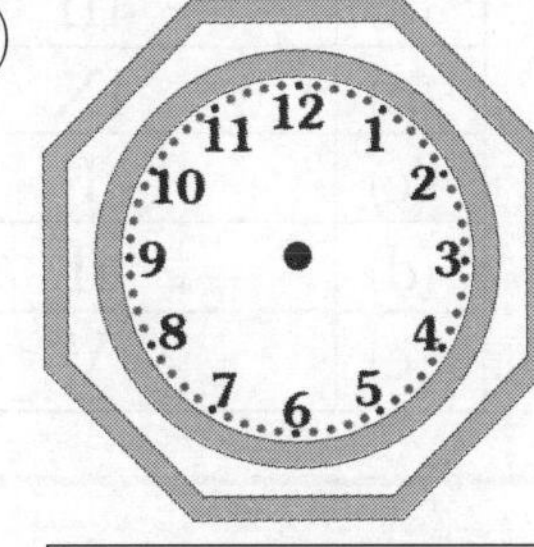

3:10

(d)

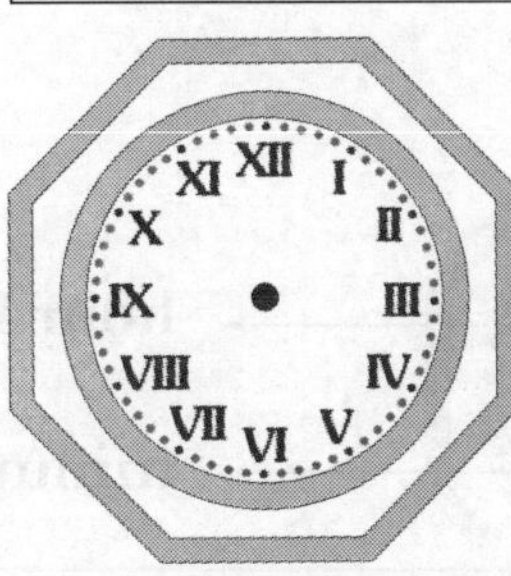

4:00

(e)

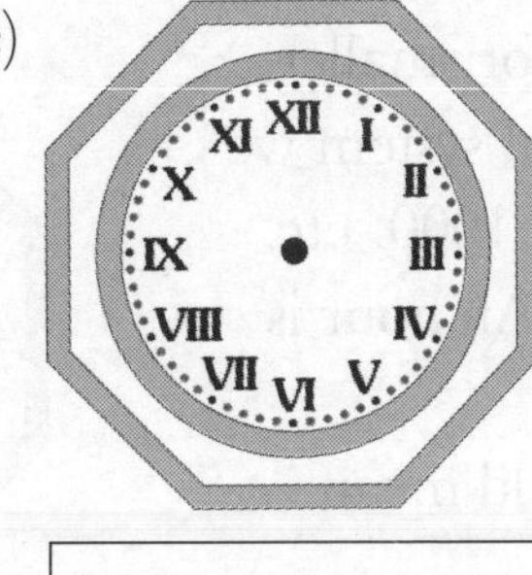

12:30

(f)

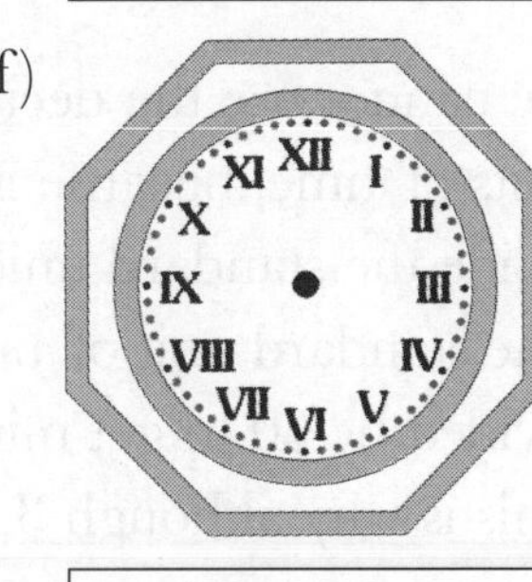

4:45

3. Write the time using the 24-hour clock.

(a) 6 a.m. = ________ (b) 10 p.m. = ________
(c) 11:30 a.m. = ________ (d) 12:30 p.m. = ________
(e) 3:45 a.m. = ________ (f) 12 midnight = ________
(g) 4:30 a.m. = ________ (h) 7:50 p.m. = ________
(i) 5:20 p.m. = ________ (j) 2:10 p.m. = ________

4. Write the time using the 12-hour clock.

(a) 1600 hours = ________ (b) 1430 hours = ________
(c) 1245 hours = ________ (d) 0045 hours = ________
(e) 1220 hours = ________ (f) 2008 hours = ________
(g) 1351 hours = ________ (h) 1540 hours = ________
(i) 1620 hours = ________ (j) 0150 hours = ________

5. Using a.m. or p.m. write at what time you:

(a) wake up in the morning ________ (b) have your breakfast ________
(c) go to school ________ (d) have lunch at school ________
(e) have your evening snack ________ (f) go out to play in the evening ________
(g) have your dinner ________ (h) go to bed ________

6. Fill in the blank spaces.

	Hour hand on	Min hand on	Part of the day	12 hour time	24 hour time
(a)	III	XII	afternoon	3 p.m.	1500 hours
(b)	IX	XII	morning		
(c)	I	VI	afternoon		
(d)	II	VI	night		
(e)	V	IV	evening		

Conversion of Units of Time

We cannot use the decimal system for smaller units of time, because in the decimal system we divide the standard unit by 10, 100, 1000, etc. The standard unit of time is **hour**. An hour is divided by 60 to get minutes.
This is why although 3.5 hours would mean $3\frac{1}{2}$ hours or 3 hours thirty minutes, it would not be very convenient to express different measures of time in decimals.

hour hand
minute hand
second hand

We know that **1 hour ÷ 60 = 1 minute**

In addition to the hour hand and minute hand, there is a third hand on the clock face that is thin and long. This hand moves the fastest of all three hands and it shows the seconds. It is called the **second hand**.

Example: What is the time on the clock face given alongside?

The hour hand is between 10 and 11. The minute hand is on the 8 hour digit.

So, $8 \times 5 = 40$ minutes

The second hand is 3 marks past the 4 hour digit.

So, $4 \times 5 = 20$ seconds and 20 seconds + 3 seconds = 23 seconds

The time is 10:40:23 or 10 hours 40 minutes 23 seconds.

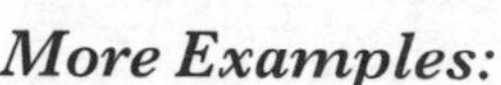

More Examples:

Example 1: Convert 3 hours 40 minutes into minutes.

3 hours 40 minutes = 3 hour + 40 minutes

= (3×60) minutes + 40 minutes

= 180 minutes + 40 minutes

= 220 minutes

Example 2: Convert 10 minutes into seconds.

1 minute = 60 seconds

So, 10 minutes = 60×10

= 600 seconds

Example 3: Convert 5 minutes 33 seconds into seconds.

5 minutes + 33 seconds

= (5×60) seconds + 33 seconds

= 300 seconds + 33 seconds

= 333 seconds

Example 4: Convert 2 hours 3 minutes 45 seconds into seconds.

2 hours + 3 minutes + 45 seconds

= (2×60) minutes + (3×60) seconds + 45 seconds

= 120 minutes + 180 seconds + 45 seconds

= (120×60) seconds + 225 seconds

= 7200 seconds + 225 seconds

= 7425 seconds

***Example* 5:** Convert 660 seconds into minutes.

60 seconds = 1 minute

To find minutes, we divide the seconds by 60.

$$
\begin{array}{r|l}
 & 11 \\
\hline
60 & 660 \\
 & -60 \\
\hline
 & 60 \\
 & -60 \\
\hline
 & \times
\end{array}
$$

Thus, 660 seconds = 11 minutes

***Example* 6:** Convert 548 seconds into minutes.

$$
\begin{array}{r|l}
 & 9 \\
\hline
60 & 548 \\
 & -540 \\
\hline
 & 8
\end{array}
$$

Quotient = 9; Remainder = 8

Thus, 548 seconds = 9 minutes 8 seconds

Operations Involving Time

Let us learn how to add, subtract, multiply and divide time.

We write h for hours, min for minutes and s for seconds.

Addition of Time

Example: Add 1 h 48 min 52 s and 2 h 25 min 38 s

	h	min	s
	1	48	52
+	2	25	38
	3	73	90

Now, 90 seconds = 60 seconds + 30 seconds

= 1 minute + 30 seconds

So, 3 h 73 min 90 s = 3 h 74 min 30 s

But, 74 minutes = 60 minutes + 14 minutes

= 1 hour + 14 minutes

Thus, 1 h 48 min 52 s + 2 h 25 min 38 s = 4 h 14 min 30 s

Try this!
Add

	h	min	s
	4	32	45
+		25	10

Subtraction of Time

Example: Subtract 1 h 45 min 40 s from 4 h 34 min 08 s

	h	min	s
	(3)	(93)	(68)
	~~4~~	~~33~~ ~~34~~	~~08~~
−	1	45	40
	2	48	28

1 minute = 60 seconds

Borrowing 1 minute from 34 minutes, we get

08 seconds + 60 seconds = 68 seconds

So, we are left with 33 minutes in the minuend.

Now, 1 hour = 60 minutes

Borrowing 1 hour from 4 hours, we get

33 minutes + 60 minutes = 93 minutes

So, we are left with 3 hours in the minuend.

Thus, 4 h 34 min 08 s − 1 h 45 min 40 s = 2 h 48 min 28 s

Try this!
Subtract

	h	min	s
	6	52	21
−	1	30	15

Multiplication of Time

Example 1: Multiply: 1 h 30 min 14 s × 2

h	min	s
1	30	14
×		2
2	60	28

Now, 60 minutes = 1 hour

We carry over 1 hour and get 3 h 00 min 28 s

Thus, 1 h 30 min 14 s × 2 = 3 h 00 min 28 s

Example 2: Multiply: 2 h 45 min 53 s × 8

h	min	s
2	45	53
×		8
16	360	424

= 16 h 367 min 04 s (as 424 s = 7 min 04 s)

= 22 h 07 min 04 s (as 367 min = 6 h 07 min)

Thus, 2 h 45 min 53 s × 8 = 22 h 07 min 04 s

Try this!

Multiply

h	min	s
1	22	08
×		3

Division of Time

Example 1: Divide 16 h 08 min 06 s by 2.

	h	min	s
	8	04	03
2	16	08	06
	−16		
	×	08	
		−08	
		×	06
			−06
			×

So, 16 h 08 min 06 s ÷ 2 = 8 h 04 min 03 s

Example 2: Divide 19 h 58 min 80 s by 7.

	h	min	s	
	2	50	80	
7	19	58	80	
	−14			
	5 →	300		(remainder 5 h × 60 = 300 min)
		+58		
		358		
		−350		
		8 →	480	(remainder 8 min × 60 = 480 s)
			+80	
			560	
			−560	
			×	

So, 19 h 54 min 80 s ÷ 7 = 2 h 50 min 80 s

Word Problems

Example 1: On Monday, Preetha slept for 7 h 15 min 35 s at night and 1 h 27 min 52 s in the afternoon. For how many hours did she sleep in all on Monday?

		h	min	s
At night, Preetha slept for	=	7	15	35
In the afternoon, she slept for	=	(+) 1	27	52
In all, she slept for	=	8	42	87

Now, 87 seconds = 60 seconds + 27 seconds

= 1 minute + 27 seconds

So, 42 min 87 seconds = 43 min 27 seconds

Thus, Preetha slept for 8 h 43 min 27 s in all on Monday.

Example 2: In an examination paper the total time allowed was 3 hours. The nib of Sahil's pen broke after 1 h 37 min 15 s. How much time was left for him to complete the paper?

		h	min	s
		(2)	(59)	(60)
Total time allowed	=	~~3~~	~~60~~ ~~00~~	~~00~~
Sahil's nib broke after	=	(−) 1	37	15
Time left	=	1	22	45

Thus, Sahil had 1 h 22 min 45 s left to complete the paper.

Example 3: Geeta practised solving mathematics problems every day for 1 h 15 minutes for a week. For how much time in all did she practise solving mathematics problems that week?

Each day Geeta practised for = 1 h 15 min

In 1 week (7 days) she practised for = 1 h 15 min × 7

h	min
1	15
×	7
7	105
8 h	45 min

Thus, Geeta practised solving mathematics problems for 8 h 45 min in all that week.

Example 4: It took Mr Ganguly 1 h 54 min to cover 8 kilometres on foot. How long did he take to cover 1 kilometre?

8 kilometres covered in 1 h 54 min. So, 1 kilometre is covered in 1 h 54 min ÷ 8.

	h	min	s
	0	14	15
8	1	54	
	−0		
	1 ⟶	60	
		+ 54	
		114	
		−112	
		2 ⟶	120
			−120
			×

So, Mr Ganguly took 14 min 15 s to cover 1 kilometre.

Exercise 12.2

Do these sums in your notebook.

1. Add the following.

(a) 10 min 10 s + 20 min 20 s
(b) 6 h 12 min + 2 h 23 min
(c) 2 h 11 min 20 s + 3 h 22 min 15 s
(d) 4 h 44 min 09 s + 3 h 04 min 20 s
(e) 3 h 07 min 40 s + 2 h 51 min 20 s
(f) 8 h 30 min 30 s + 1 h 50 min 50 s
(g) 5 h 40 min 10 s + 4 h 30 min 20 s
(h) 9 h 20 min 5 s + 3 h 25 min 15 s
(i) 11 h 01 min 3 s + 2 h 4 s
(j) 12 h 23 min 5 s + 3 h 6 s

2. Subtract the following.

(a) 7 h 48 min – 4 h 12 min
(b) 12 min 53 s – 10 min 22 s
(c) 6 h 35 min 48 s – 3 h 13 min 27 s
(d) 9 h 44 min 37 s – 9 h 03 min 17 s
(e) 5 h 08 min 10 s – 2 h 02 min 50 s
(f) 3 h 38 min 05 s – 21 min 55 s
(g) 4 h 48 min 20 s – 11 min 8 s
(h) 8 h 52 min 30 s – 22 min 9 s
(i) 5 h 28 min 40 s – 33 min 11 s
(j) 7 h 04 min 50 s – 43 min 13 s

3. Multiply the following.

(a) 3 h 04 min × 2
(b) 3 min 23 s × 3
(c) 4 h 12 min 24 s × 2
(d) 2 h 02 min 12 s × 4
(e) 5 h 06 min 15 s × 6
(f) 6 h 10 min 21 s × 5
(g) 6 h 20 min 30 s × 3
(h) 9 h 30 min 30 s × 5
(i) 7 h 10 min 40 s × 4
(j) 7 h 10 min 40 s × 5

4. Divide the following.

(a) 4 h 08 min ÷ 2
(b) 9 min 36 s ÷ 3
(c) 6 h 42 min 36 s ÷ 2
(d) 6 h 18 min 27 s ÷ 3
(e) 12 h 48 min 28 s ÷ 4
(f) 5 h 50 min 25 s ÷ 5
(g) 8 h 16 min 24 s ÷ 8
(h) 8 h 48 min 32 s ÷ 8
(i) 9 h 27 min 36 s ÷ 9
(j) 9 h 45 min 36 s ÷ 9

5. Solve the following word problems.

(a) A baker got all the materials for making a cake together in 5 min 14 s. Then, he mixed all the ingredients together for 3 min 21 s. He then baked the cake in an oven for 32 min 5 s. How long did the baker take to make the cake?

(b) Arvind jogged to a park in 57 min 38 s. There he took a break and sat on a bench for 5 min 45 s. He jogged back home in 55 min 28 s. How much time did he spend jogging?

(c) Pratima took 2 h 35 min 15 s to complete her homework on Tuesday. On Wednesday, she took 48 min 20 s less than the time she took on Tuesday. How much time did she take to finish her homework on Wednesday?

(d) The school bell rings at 10:00 a.m. sharp and it is already 09:50:10 a.m. How much time remains for the bell to ring?

(e) Divya woke up at 7:00 a.m. after sleeping for 7 hours. At what time did she go to bed?

(f) If Divya has spent 600 seconds practising on the harmonium, how many minutes has she spent?

(g) A television programme had 15 minutes of advertisements in it. How many seconds were the advertisements for?

(h) A machine takes 5 seconds to fix the cap on a bottle of cold drink. How many caps will it fix in 10 minutes? [**Hint:** Convert 10 minutes to seconds first]

Revision Exercise

Do these sums in your notebook.

1 Write the time using the 24-hour clock.

(a) 9:00 a.m. (b) 6:15 p.m. (c) 7:35 a.m.
(d) 6:50 p.m. (e) 8:10 a.m. (f) 9:10 a.m.

2 Write the time using the 12-hour clock.

(a) 0540 hours (b) 1315 hours (c) 1720 hours
(d) 0120 hours (e) 0000 hours (f) 12 noon

3 Convert the following.

(a) 4 days into hours (b) 2.5 days into hours
(c) 1 h 23 min into minutes (d) 6 min 14 s into seconds
(e) 480 s into minutes (f) 4200 s into h and minutes

4 Solve the following.

(a) 30 min 6 s + 20 min 11 s (b) 1 h 58 min 34 s + 2 h 6 min 48 s
(c) 2 h 23 s + 45 min 45 s (d) 46 min 29 s – 30 min 4 s
(e) 6 h 6 min 6 s – 1 h 8 min 8 s (f) 5 h – 1 h 18 min 44 s
(g) 4 min 4 s × 4 (h) 1 h 20 min 30 s × 5
(i) 3 h 38 min 16 s × 7 (j) 39 min 42 s ÷ 3
(k) 3 h 34 min 48 s ÷ 4 (l) 7 h 31 min 54 s ÷ 6
(m) 1 h 48 min 52 s + 2 h 25 min 38 s (n) 4 h 34 min 08 s – 1 h 45 min 40 s
(o) 1 h 30 min 14 s × 2 (p) 2 h 45 min 53 s × 8
(q) 16 h 08 min 6 s ÷ 2 (r) 19 h 58 min 80 s ÷ 7

5 On annual Sports Day, a flag had to be held aloft for 3 hours. Achla held the flag for 57 min 23 s and when she got tired, Kulsoom held it for 1 h 14 min 16 s. Finally, Poorva held the flag for the rest of the time. For how long did Poorva hold the flag aloft?

6 A boat takes 8 min 15 s to cross a river. If it made 15 crossings in one day, for how long did it travel throughout the day?

7 If a cook can bake 15 cakes one after the other in 5 h 45 min, how long does he take to bake each cake?

8 The Earth takes 24 hours to complete one rotation about its axis. How many hours does it take to rotate 5 times?

13 UNITARY METHOD

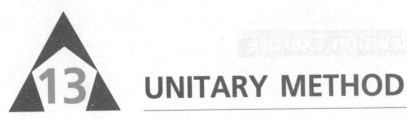

Rahul went to a fruit seller to buy 6 bananas for the elephants. The bananas were for Rs 24 a dozen.

Unitary Method

A single object or person is known as a *unit.* The word **unitary** is derived from the word unit. In this chapter we will use the unitary method to find the value of many, given the value of one and *vice versa.*

Finding the Value of Many

To find out the value of **many**, when we know the value of one, we **multiply**

Example 1: A car has 4 wheels. How many wheels will 10 cars have?

One car has = 4 wheels

10 cars will have = $4 \times 10 = 40$ wheels

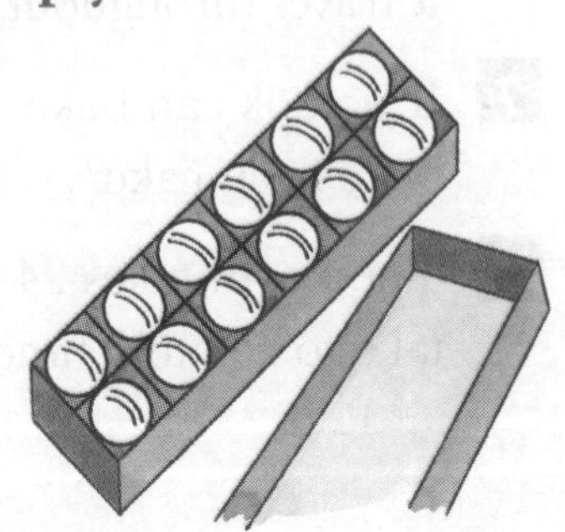

Example 2: How much will 12 balls cost, if each ball costs Rs 4?

Cost of 1 ball = Rs 4

Cost of 12 balls = Rs 4×12 = Rs 48

Finding the Value of One

To find out the value of **one**, when we know the value of many, we **divide**.

Example 1: 12 bananas cost Rs 24. How much will 1 banana cost?

Cost of 12 bananas = Rs 24

Cost of 1 banana = Rs 24 ÷ 12 = Rs 2

Example 2: 12 coaches in a train have 360 seats in all. How many seats are there in one coach?

12 coaches have = 360 seats

1 coach will have = 360 seats ÷ 12 = 30 seats

Example 3: Alex needs to buy a packet of sharpeners. When he goes to the market he finds that 10 orange sharpeners cost Rs 20 and 12 blue sharpeners cost Rs 36. If both the sharpeners are of the same quality, which is a better buy?

Here, we need to find out which of the two sharpeners is cheaper. As the quality of both is the same, the cheaper sharpener is a better buy.

Cost of 10 orange sharpeners = Rs 20

Cost of 1 orange sharpener = Rs 20 ÷ 10

= Rs 2

Cost of 12 blue sharpeners = Rs 36

Cost of 1 blue sharpener = Rs 36 ÷ 12

= Rs 3

So, the price of one orange sharpener is less than the price of one blue sharpener. Therefore, it is a better buy.

- *Many units are more than one unit. So to find out the value for many units, when that for one is known, we multiply.*
- *One unit is less than many units. So to find out the value for one unit, when that for many units is known, we divide.*

Finding Out for Many When We Know for Some

If we know the price for some units, we first find out the price for one unit by dividing. Then, we find how much many units would cost by multiplying.

We write the known quantity on the left-hand side. On the right-hand side, we write what is to be found out.

Example 1: 8 rows of flowers have 720 flowers. How many flowers are there in 6 rows?

8 rows have	=	720 flowers
1 row has	=	720 flowers ÷ 8 = 90 flowers
Now, 1 row has	=	90 flowers
So, 6 rows have	=	90 flowers × 6 = 540 flowers

Example 2: Let us now solve Rahul's problem.

Cost of 12 bananas	=	Rs 24
So, cost of 1 banana	=	Rs 24 ÷ 12 = Rs 2
Now, cost of 1 banana	=	Rs 2
So, cost of 6 bananas	=	Rs 2 × 6 = Rs 12

Remember that the unitary method does not work in some situations.

For instance, in solving Example 1 above, it is assumed that each row has an equal number of flowers, or else we cannot apply the unitary method.

The units which are divided and then multiplied need to be of the same object as the units of the answer, else we cannot apply the unitary method.

For example, if we know the price of a dozen apples, we can find the price of 6 apples. But we cannot find the price of 6 oranges, given the price of a dozen apples.

Similarly, if we know that a car has four wheels, we can find out how many wheels 8 such cars will have. But we cannot find out how many wheels 10 vehicles will have. This is because some vehicles may be trucks with 6 wheels and some may be scooters with 2 wheels.

If we know that 1 tree has 420 mangoes, we cannot tell how many mangoes will be there on 6 trees, unless it is given that all trees contain 420 mangoes each. This is because some trees may have more and some may have less number of mangoes.

Revision Exercise

Do these sums in your notebook.

1 Use the unitary method to fill in the boxes.

(a) 1 bag weighs 4 kg, so 7 bags will weigh = ☐ kg
(b) 1 ice cream costs Rs 3, so 20 ice creams will cost = ☐ Rs
(c) 1 teddy-bear costs Rs 32, so 3 teddy-bears will cost = ☐ Rs
(d) 1 cold drink bottle contains 200 $m\ell$, so 3 cold drink bottles will contain = ☐ $m\ell$
(e) 1 step in a staircase is 25 cm high, so 8 steps in the staircase will be = ☐ cm
(f) 7 pens cost Rs 49, so 1 pen will cost = ☐ Rs
(g) 8 bags of flour have 120 kg, so 1 bag of flour will have = ☐ kg
(h) 3 drums of water have 210 ℓ, so 1 drum of water will have = ☐ ℓ
(i) 1 dozen pencils cost Rs 12, so 1 pencil will cost = ☐ Rs
(j) 8 dozen bangles cost Rs 96, so 1 dozen bangles will cost = ☐ Rs

2 Fill in the boxes.

You may need to use both division and multiplication in some cases.

(a) 1 book = Rs 23; 56 books = ☐
(b) 8 pencils = Rs 56; 3 pencils = ☐
(c) 4 chairs = Rs 464; 7 chairs = ☐
(d) 72 students need 24 benches; 93 students will need ☐ benches.
(e) 48 boxes contain 576 crayons; 3 boxes will contain ☐ crayons.

3 Solve the following word problems using the unitary method.

(a) 10 ℓ of kerosene oil costs Rs 50. How much will 5 ℓ of kerosene oil cost?
(b) A farmer tills 3 acres of land in 6 days. How many days will he take to till his entire field of 18 acres?
(c) 4 toy guns cost Rs 48. How much would 5 toy guns cost?
(d) A matchbox has 52 matchsticks. How many matchsticks will 4 matchboxes have?
(e) 2 school buses can seat 110 students in all. How many students can be seated in 6 such buses?
(f) 7 kg of rice costs Rs 98. How much would 15 kg of rice cost?
(g) A weaving mill produces 448 sarees in 8 days. How many sarees will it produce in 15 days?
(h) There are 7 days in 1 week. How many days are there is 52 weeks?
(i) 36 boxes of crayons have 864 crayons in all. How many crayons are there in each box?
(j) 10 toys cost Rs 500. How much would 17 toys cost?

GEOMETRY

Let's Recap

1. Draw lines of symmetry to divide these shapes into symmetrical halves.

(a)  (b) 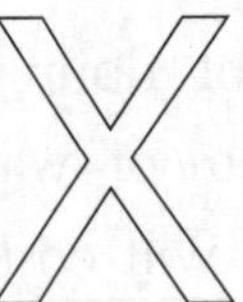 (c) 

2. Draw a line segment AB measuring 7 cm.

3. Measure the lengths of the line segments and fill in the blanks.

(a)

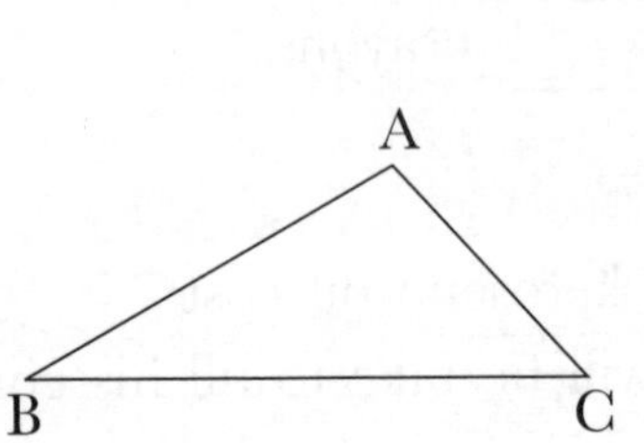

AB = __________ cm
BC = __________ cm
AC = __________ cm
Perimeter = AB + BC + AC
Perimeter = __________ cm

(b)

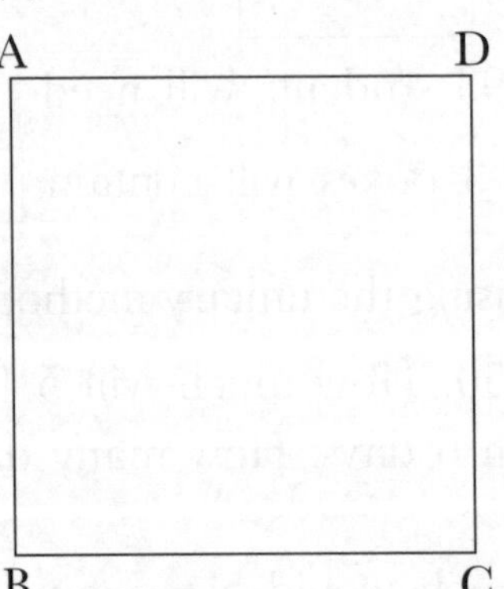

AB = __________ cm
BC = __________ cm
CD = __________ cm
AD = __________ cm
Perimeter = AB + BC + CD + AD
Perimeter = __________ cm

(c)

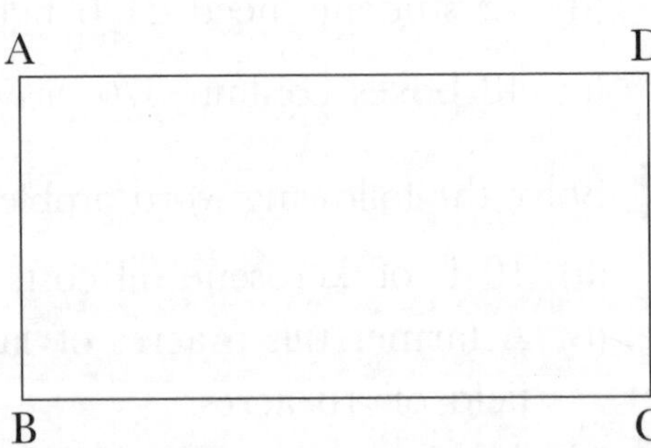

AB = __________ cm
BC = __________ cm
CD = __________ cm
AD = __________ cm
Perimeter = AB + BC + CD + AD
Perimeter = __________ cm

4. How many lines can be drawn through a point? __________

5. How many lines can be drawn through two points? __________

Just before leaving the zoo, the three friends reached the lion's cage. When the lion growled, they got scared and stepped back.

Line Segments

A line segment is a part of a line. It has two end-points. In Class III we have learnt how to draw and measure line segments.

A 4 cm B

This is line segment AB (or BA). It has two end-points A and B, and measures 4 cm.

If you observe your centimetere ruler carefully, you will notice that each centimetre is again divided into 10 smaller divisions. One small division is called a millimetre (mm). Thus 1 cm = 10 mm.

Look at the line segment AB. It measures 3 cm and 5 mm or 3.5 cm.

Measure the following line segments using your centimetre ruler.

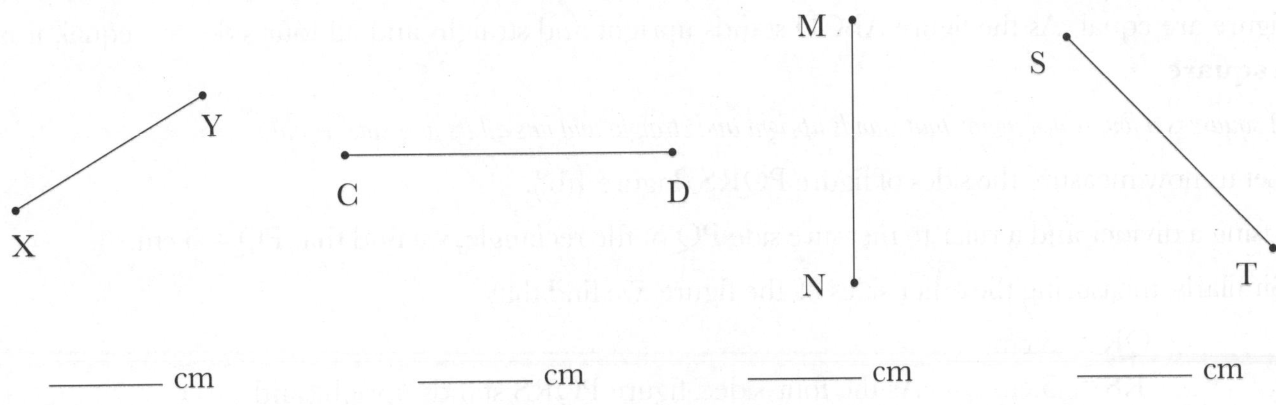

_______ cm _______ cm _______ cm _______ cm

Figures Formed Using Line Segments

Closed figures like squares, rectangles, triangles, etc., are formed using line segments. By measuring the sides of these closed figures we can find out what type of figure they are.

Squares and Rectangles

Let us measure the sides of the following four-sided figures to find out if they are squares or rectangles.

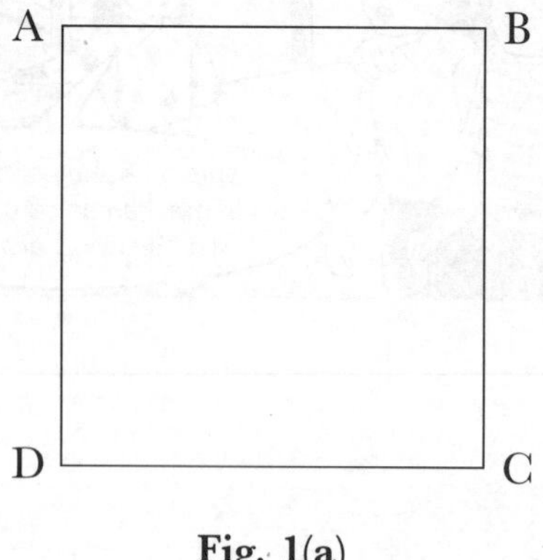

Fig. 1(a)

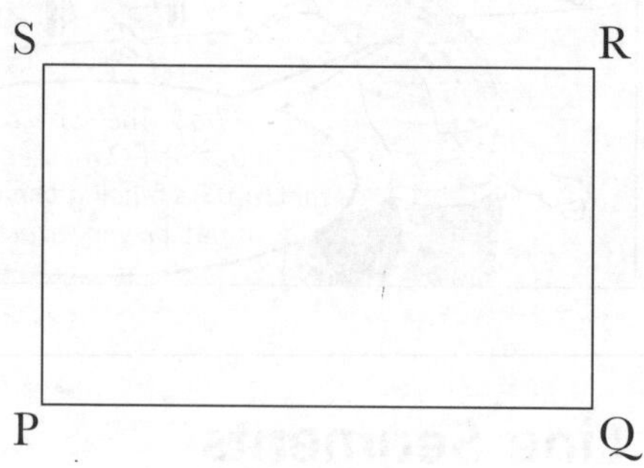

Fig. 1(b)

Let us measure the sides of Figure 1(a) using a divider and a ruler.

Place one end-point of the divider on point C. Then, adjust the other arm of the divider such that the other end-point rests on point D. Now lift the divider from points D and C and compare the gap between the two end-points against the ruler.

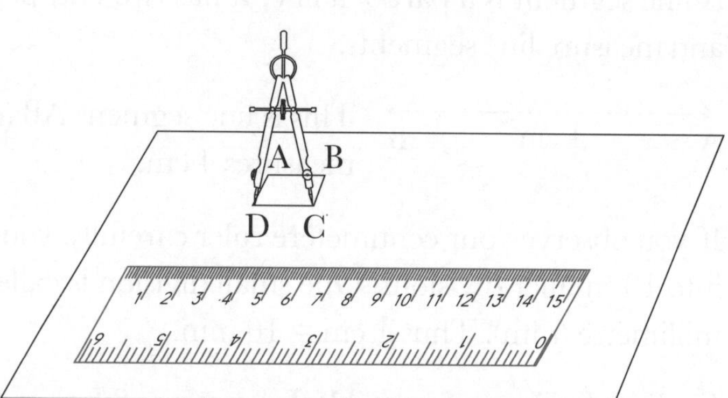

When one end-point is placed on the 0 cm mark of the ruler, we find that the other end-point rests on the 4 cm mark. Thus, the length of side DC = 4 cm.

Similarly, if we measure the sides AD, AB and BC, we find that all the sides of this four-sided figure are equal. As the figure ABCD stands upright and straight and all four sides are equal, it is a **square**

A square is a four-sided figure, that stands upright and straight and has all its four sides equal.

Let us now measure the sides of figure PQRS (Figure 1(b)).

Using a divider and a ruler to measure side PQ of the rectangle, we find that PQ = 5 cm.

Similarly, measuring the other sides of the figure, we find that

QR = 3 cm
RS = 5 cm
SP = 3 cm

As the four-sided figure PQRS stands upright and straight and its opposite sides are equal, it is a **rectangle**

A rectangle is a four-sided figure that stands upright and straight and has its opposite sides equal.

Note:

- If a square leaned on one side, it would become a rhombus.
- If a rectangle leaned on one side, it would become a parallelogram.

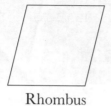

Square

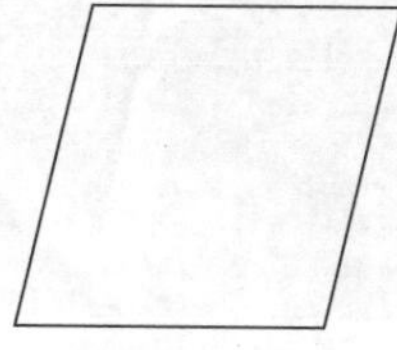

Rhombus

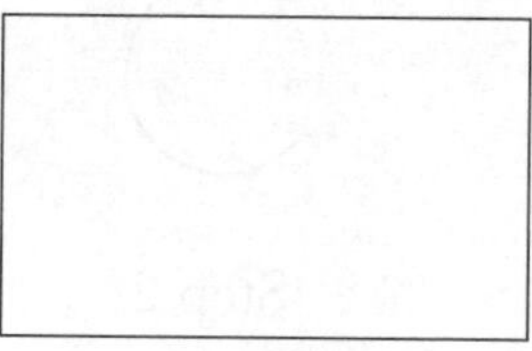

Rectangle

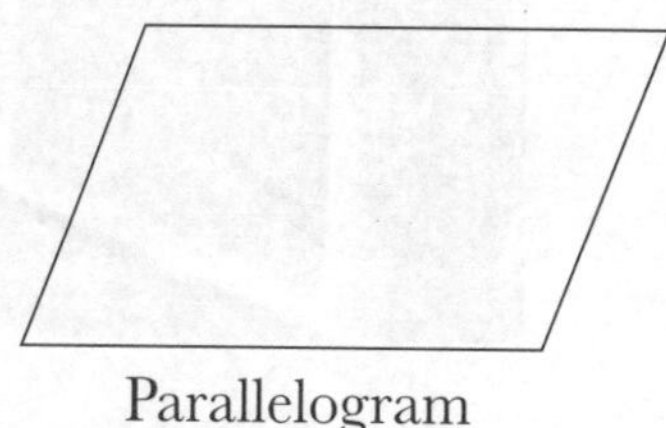

Parallelogram

Triangles

A triangle is a plane figure formed by three line segments.

The segments meet each other at points called **vertices**.

We use the symbol Δ to represent a triangle.

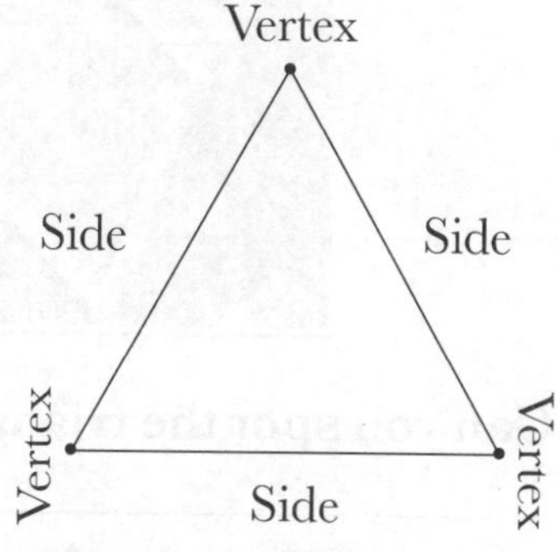

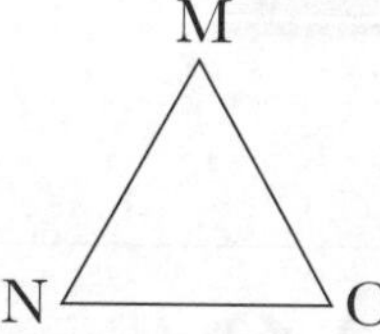

This is ΔMNO.

It has three vertices: M, N and O

It has three sides: MN, NO and OM

A triangle is a closed figure with the least number of vertices. This is why a triangular shape is rigid or strong. This activity shows us how a square shape is not as rigid as a triangular one.

Try this out!

Strips of cardboard (for the sides) are held together with paper clips (at the vertices) to make a square and a triangular shape.

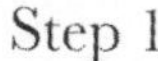

Step 1

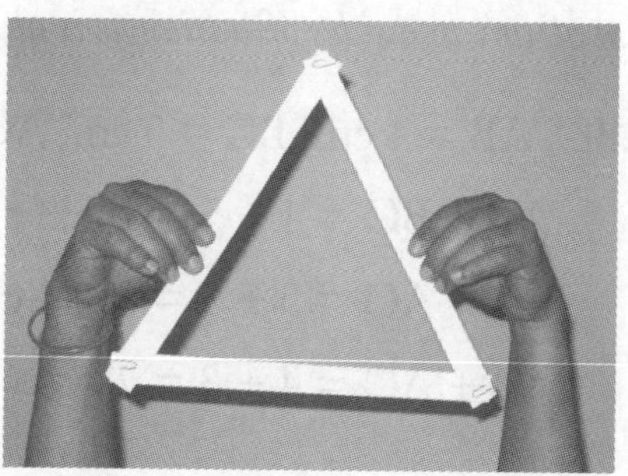

See what happens when the shapes are turned. The square shape leans to become a rhombus, but the triangular shape is unchanged.

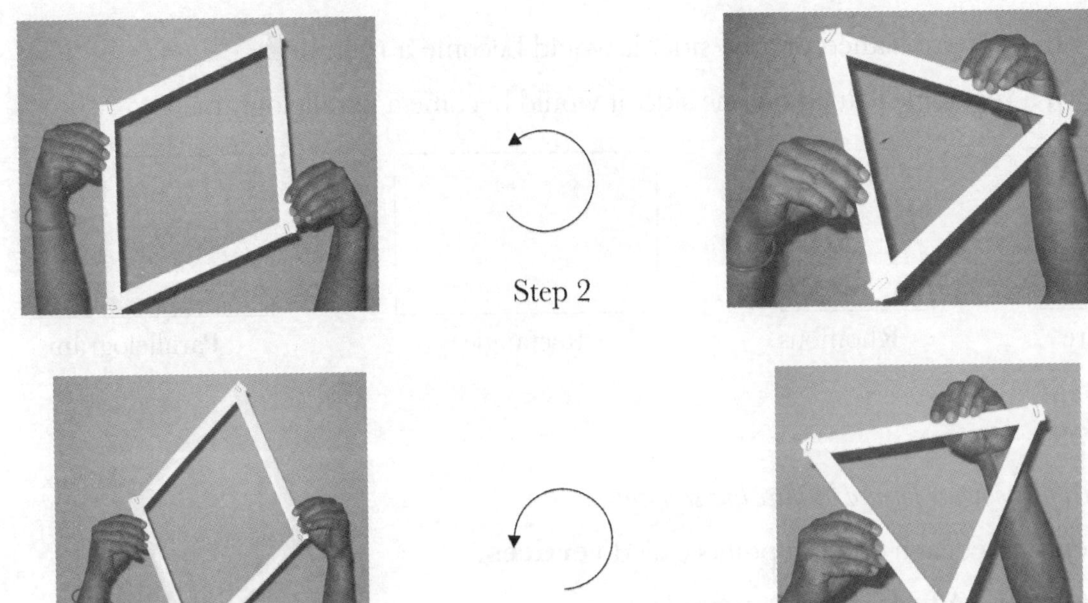

Can you spot the triangular shapes in these strong structures?

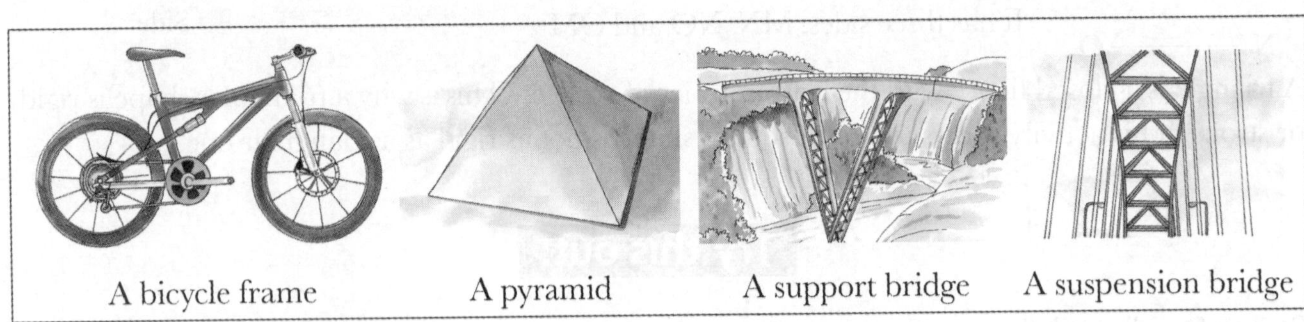

A bicycle frame | A pyramid | A support bridge | A suspension bridge

Measure of Sides of Triangle

The sum of any two sides of a triangle is always greater than the third side.

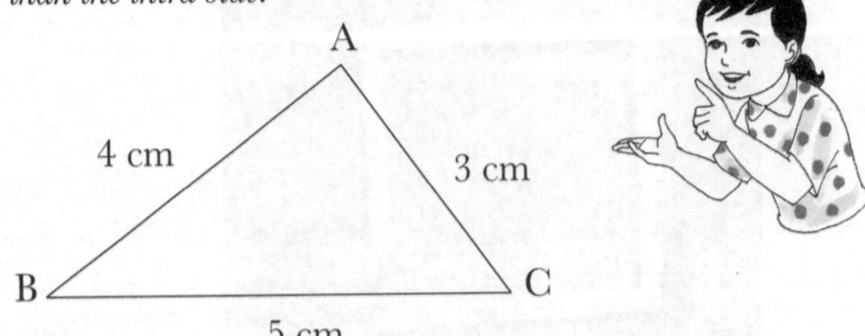

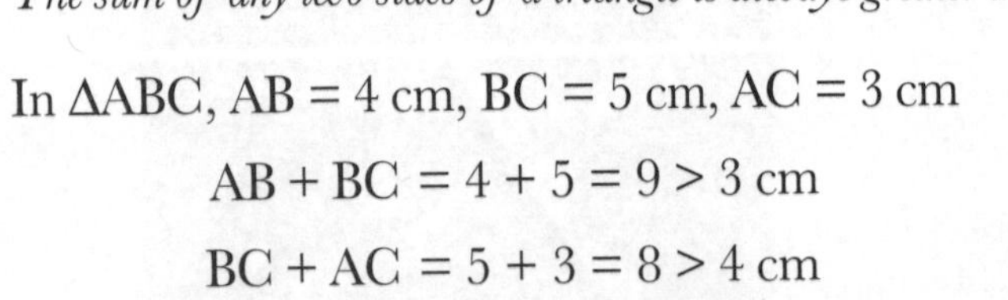

In ΔABC, AB = 4 cm, BC = 5 cm, AC = 3 cm

$AB + BC = 4 + 5 = 9 > 3$ cm

$BC + AC = 5 + 3 = 8 > 4$ cm

$AB + AC = 4 + 3 = 7 > 5$ cm

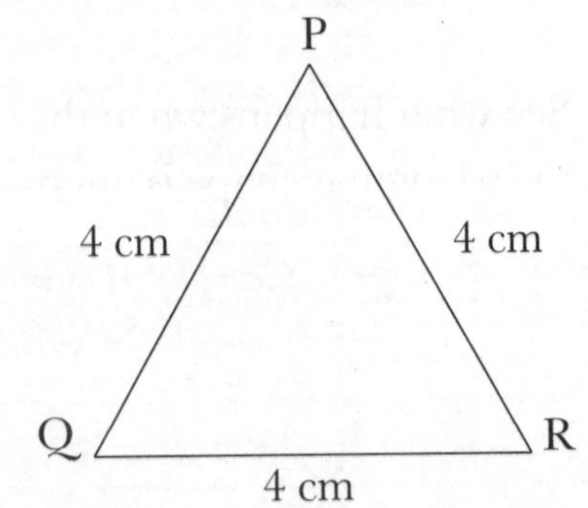

In ΔPQR, PQ = 4 cm, QR = 4 cm, PR = 4 cm

$PQ + QR = 4 + 4 = 8 > 4$ cm

$PQ + PR = 4 + 4 = 8 > 4$ cm

$QR + RP = 4 + 4 = 8 > 4$ cm

In ΔLMN, LM = 3 cm, MN = 4 cm, LN = 5 cm

$LM + MN = 3 + 4 = 7 > 5$ cm

$MN + LN = 4 + 5 = 9 > 3$ cm

$LM + LN = 3 + 5 = 8 > 4$ cm

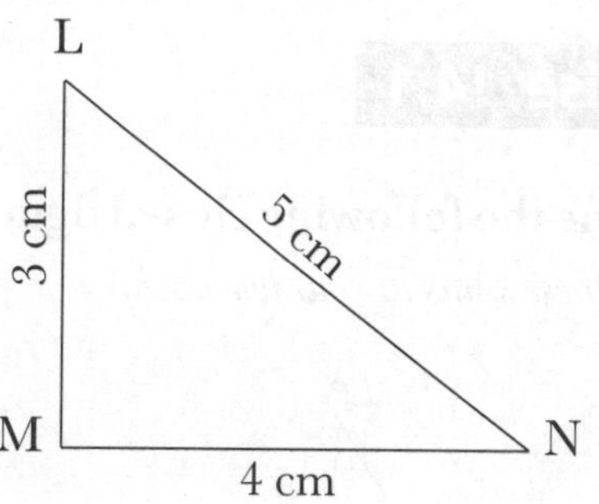

Types of Triangles

Let us measure the sides of the following three triangles, using a divider and a ruler, to find out how these triangles are different.

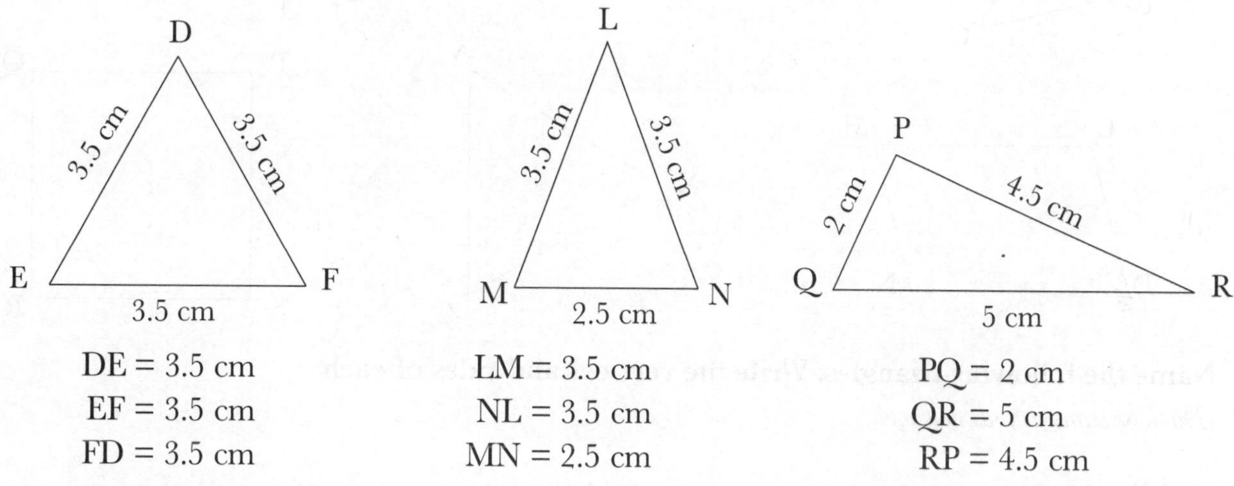

We observe that:

1. In ΔDEF, all the three sides are equal. Such *a triangle in which all the three sides are equal is known as an equilateral triangle.*
2. In ΔLMN, two of the sides, LM and LN, are equal. Such a *triangle in which two of the sides are equal is known as an isosceles triangle.*
3. In ΔPQR, none of the sides are equal. Such *a triangle in which none of the sides are equal is known as a scalene triangle.*

Note:

- A square is a four-sided figure and has all its sides equal.
- A rectangle is a four-sided figure and has opposite sides equal.
- A triangle is a three-sided figure.
- The sum of any two sides of a triangle is always greater than the third side.
- A triangle in which all the three sides are equal is known as an equilateral triangle.
- A triangle in which two of the sides are equal is known as an isosceles triangle.
- A triangle in which none of the sides are equal is known as a scalene triangle.

Exercise 14.1

1. Name the following closed figures and measure their sides.

(*Do these sums in your notebook.*)

(a)
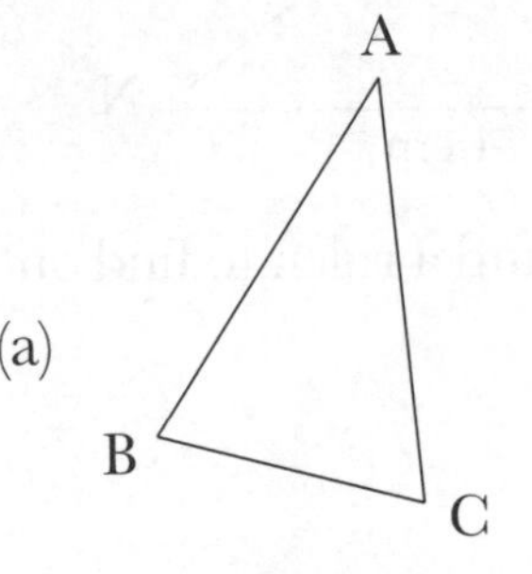

(b)
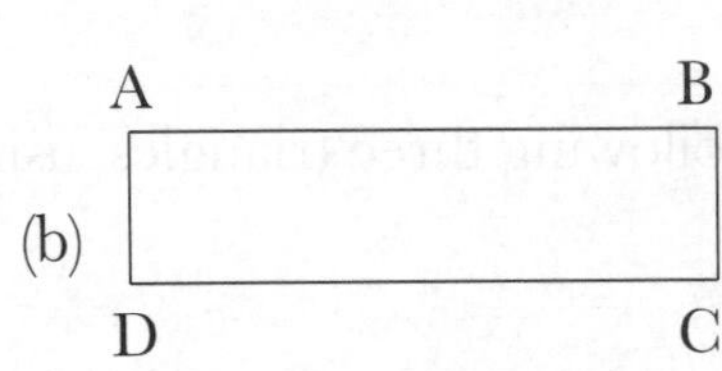

(c)
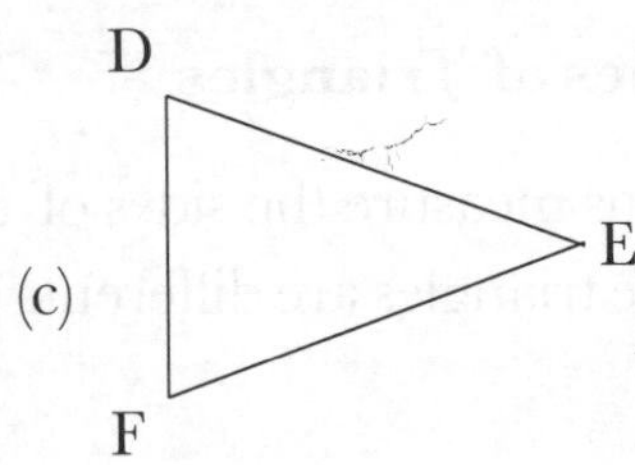

(d)
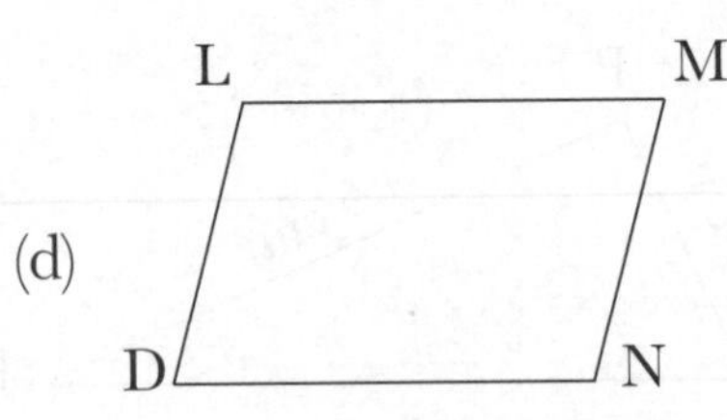

(e)
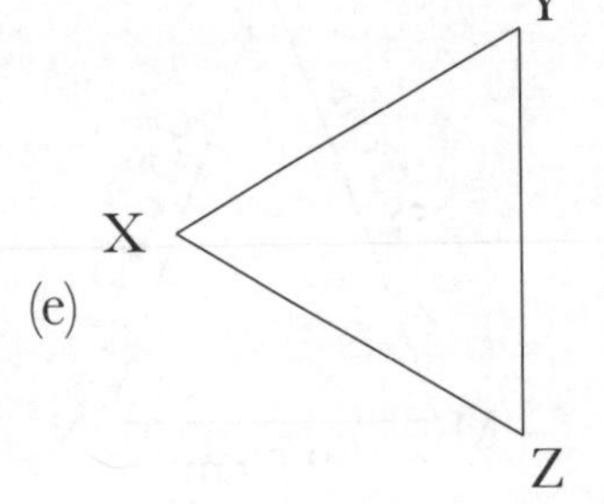

(f)
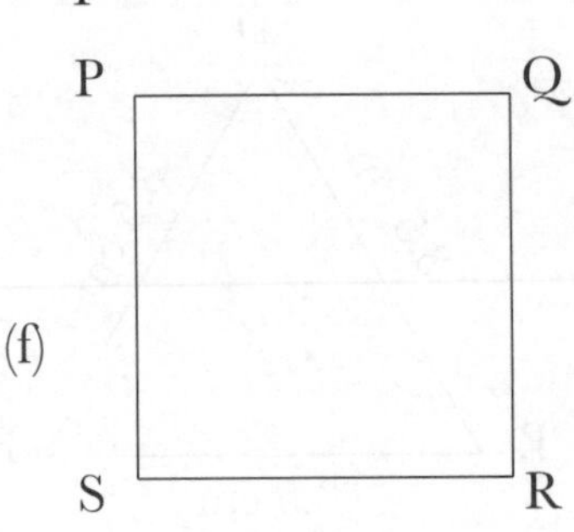

2. Name the following triangles. Write the vertices and sides of each.

(*Do these sums in your notebook.*)

(a)
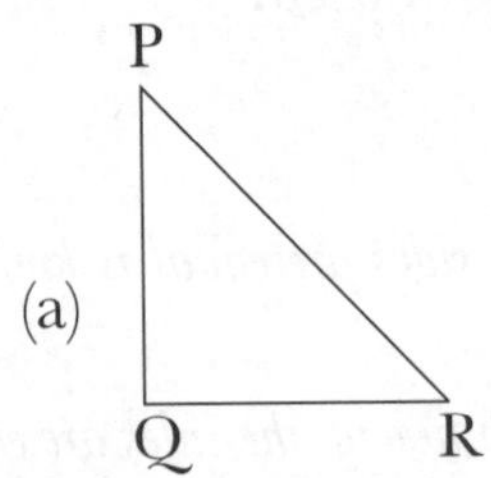

(b)
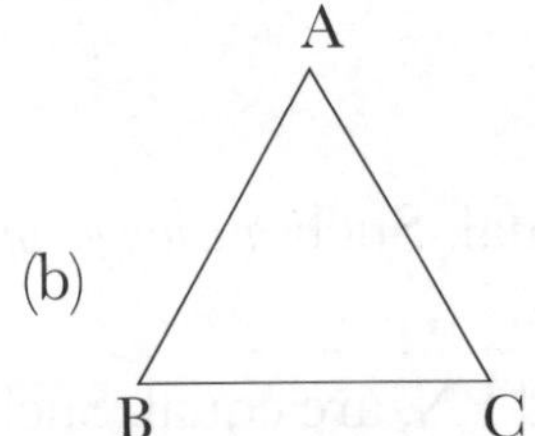

(c)
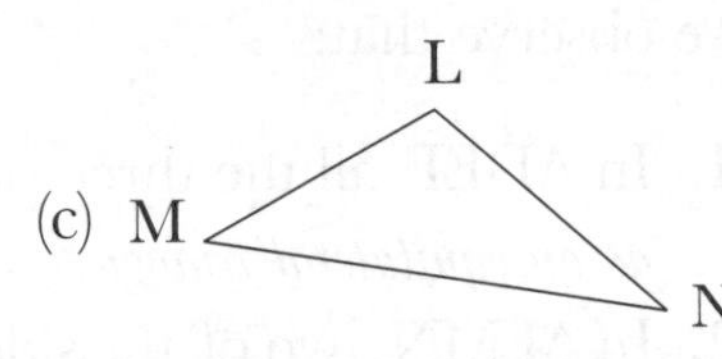

3. Fill in the blanks.

(a) A plane figure that stands upright and has all its four sides equal is a _________

(b) A plane figure that stands upright and has opposite sides equal is a _________

(c) An equilateral triangle has _________ equal sides.

(d) An isosceles triangle has _________ of its sides equal.

(e) A scalene triangle has _________ of its sides equal.

4. The sum of any two sides of a triangle is greater than the third side. Using this information answer the following.

(a) Can a triangle XYZ be constructed with sides 3 cm, 5 cm and 9 cm? _________

(b) Can a triangle PQR be constructed with sides 2 cm, 4 cm and 5 cm? _________

(c) Can a triangle ABC be constructed with sides 1 cm, 2 cm and 4 cm? _________

Area

Take a square piece of paper. Dip it in water and place it on another piece of paper. Now remove the wet paper. Notice that it leaves a wet square patch that matches exactly with its square shape. This wet patch is the **area** which the square paper occupied.

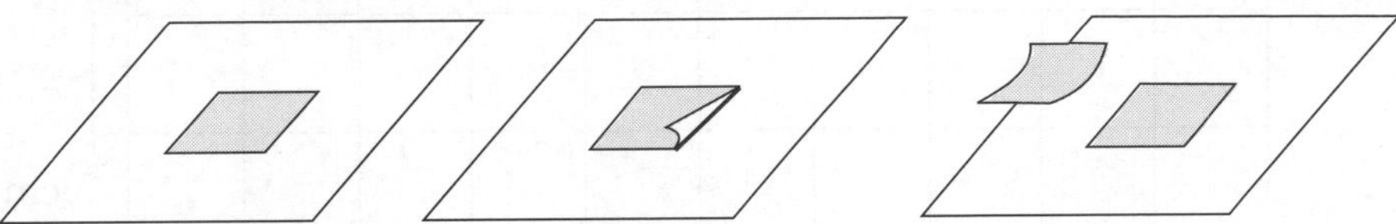

Measurement of Area by the Tiling Method

If one side of a square is equal to 1 cm, the area of the square is said to be 1 square centimetre. It is written as 1 sq. cm or 1 cm^2.

Using this information, let us find the area of a square with side 5 cm.

ABCD is a square with each side measuring 5 cm.

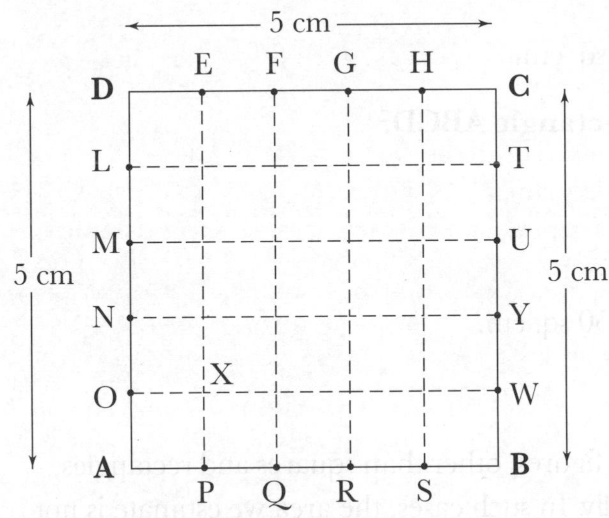

To find its area,

1. With the help of a ruler we mark points P, Q, R and S on side AB, each point 1 cm away.
2. Similarly, we mark points with a 1 cm gap on sides BC, CD and DA.
3. Now, we use a pencil and ruler to join the points we marked with those on the opposite side. For example, join P (on AB) and E (on CD), join O (on DA) and W (on BC), etc.

Now consider figure APXO. There is no need to measure its sides, as we have marked the points at 1 cm gaps.

So, we have AP = 1 cm; OA = 1 cm;

XP = WB = 1 cm; XO = ED = 1 cm

Thus, APXO is a square with each side measuring 1 cm. We know that the area of a square with sides 1 cm is 1 sq. cm.

Thus, the area of square APXO = 1 sq. cm.

How many such squares with 1 cm sides are there in all?

There are 25 such squares within ABCD.

Thus, the area of ABCD = 25 × 1 sq. cm = 25 sq. cm

The method by which we found the area of square ABCD is known as the **tiling method**

Now, let us find the area of rectangle ABCD, given the following:

AB = CD = 10 cm

BC = DA = 5 cm

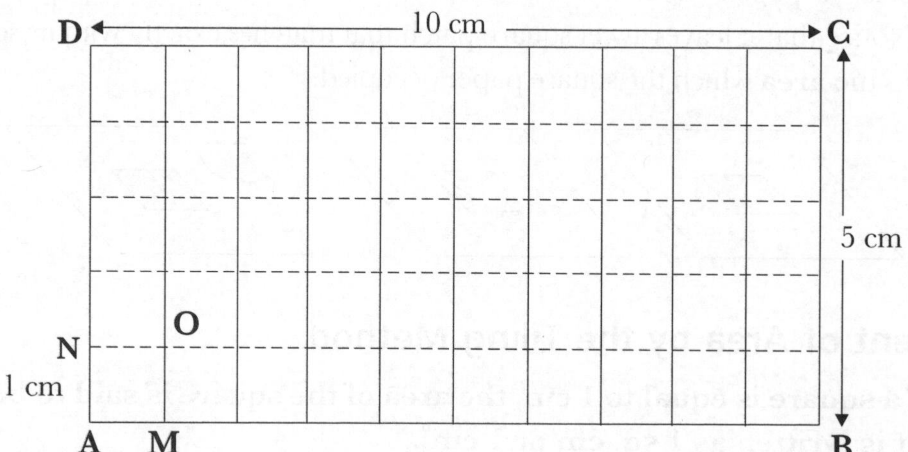

As we did earlier while finding the area of a square, we again mark points 1 cm away from each other on all the sides of rectangle ABCD. This way we divide the figure into small squares of side 1 cm each.

One such square is AMON. The area of AMON = 1 sq. cm.

How many such squares are there within the rectangle ABCD?

There are 10 such squares along the length.

There are 5 such squares along the breadth.

There are $10 \times 5 = 50$ such squares in all.

Thus, the area of rectangle ABCD = 50×1 sq. cm = 50 sq. cm.

Estimation of Area

We can use the tiling method to **estimate** the area of figures, other than squares and rectangles, that cover some squares fully and some squares partially. In such cases, the area we estimate is not the exact area of the figure but it is close to the actual area.

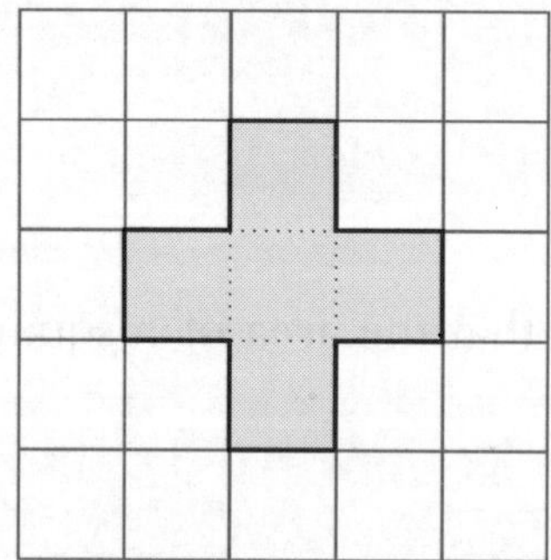

This shape covers 5 whole squares. So if each square is of 1 sq. cm area, then area of this shape = 1 sq. cm × 5 = 5 sq. cm.

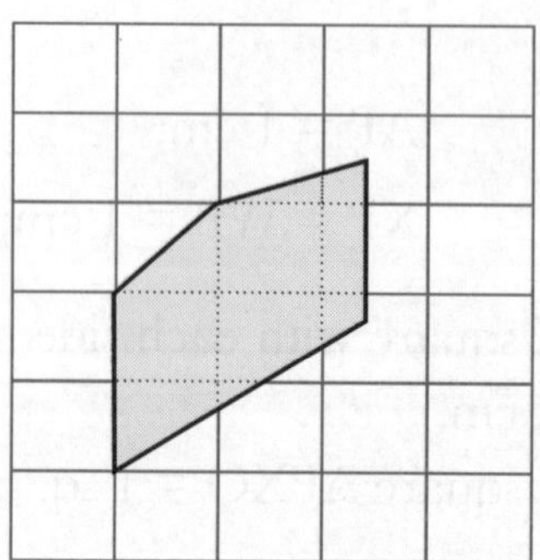

This shape covers 2 whole squares and 8 partial squares. So we can only estimate the area of this shape.

Let us estimate the area of the following two figures using the tiling method.

As none of these figures can be marked into equal square tiles, we draw the tiles over the figures as shown. Each side of the square tile is 1 cm long.

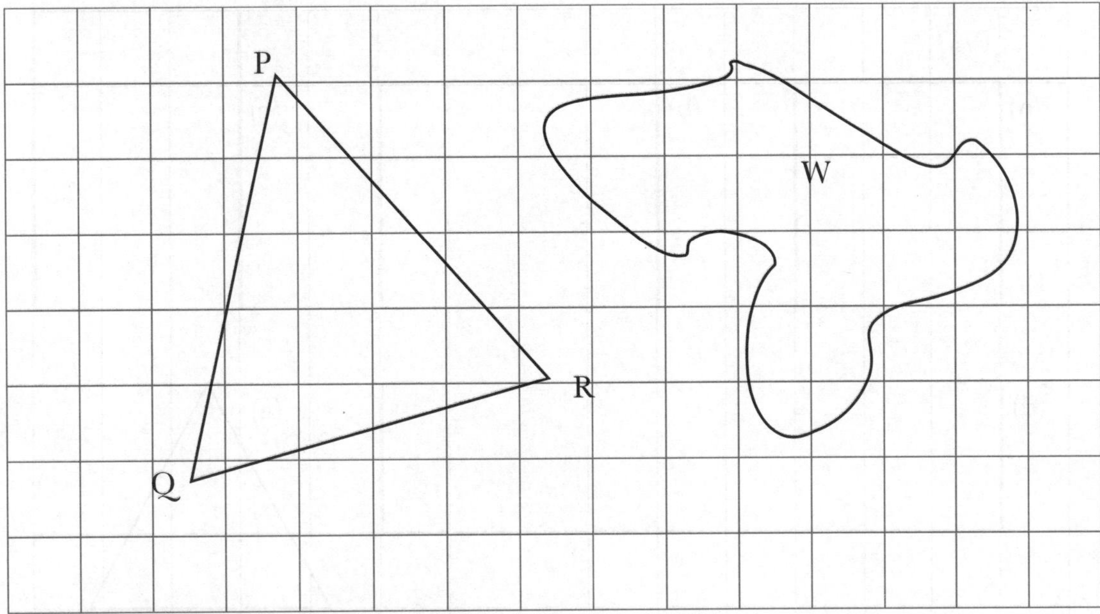

Let us now estimate the area of triangle PQR.

(a) Number of tiles that fall completely within PQR = 4
(b) Number of tiles that fall mostly within PQR = 7
(c) Number of tiles with less than half within PQR = 10

Thus 4 + 7 = 11 tiles are either fully or mostly within PQR. As the area of each tile is 1 sq. cm, the area of triangle PQR will be about 11 square centimetres.

Similarly, we can estimate the area of shape W.

(a) Number of tiles that fall completely within W = 4
(b) Number of tiles that fall mostly within W = 11
(c) Number of tiles with less than half within W = 7

Thus 4 + 11 = 15 tiles are either fully or mostly within W. As the area of each tile is 1 sq. cm, the area of shape W will be about 15 sq. cm.

- *Count all complete squares.*
- *Count all squares that are more than half within the area.*
- *Add the two.*
- *Do not add squares that are less than half within the area.*

Exercise 14.2

Find the area of figures from (a) to (d) and estimate the area of figures from (e) to (j).

Take each box to be of 1 sq. cm area.

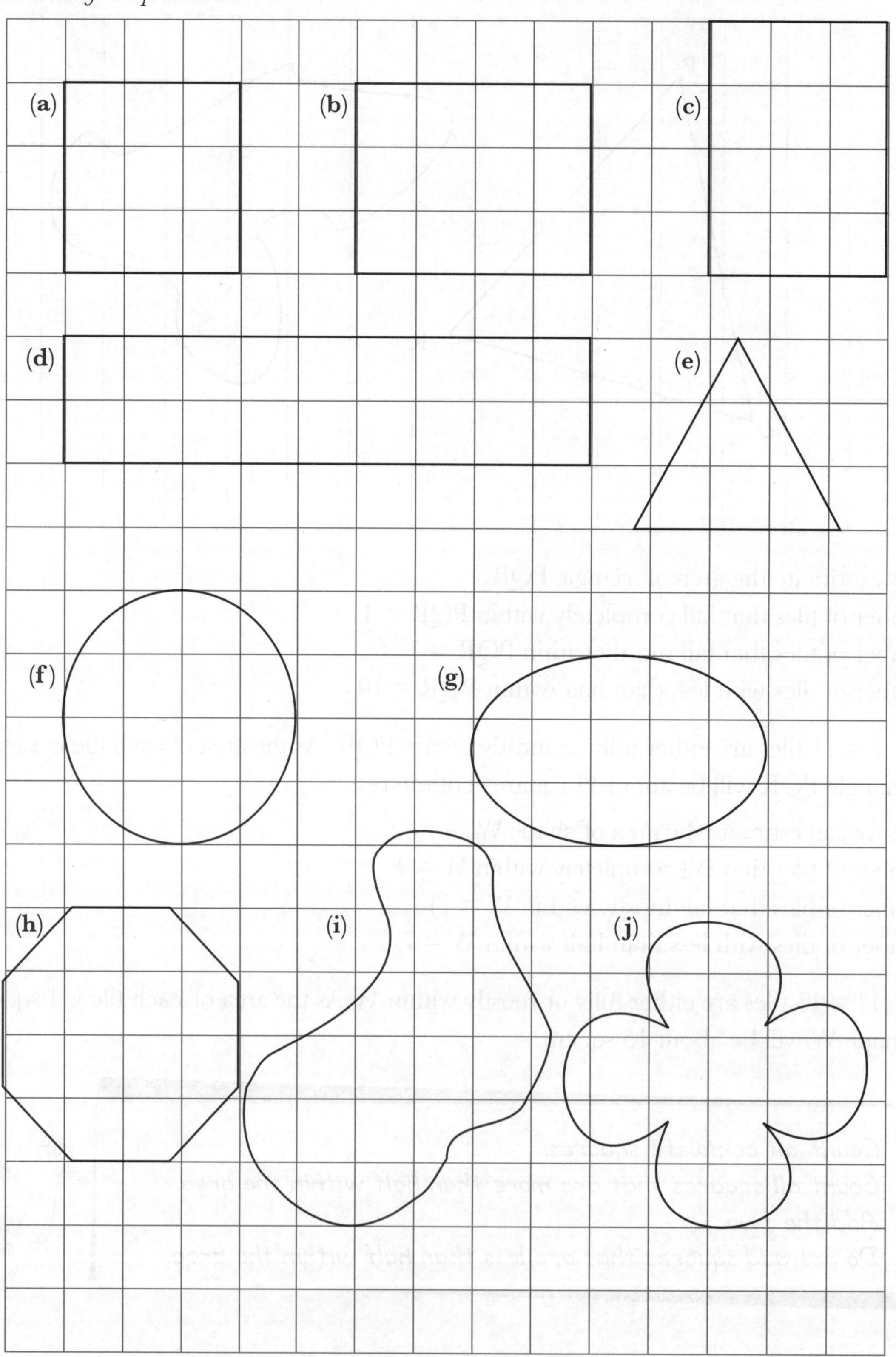

Perimeter

The length of the boundary of any plane figure is known as its **perimeter**

The perimeter is the sum of all the sides of a plane figure.

Example 1: If we measure all the sides of the square ABCD, we find,

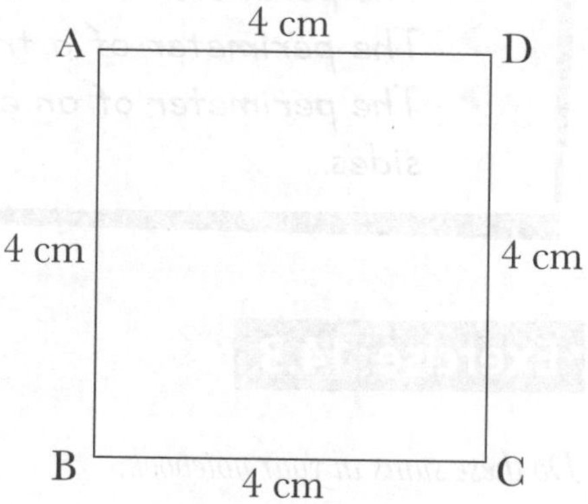

AB = 4 cm BC = 4 cm

CD = 4 cm DA = 4 cm

Thus, the perimeter of square ABCD = 4 + 4 + 4 + 4 = 16 cm

or $4 \times 4 = 16$ cm

The perimeter of a square is four times the length of one side.

Example 2: The length of the sides PS and QR of the rectangle PQRS are 5 cm each and the length of the sides PQ and RS are 3 cm each.

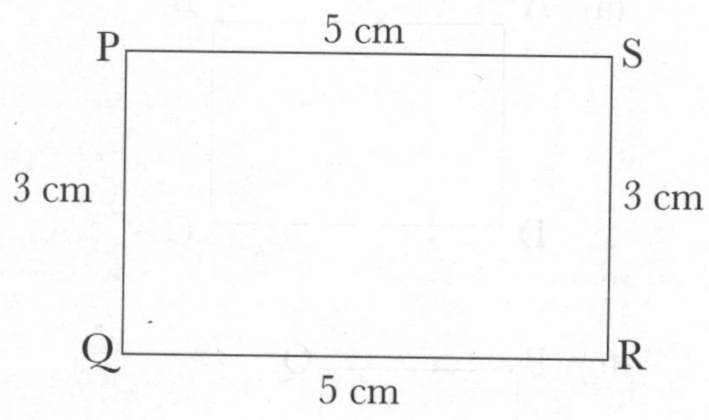

Thus, the perimeter of rectangle PQRS

= 5 + 3 + 5 + 3 = 16 cm

$= 2 \times (5 + 3)$

$= 2 \times 8 = 16$ cm

The perimeter of a rectangle is twice the sum of its length and breadth.

Example 3: Triangle EFG is an equilateral triangle with all the sides measuring 4 cm each.

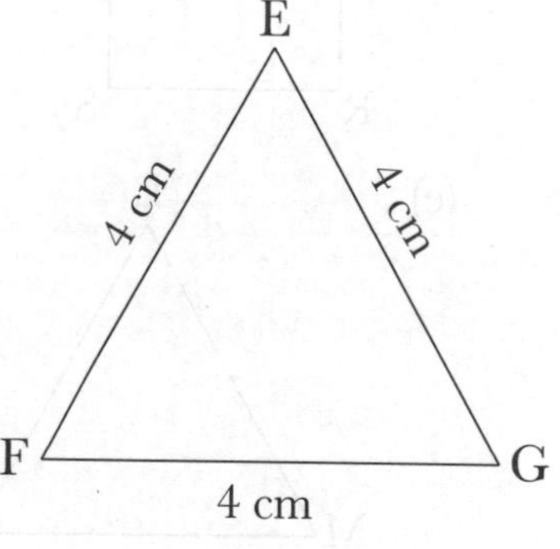

The perimeter of the equilateral triangle EFG = 4 + 4 + 4 = 12 cm

or $3 \times 4 = 12$ cm

The perimeter of an equilateral triangle is thrice the length of one of its sides.

Example 4: Triangle MNO is a scalene triangle with no two sides equal. On measurement of the three sides using a divider and ruler, we find MN = 2 cm, NO = 5 cm and OM = 6 cm. The perimeter of the scalene triangle MNO = 2 + 6 + 5 = 13 cm.

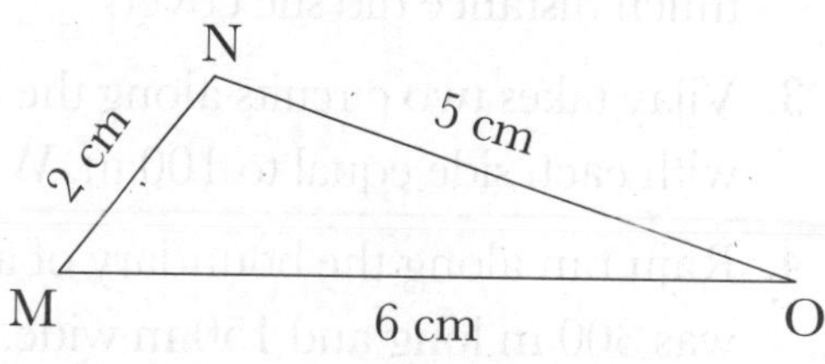

The perimeter of a triangle is the sum of the lengths of its three sides.

- The length of the boundary of any plane figure is known as its perimeter.
- The perimeter of a square is four times the length of one side.
- The perimeter of a rectangle is twice the sum of its length and breadth.
- The perimeter of a triangle is the sum of the lengths of its three sides.
- The perimeter of an equilateral triangle is thrice the length of one of its sides.

Exercise 14.3

Do these sums in your notebook.

1. Measure the sides of the following shapes using a divider and a ruler and find out the perimeter of each.

(a)

(b)

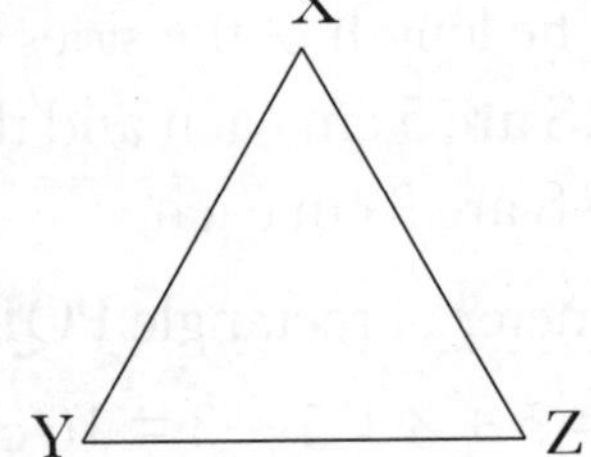

(c)

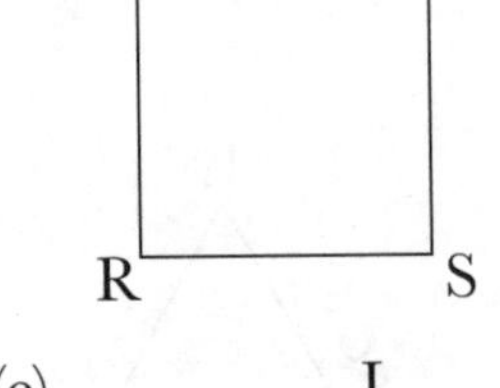

(d)

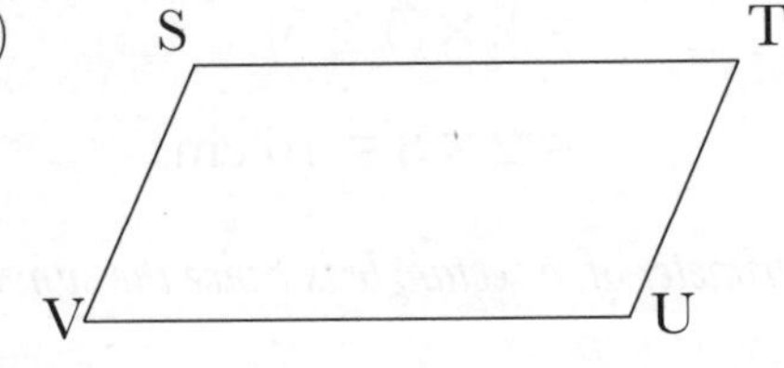

(e)

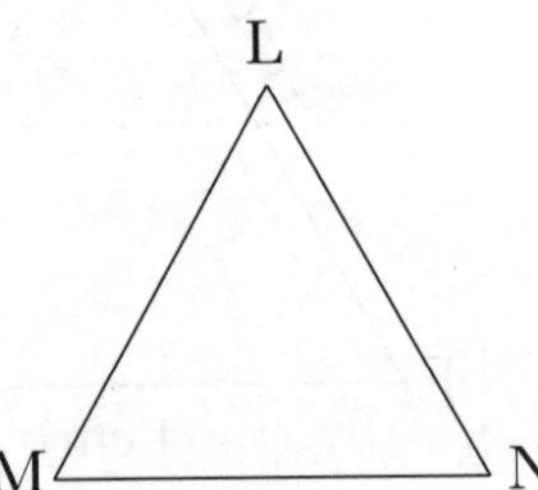

(f)

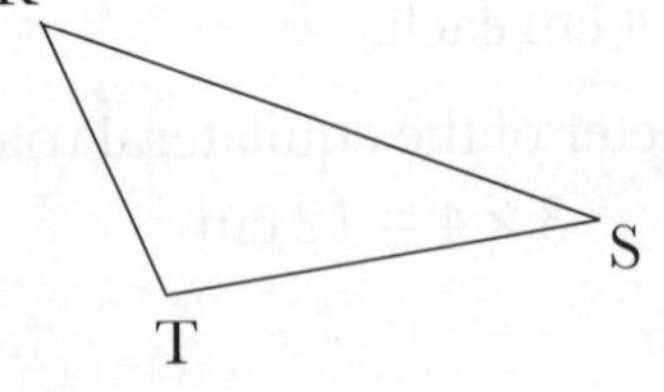

2. Jyoti walked along the entire boundary of a square field, with each side equal to 80 m. How much distance did she cover?

3. Vijay takes two circuits along the boundary of a square field with each side equal to 100 m. What distance does he cover?

4. Raju ran along the boundary of a rectangular park. If the park was 300 m long and 150 m wide, how much distance did Raju cover in all in completing one circuit around the park?

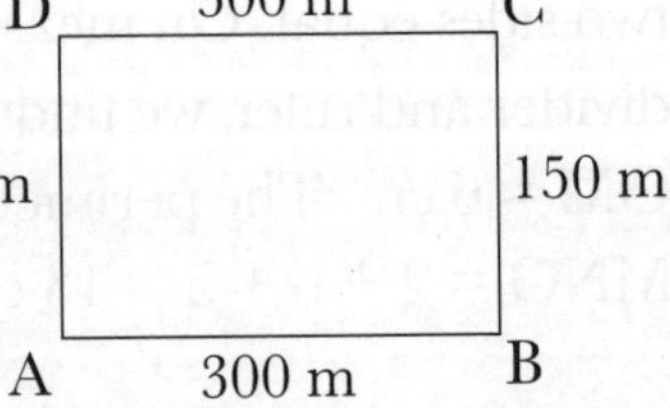

Angle

We have learnt about triangles. We know that a triangle is bound by three line segments. In the word triangle, the first half—**tri**—signifies the number three, whereas the second half—**angle**—describes a feature of all intersecting lines and closed figures with straight line segments.

Before defining an angle, let us understand what a **ray** is.

A B

This is line segment AB. But having started at point A if we do not stop at point B but keep on drawing a line that never ends, we get a ray, represented as $\overrightarrow{AB}$.

A is the only end-point of $\overrightarrow{AB}$.

A B

Thus, a ray has one end-point.

When two rays have a common end-point, they form an angle.

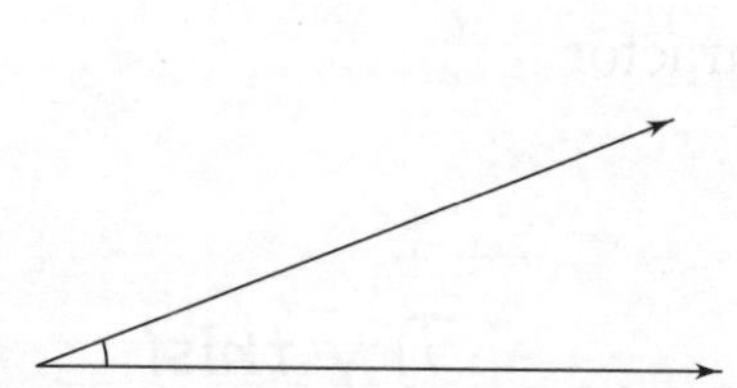
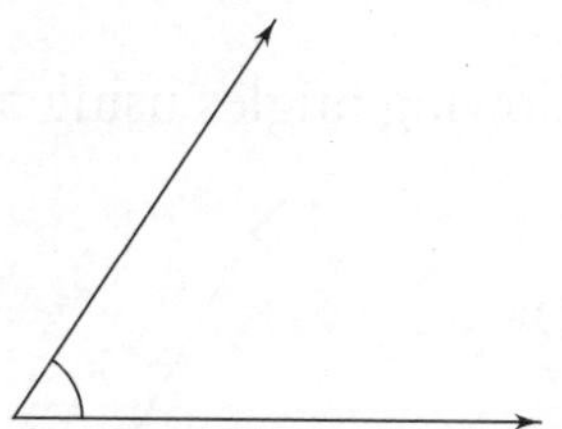
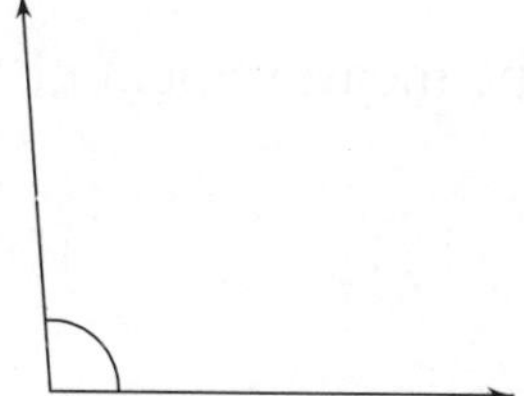

We see angles around us all the time.

Parts of an Angle

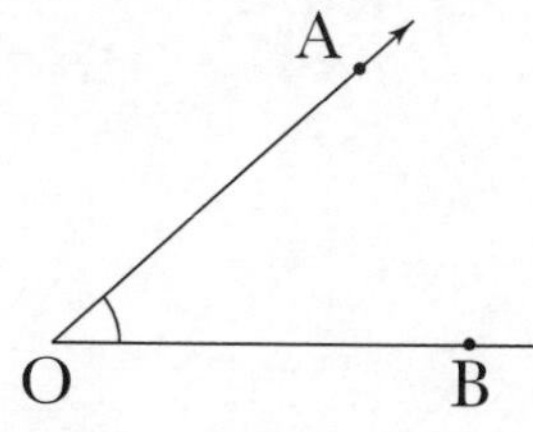

The rays $\overrightarrow{OA}$ and $\overrightarrow{OB}$ form an angle at their common end-point O. This common end-point, O, is called the **vertex** of the angle.

OA and OB are the **arms** of the angle.

The above angle is called **angle AOB** or **angle BOA**. We use the symbol ∠ to represent an angle. So, **∠AOB** means angle AOB and **∠BOA** means angle BOA.

The middle letter is always the vertex of the angle.

Measurement of an Angle

Degree is the unit in which an angle is measured. It is represented by the symbol °.

For example, 30° is read as thirty degrees. A **protractor** is used to measure angles. A protractor is an instrument in your geometry box, shaped like a D.

Observe the figure of the protractor given below. The curved side has angle measurements from 0° to 180°. The straight side of the protractor has a mid-point clearly marked which we place over the vertex of the angle that we need to measure.

The line on the straight side that runs through the mid-point is placed over one arm of the angle—OB, such that the mid-point is over the vertex of the angle as shown in the figure.

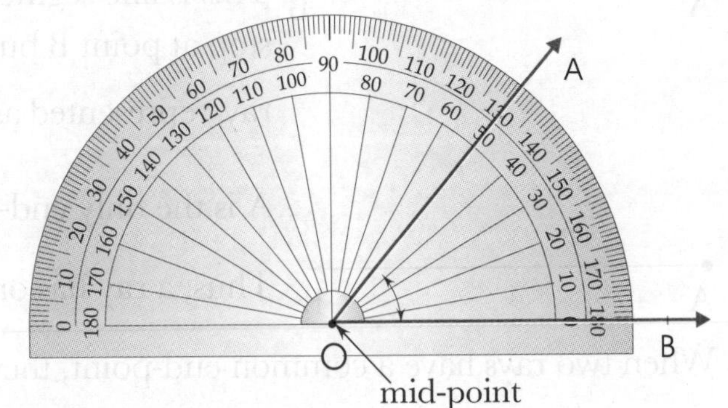

The angle is then read off on the protractor, counting from 0° to where the other arm OA lies. In the given figure, the angle is measured as 50°.

Confirm the measurement of the following angles using a protractor.

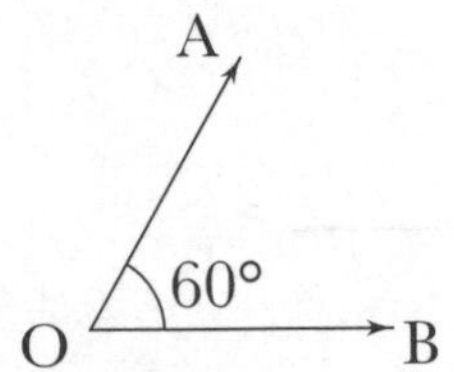

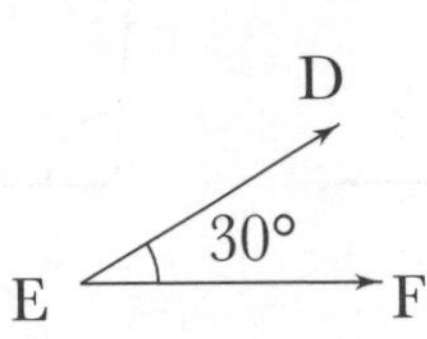

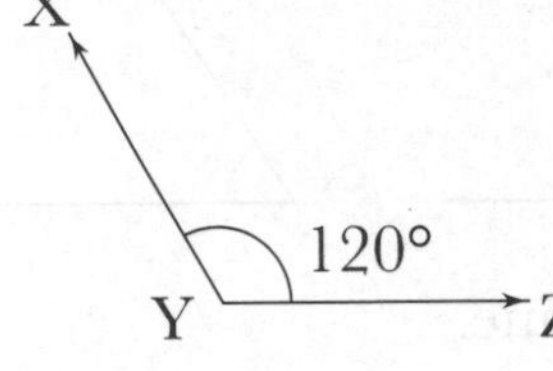

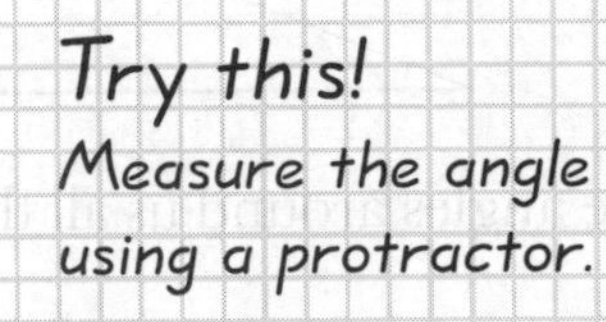

Try this!
Measure the angle using a protractor.
A
110°
O
B

Types of Angles

When rays or line segments meet, different types of angles are formed.

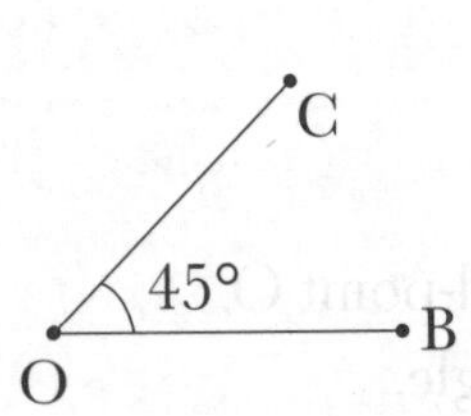

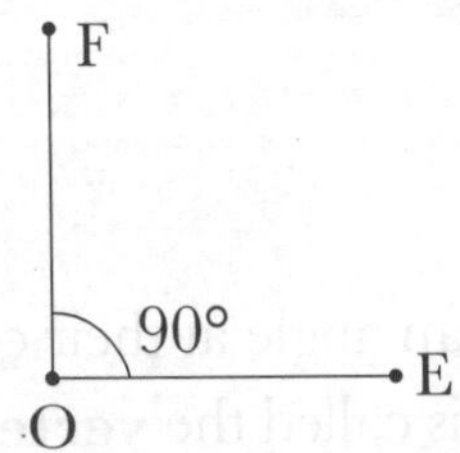

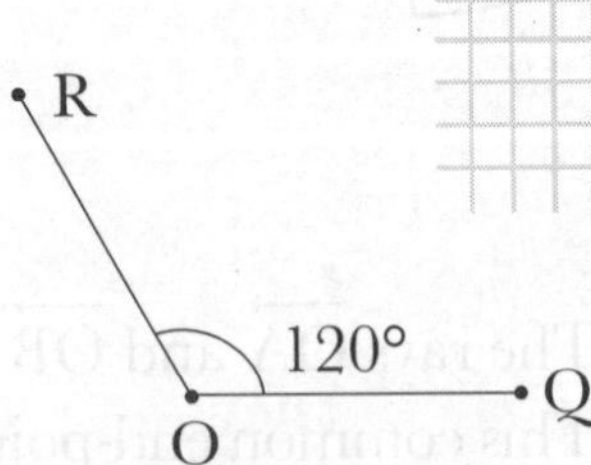
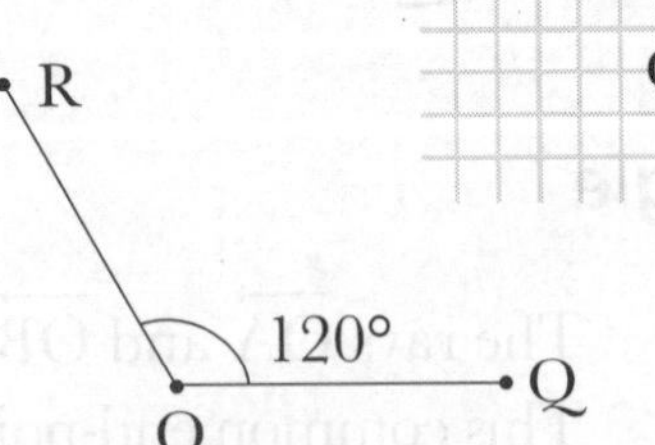

1. **Acute angles** measure less than 90°. Thus, ∠COB is an acute angle
2. **Right angles** measure exactly 90°. Thus, ∠FOE is a right angle.
3. **Obtuse angles** measure more than 90°. Thus, ∠ROQ is an obtuse angle.

Solid Figures and Plane Figures

You have learnt about plane figures and solid figures in your earlier classes. You know that we can make plane shapes by tracing the flat face of the corresponding solid figures.

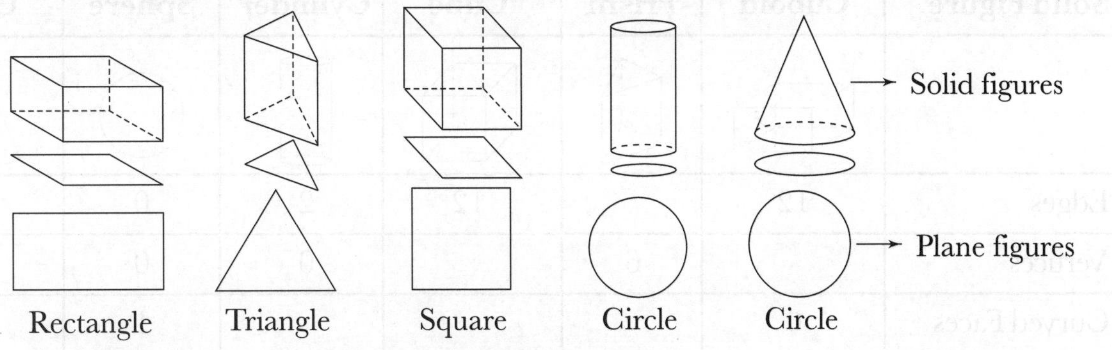

We can find these shapes in objects of use in daily life.
For example, a ball is spherical, a bangle is circular, a dice is a cube, a tent is pyramidal in shape, etc.

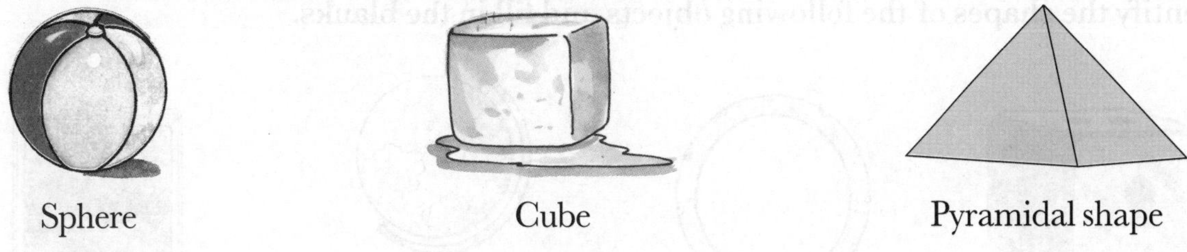

Sphere Cube Pyramidal shape

Symmetry

Symmetry refers to the exact match in size and shape between two halves, parts or sides of an object or figure.

The following figures are symmetrical. The dotted lines show the lines of symmetry.

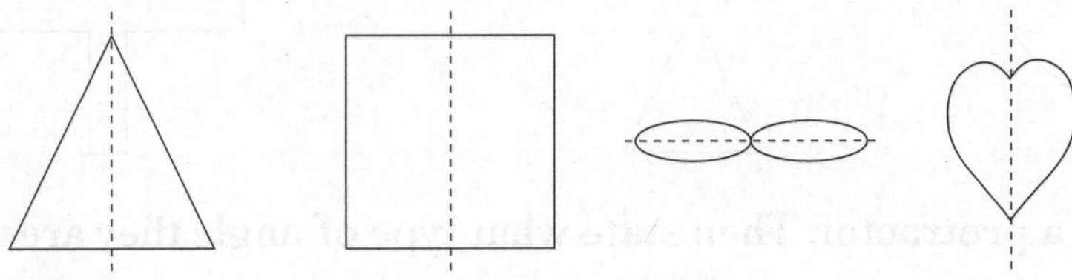

The following shapes do not have symmetry.

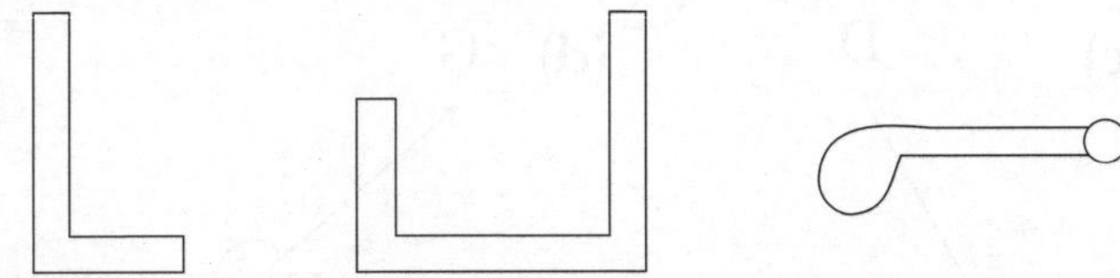

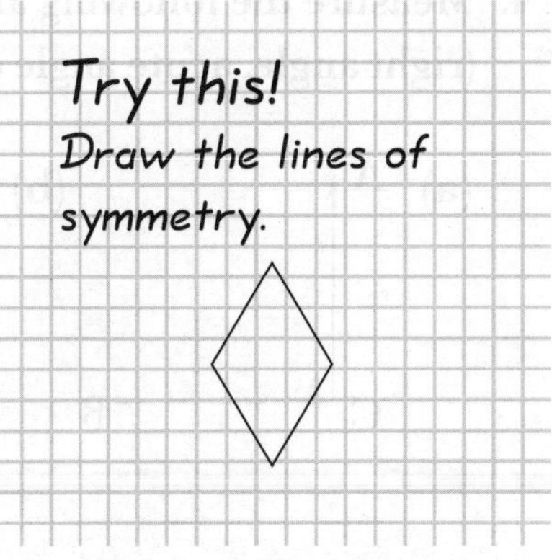

The following shapes have more than one line of symmetry.

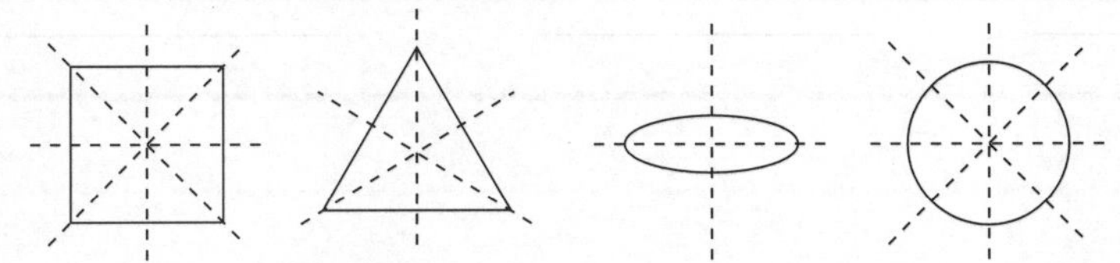

Exercise 14.4

1. Complete the following table.

Solid Figure	Cuboid	Prism	Cube	Cylinder	Sphere	Cone
Edges	12		12	2	0	
Vertices		6		0	0	1
Curved Faces	0				1	
Plane Faces			6	2		1

2. Identify the shapes of the following objects and fill in the blanks.

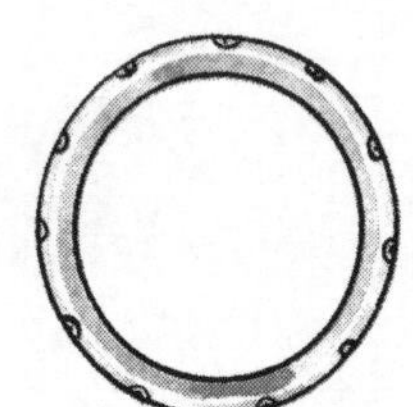

3. Draw the lines of symmetry for the following figures.

(a)
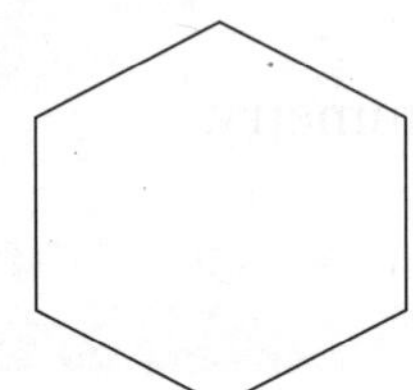

(b)
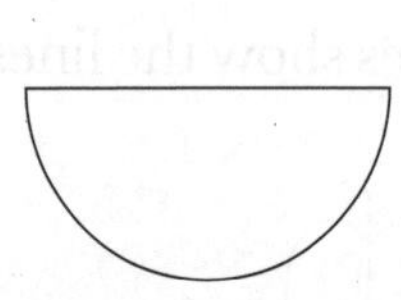

(c)
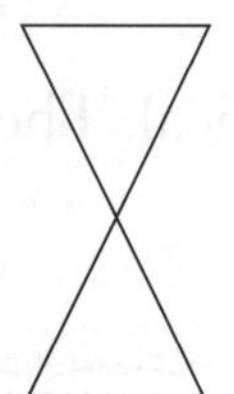

(d)
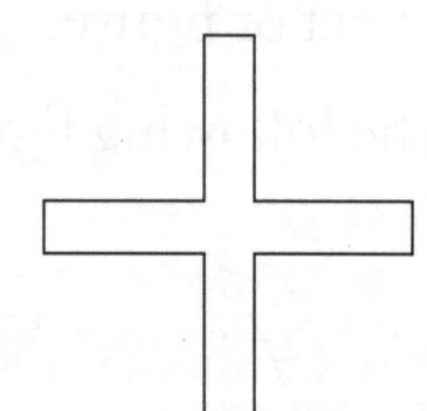

4. Measure the following angles using a protractor. Then state what type of angle they are (right angle, acute angle or obtuse angle).

(a)
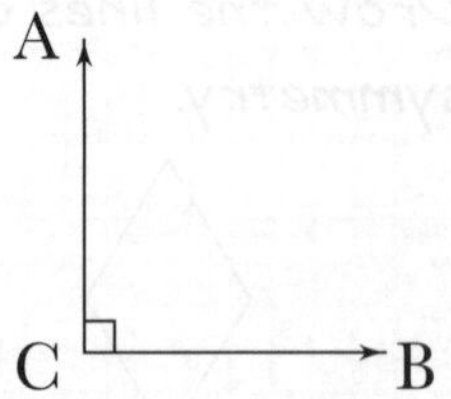

(b)
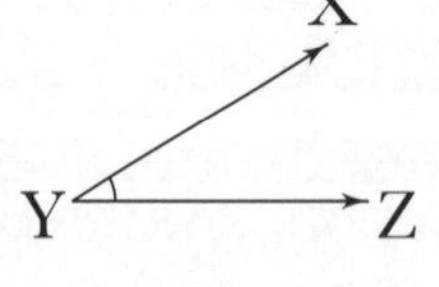

(c)
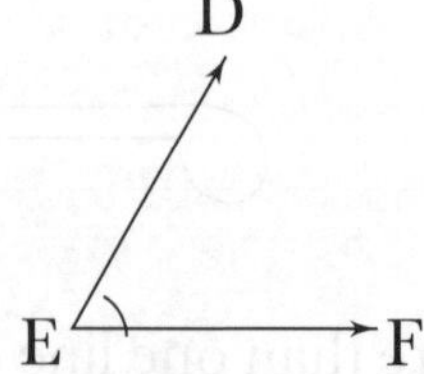

(d)
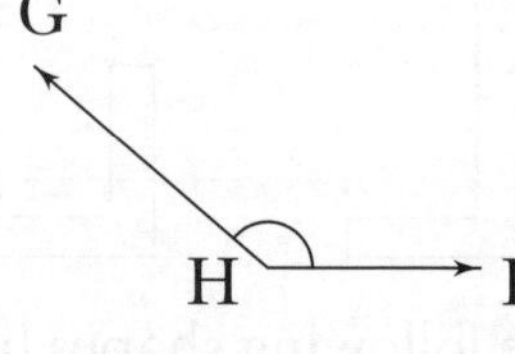

Revision Exercise

Do these sums in your notebook.

1 Measure the sides of the following figures.

(a)

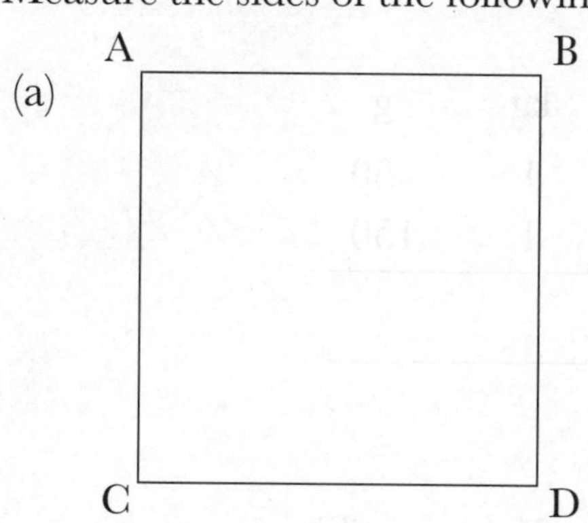

(b)

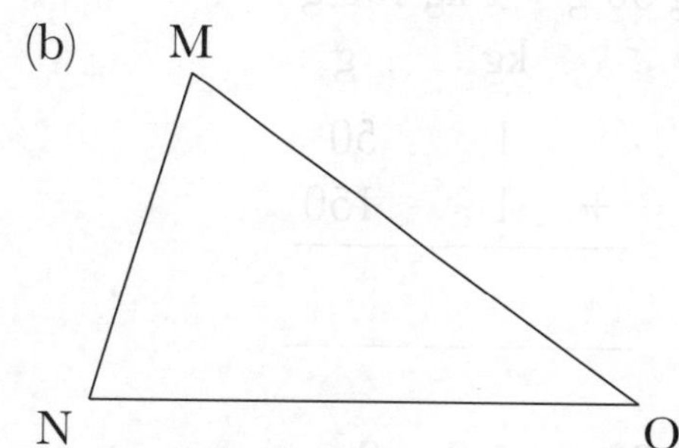

(c)

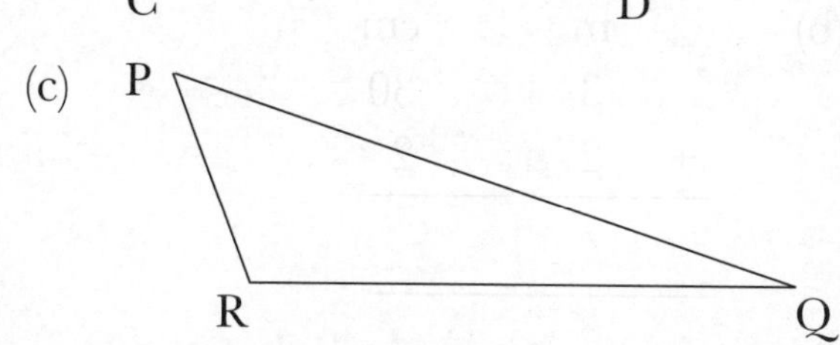

(d)

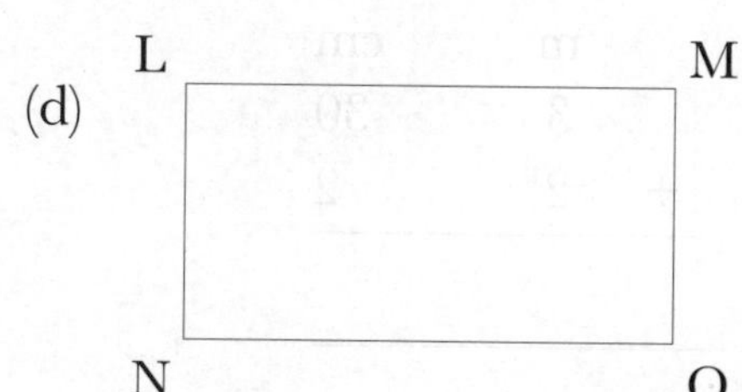

2 Say whether the following statements are true or false. If a statement is false, write the correct one.

(a) A line has two end-points.
(b) A rectangle has all its sides of equal length.
(c) If a square leaned on one side, it would form a rhombus.
(d) A scalene triangle has none of its sides equal.
(e) An isosceles triangle has two of its sides equal.
(f) The area of a square with each side 1 cm is 2 sq. cm.
(g) The perimeter of a square is 6 times the length of one of its sides.

3 Fill in the blanks.

(a) A square is a _____ figure, while a cube is a _____ figure.
(b) A cylinder has _____ plane faces.
(c) A cone has _____ curved face.
(d) An isosceles triangle has _____ line(s) of symmetry.

4 Use your protractor to measure the following angles.

(a)

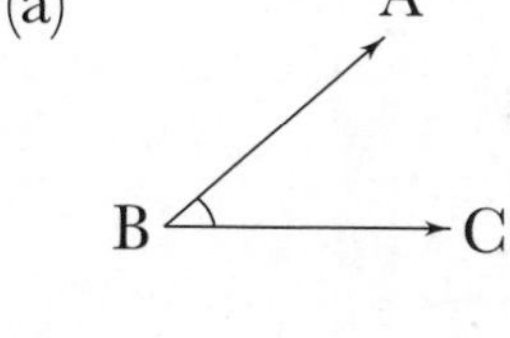

(b)

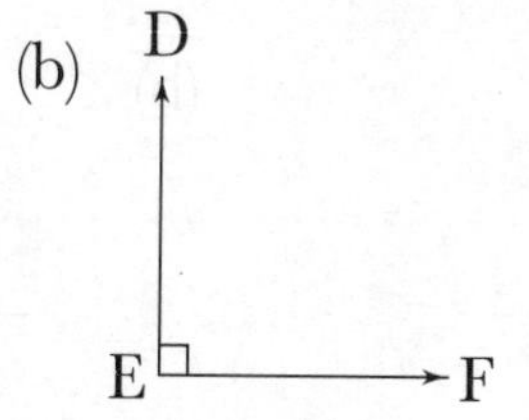

(c)

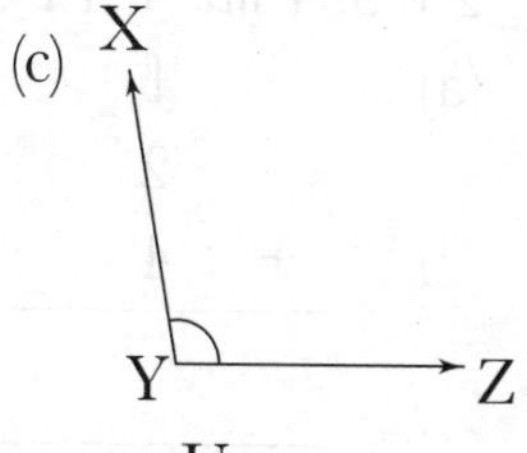

(d)

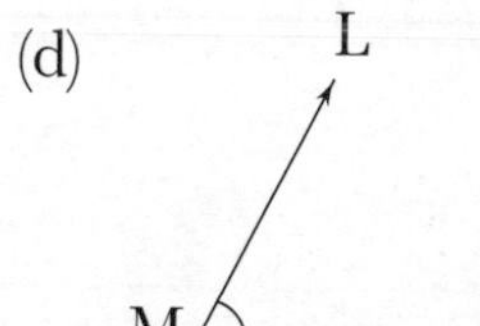

(e)

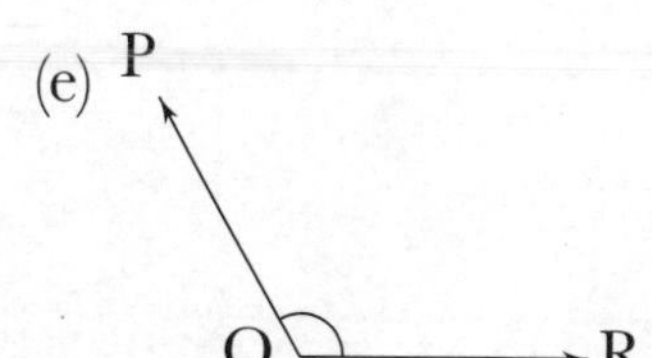

(f)

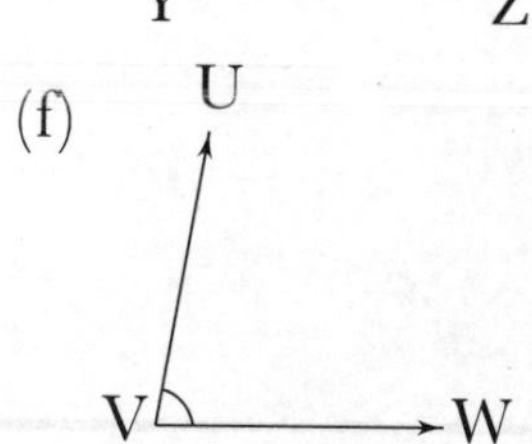

Worksheet 1 – Addition

Choose the correct vertical arrangement and add.

1. 1 kg 50 g + 1 kg 150 g

(a)

	kg	g
	1	50
+	1	150

(b)

	kg	g
	1	50
+	1	150

2. 3 m 30 cm + 2 m 2 cm

(a)

	m	cm
	3	30
+	2	2

(b)

	m	cm
	3	30
+	2	2

3. 4 km 222 m + 2 km 1 m

(a)

	km	m
	4	222
+	2	1

(b)

	km	m
	4	222
+	2	1

4. 6 ℓ 415 mℓ + 3 ℓ 52 mℓ

(a)

	ℓ	mℓ
	6	415
+	3	52

(b)

	ℓ	mℓ
	6	415
+	3	52

5. 2 ℓ 994 mℓ + 4 ℓ 9 mℓ

(a)

	ℓ	mℓ
	2	994
+	4	9

(b)

	ℓ	mℓ
	2	994
+	4	9

Worksheet 2 – Subtraction

Choose the correct vertical arrangement and subtract.

1. 5 kg 5 g – 3 kg 500 g

(a)

	kg	g
	5	5
–	3	500

(b)

	kg	g
	5	5
–	3	500

2. 6 m 60 cm – 3 m 3 cm

(a)

	m	cm
	6	60
–	3	3

(b)

	m	cm
	6	60
–	3	3

3. 8 km 548 m – 4 km 23 m

(a)

	km	m
	8	548
–	4	23

(b)

	km	m
	8	548
–	4	23

4. 9 ℓ 288 mℓ – 4 ℓ 4 mℓ

(a)

	ℓ	mℓ
	9	288
–	4	4

(b)

	ℓ	mℓ
	9	288
–	4	4

5. 7 ℓ 14 mℓ + 3 ℓ 3 mℓ

(a)

	ℓ	mℓ
	7	14
–	3	3

(b)

	ℓ	mℓ
	7	14
–	3	3

Worksheet 3 – Angles

Identify the marked angles formed by the hands of the following clocks.

Acute ∠ ☐
Right ∠ ☐
Obtuse ∠ ☐
Straight ∠ ☐
Reflex ∠ ☐

Acute ∠ ☐
Right ∠ ☐
Obtuse ∠ ☐
Straight ∠ ☐
Reflex ∠ ☐

Acute ∠ ☐
Right ∠ ☐
Obtuse ∠ ☐
Straight ∠ ☐
Reflex ∠ ☐

Acute ∠ ☐
Right ∠ ☐
Obtuse ∠ ☐
Straight ∠ ☐
Reflex ∠ ☐

Acute ∠ ☐
Right ∠ ☐
Obtuse ∠ ☐
Straight ∠ ☐
Reflex ∠ ☐

Acute ∠ ☐
Right ∠ ☐
Obtuse ∠ ☐
Straight ∠ ☐
Reflex ∠ ☐

Acute ∠ ☐
Right ∠ ☐
Obtuse ∠ ☐
Straight ∠ ☐
Reflex ∠ ☐

Acute ∠ ☐
Right ∠ ☐
Obtuse ∠ ☐
Straight ∠ ☐
Reflex ∠ ☐

Worksheet 4 – Shapes with Matchsticks

1. 15 matchsticks have been used to make two squares.

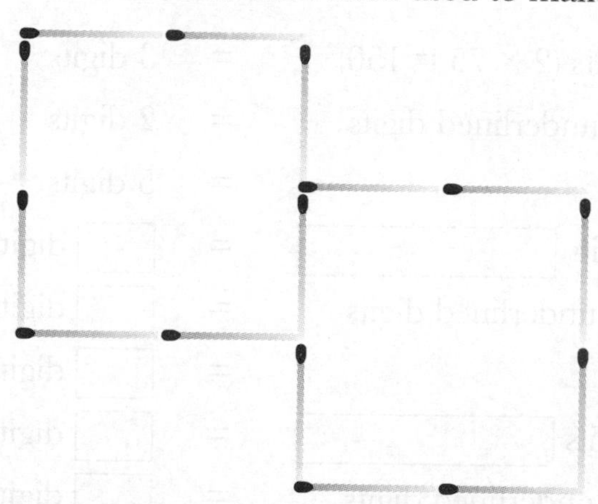

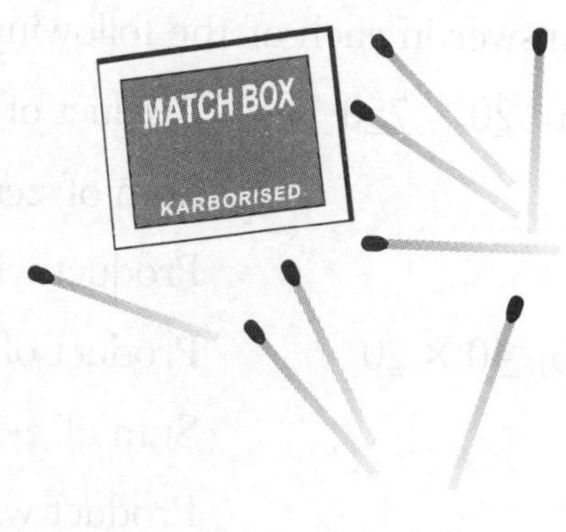

2. Now make two squares using exactly
   (a) 7 matchsticks (b) 10 matchsticks (c) 11 matchsticks (d) 18 matchsticks
3. Now make three squares using exactly
   (a) 9 matchsticks (b) 10 matchsticks (c) 12 matchsticks (d) 15 matchsticks
   (e) 16 matchsticks (f) 20 matchsticks (g) 21 matchsticks (h) 22 matchsticks
4. Make a square grid 3 matchsticks long. A shape with two squares has been made using 7 matchsticks.
   (a) Can you make a shape with one square using
   (i) 4 (ii) 8 (iii) 12 matchsticks?
   (b) Can you make a shape with two squares using
   (i) 8 (ii) 10 (iii) 11 (iv) 12 matchsticks?
   (c) Can you make a shape with three squares using
   (i) 10 (ii) 11 (iii) 12 matchsticks?
   (d) Can you make a shape with five squares using 12 matchsticks?
   (e) Can you make a shape with four squares using 12 or less matchsticks?

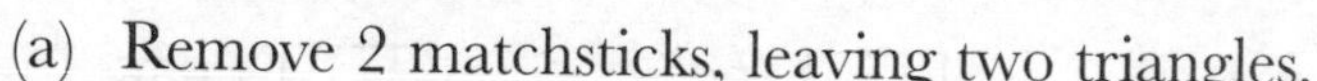

5. The shape on the right has 9 matchsticks and makes five triangles.
   (a) Remove 2 matchsticks, leaving two triangles.
   (b) Remove 3 matchsticks, leaving two triangles.
   (c) Remove 3 matchsticks, leaving one triangle.
   (d) Remove 6 matchsticks, leaving one triangle.
6. The shape on the right has 16 matchsticks.
   (a) Remove 2 matchsticks, leaving eight triangles.
   (b) Remove 4 matchsticks, leaving four triangles.
   (c) Remove 6 matchsticks, leaving four triangles.

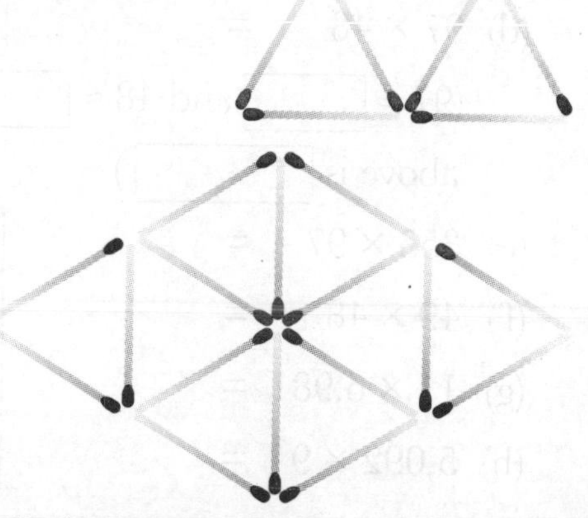

Worksheet 5 – Mental Maths

1. Answer in each of the following.

   (a) $\underline{20} \times \underline{75}0$ Product of underlined digits ($2 \times 75 = 150$) = 3 digits
   Sum of zeroes to right of underlined digits = 2 digits
   Product will have = 5 digits

   (b) $\underline{4}0 \times \underline{2}0$ Product of underlined digits ☐ = ☐ digits
   Sum of zeroes to right of underlined digits = ☐ digits
   Product will have = ☐ digits

   (c) $\underline{7} \times \underline{8}0$ Product of underlined digits ☐ = ☐ digits
   Sum of zeroes to right of underlined digits = ☐ digits
   Product will have = ☐ digits

   (d) $\underline{11}0 \times \underline{11}0$ Product of underlined digits ☐ = ☐ digits
   Sum of zeroes to right of underlined digits = ☐ digits
   Product will have = ☐ digits

2. Put a tick mark (✓) against the correct answer.

   (a) 398 × 49 = ☐ 9,502 ☐ 19,502 ☐ 1,952
   (398 ≈ 400 and 49 ≈ 50, so 398 × 49 ≈ 400 × 50 = 20,000. Nearest choice above is 19,502.)

   (b) 295 × 55 = ☐ 16,225 ☐ 61,225 ☐ 6,225
   (295 ≈ ☐ and 55 ≈ ☐ and ☐ × ☐ = ☐. Nearest choice above is ☐)

   (c) 413 × 9 = ☐ 37,171 ☐ 3,717 ☐ 7,317
   (413 ≈ ☐ and 9 ≈ ☐ and ☐ × ☐ = ☐. Nearest choice above is ☐)

   (d) 97 × 48 = ☐ 465 ☐ 456 ☐ 4,656
   (97 ≈ ☐ and 48 ≈ ☐ and ☐ × ☐ = ☐. Nearest choice above is ☐)

   (e) 355 × 97 = ☐ 34,435 ☐ 53,435 ☐ 54,435

   (f) 49 × 48 = ☐ 352 ☐ 2,352 ☐ 23,522

   (g) 11 × 6,981 = ☐ 7,791 ☐ 17,791 ☐ 76,791

   (h) 5,092 × 9 = ☐ 4,828 ☐ 45,828 ☐ 4,85,828

COMPREHENSIVE TEST PAPERS

Complete these test papers in your notebook.

Test Paper I

1. Insert commas and write the numerals in the required system of numeration.

Numeral	Indian place-value system	International place-value system
3567		
99000		
105000		
388956		

2. Arrange the following numbers in ascending order.
   6,78,463; 6,78,436; 6,76,863; 6,76,836; 6,78,643
   1,01,010; 1,10,010; 1,01,101; 1,01,100; 1,01,011
   8,98,989; 8,98,898; 8,98,899; 8,98,988; 8,98,998
3. Arrange the Roman numerals C, M, X, L, I, D, V in descending order.
4. Perform the following fundamental operations.
   (a) 4,63,489 + 2,91,045 (b) 1,07,995 + 6,89,546 (c) 3,62,116 + 54,780 + 5,040
   (d) 8,54,786 – 2,68,775 (e) 5,00,000 – 2,35,217 (f) 3,85,684 + 2,15,732 – 2,84,552
   (g) 638 × 16 (h) 535 × 208 (i) 1,862 × 168
   (j) 59,045 ÷ 7 (k) 2,06,964 ÷ 18 (l) 2,93,556 ÷ 34
5. Fill in the missing digits to complete the following.

(a)
```
    2 4 5 3 7 8
  + □ 4 □ 3 □ 9
  -------------
    6 □ 8 □ 0 □
```

(b)
```
    □ 6 8 5 □ 3
  – 6 2 □ 0 4 3
  -------------
    1 □ 9 □ 5 □
```

(c)
```
    □ 3 0 1 □ 8
  + 2 2 5 □ 8 5
  + 3 0 □ 9 6 7
  -------------
    8 □ 8 8 9 □
```

6. List the first three even multiples of 7.
7. List the even factors of 24.
8. Find the HCF of 624 and 330.
9. Find the LCM of 504 and 756.
10. Perform the following operations with fractions.
    (a) $\frac{5}{6}-\frac{2}{5}$ (b) $\frac{1}{2}+\frac{3}{7}$ (c) $2\frac{3}{4}-1\frac{1}{5}$
11. Arrange the following decimals vertically and perform the following operations.
    (a) 6.06 + 2.2 (b) 7.86 + 5.9 + 3.09 (c) 8 – 2.64
12. Convert the following.
    (a) 7,638 cg into g and cg (b) 3 ℓ into cℓ (c) 434 m into dam and dm
13. Perform the following operations with time.
    (a) 1 h 22 min 48 s + 34 min 22 s (b) 3 h 28 min 30 s – 1 h 28 min 50 s
14. Is a triangle ABC possible where AB = 6 cm, BC = 12 cm and AC = 6 cm?
15. How many lines of symmetry can be drawn through the star figure shown alongside?

Test Paper II

1. Write the successors and predecessors of the following numbers.

Predecessor	Number	Successor
	48,729	
	23,499	
	6,14,910	
	5,00,000	

2. Arrange the following numbers in descending order.
   82,597; 82,759; 82,579; 82,795; 82,599
   1,10,110; 1,00,100; 1,01,110; 1,01,100; 1,00,110
   3,25,523; 3,23,523; 3,25,532; 3,25,253; 3,23,253
3. Write the Hindu–Arabic numeral for XL.
4. Perform the following fundamental operations.
   (a) 2,56,985 + 1,85,090 (b) 7,13,629 + 1,89,647 (c) 4,06,733 + 88,564 + 9,187
   (d) 8,79,667 – 6,14,537 (e) 8,50,000 – 4,81,089 (f) 4,58,653 + 3,21,569 – 1,18,659
   (g) 764 × 18 (h) 498 × 317 (i) 2,543 × 164
   (j) 1,98,888 ÷ 8 (k) 1,10,147 ÷ 23 (l) 1,01,379 ÷ 47
5. Fill in the missing digits to complete the following.

   (a)
   7 0 3 2 6 1
   + □ 8 □ 3 □ 9
   9 □ 6 □ 9 □

   (b)
   □ 3 5 9 □ 0
   – 2 3 □ 1 6 5
   2 □ 8 □ 2 □

   (c)
   □ 8 3 5 □ 1
   + 4 6 4 □ 0 9
   + 1 3 □ 4 7 2
   9 □ 9 5 0 □

6. Find the HCF of the first 10 prime numbers.
7. Find the LCM of the first 5 multiples of 5.
8. Find the HCF of 147 and 189.
9. Find the LCM of 204 and 306.
10. Perform the following operations with fractions.
    (a) $\frac{3}{4} + \frac{5}{7}$ (b) $\frac{2}{5} + \frac{4}{9}$ (c) $3\frac{1}{3} - 1\frac{2}{5}$
11. Express the following fractions as decimals.
    (a) $\frac{3}{5}$ (b) $\frac{7}{10}$ (c) $\frac{13}{100}$
12. Convert the following.
    (a) 23 g into cg (b) 540 cℓ into ℓ (c) 85 m into km
13. Perform the following operations with time.
    (a) 3 h 4 min 4 s × 5 (b) 1 h 15 min 22 s × 8
14. If 4 oranges cost Rs 28, how much will 12 oranges cost?
15. What is the perimeter of an equilateral triangle in which one side measures 2.5 cm?

Test Paper III

1. Write the following in expanded form.

Numeral	Expanded form
3,03,030	
5,84,253	
7,00,967	
8,59,000	

2. Arrange the digits 2, 6, 3, 0, 1 and 9 to make the greatest 6-digit numeral without repeating any digit.
3. Find the difference: XL – XXVIII
4. Perform the following fundamental operations.

(a) 67,894 + 7,98,543　(b) 9,06,754 + 74,689　(c) 2,89,547 + 66,385 + 7,998
(d) 7,10,000 – 3,54,658　(e) 6,20,176 – 2,90,466　(f) 5,07,586 + 1,82,254 – 3,42,779
(g) 836 × 19　(h) 296 × 178　(i) 2,518 × 185
(j) 3,32,289 ÷ 9　(k) 2,13,122 ÷ 26　(l) 2,45,947 ÷ 38

5. Fill in the missing digits to complete the following.

(a)
4 1 0 8 7 9
\+ □ 8 □ 5 □ 1
8 □ 6 □ 2 □

(b)
□ 3 7 0 □ 8
– 2 8 □ 1 7 5
3 □ 2 □ 5 □

(c)
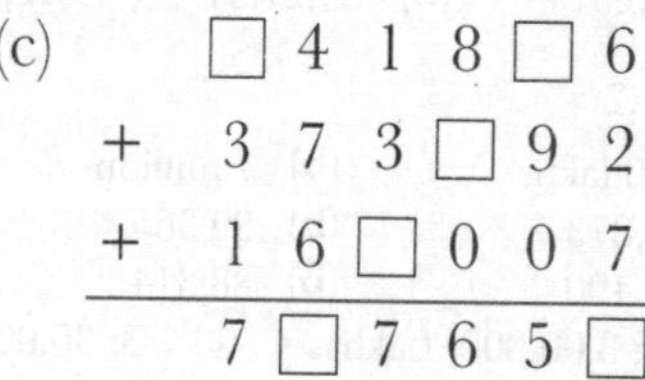
□ 4 1 8 □ 6
\+ 3 7 3 □ 9 2
\+ 1 6 □ 0 0 7
7 □ 7 6 5 □

6. List the first three odd multiples of 5.
7. List the odd factors of 420.
8. Find the HCF of 648 and 756.
9. Find the LCM of 504 and 756.
10. Seema's height is $1\frac{3}{10}$ m. If her father is $\frac{23}{40}$ m taller, what is Seema's father's height?
11. Expess the following decimals as fractions.
(a) 0.5　(b) 1.75　(c) 2.25
12. Convert the following.
(a) 1,051 g into hg and dg　(b) 7 $k\ell$ into $d\ell$　(c) 78 dm into dam
13. Clock A runs on time while Clock B loses 4 minutes every hour. If both clocks are set at 1:00 p.m., what time will clock B show at 1:00 pm the next day?
14. If three FM radios cost Rs 336, how much would five such radios cost?
15. There are three triangles. One is equilateral, the other is isosceles and the third one is a scalene triangle. Through which triangle will you not be able to draw a line of symmetry?

Answers to Select Questions

Chapter 1: Large Numbers

Let's Recap

1. (a) Seven thousand eight hundred and fourteen
   (b) Ten thousand five hundred and thirty-two
   (c) Sixty-seven thousand three hundred and ninety-one
2. (a) 9871 (b) 20780
3. (a) 40; 4 (b) 900; 9 (c) 3000; 3 (d) 50000; 5
4. (a) 7231, 7563, 7653, 8930 (b) 1213, 3012, 10123, 11023
5. (a) 2980, 2561, 2190, 2109 (b) 64291, 25381, 4382, 4328

Exercise 1.1

1. (a) 99,999; Ninety-nine thousand nine hundred and ninety-nine (b) 1,00,000; One lakh (c) 10,00,000; Ten lakhs
   (d) 99,99,999; Ninety-nine lakhs ninety-nine thousand, nine hundred and ninety-nine
   (e) 9,99,999; Nine lakhs ninety-nine thousand nine hundred and ninety-nine
2. (a) Six lakh thirty-four thousand five hundred and twenty-one
   (b) Two lakh thirty-five thousand one hundred and sixty-five
   (c) Thirty-five lakh fifty-eight thousand one hundred fifty-four
   (d) Fifty lakh thirty-three thousand eight hundred and forty-seven
3. (a) 6,34,205 (b) 8,07,009 (c) 53,38,249 (d) 77,00,707
4. (a) 6,74,354; Six lakhs seventy-four thousand three hundred and fifty-four
   (b) 46,25,417; Forty-six lakhs twenty-five thousand four hundred and seventeen
6. (a) 3,21,697 (b) 73,48,720 (c) 4,00,000 (d) 40,001 (e) 8,67,429 (f) 48,75,565 (g) 56,90,000 (h) 10,00,000
7. (a) 76,314 (b) 69,21,347 (c) 12,99,999 (d) 3,00,000 (e) 88,23,935 (f) 37,48,209 (g) 43,88,887 (h) 21,00,007

Exercise 1.2

3. (a) 10 lakhs (b) 7 million (c) 3 lakhs (d) 2 million 6 hundred thousands
4. (a) 1,873 (b) 29,365 (c) 6,32,786 (d) 73,42,630 (e) 54,98,139 (f) 42,10,367
5. (a) 3,490 (b) 88,314 (c) 378,177 (d) 653,210 (e) 1,789,360 (f) 7,304,059
6. (b) 3; 3,00,000; Lakhs (c) 3; 30,000; Thousands (d) 3; 3,00,000; Lakhs (e) 3; 3; Ones (f) 3; 3,00,000; Lakhs
7. (a) 60000 + 8000 + 400 + 80 + 1 (b) 500000 + 20000 + 3000 + 700 + 80 + 4
   (c) 900000 + 60000 + 5000 + 400 + 10 + 2 (d) 700000 + 50 + 1000 + 300 + 10 + 4
   (e) 1000000 + 300000 + 40000 + 1000 + 100 + 80 + 7 (f) 6000000 + 800000 + 200 + 10 + 8
   (g) 4000000 + 100000 + 20000 + 9000 + 700 + 3 (h) 3000000 + 900000 + 60000 + 1000 + 400 + 50 + 5
   (i) 8000000 + 30000 + 6000 (j) 800000 + 60000 + 7000
8. (a) 1,000 tens (b) 10 lakhs (c) 10,000 tens (d) 10 thousands (e) 10 lakhs (f) 10 lakhs

Exercise 1.3

1. (a) < (b) > (c) < (d) < (e) < (f) >
2. (a) 2,99,510 (b) 17,645 (c) 12,46,846
3. (a) 9,96,543 (b) 27,01,010 (c) 78,25,306
4. (a) 33,333; 3,33,033; 3,33,333; 33,03,303; 33,33,333 (b) 7,25,485; 7,25,548; 7,25,584; 7,25,845; 7,25,854
   (c) 7,37,241; 7,98,147; 8,12,939; 8,21,120; 8,92,347 (d) 44,25,617; 45,22,671; 54,52,716; 54,52,761; 55,22,176
5. (a) 6,83,765; 6,83,675; 6,83,657; 6,83,576; 6,83,567 (b) 79,88,462; 77,88,462; 76,88,462; 75,88,462; 73,88,462
   (c) 78,93,174; 38,71,348; 29,84,562; 8,36,245; 2,76,209
6. (a) Greatest: 8,76,541 and Smallest: 1,45,678 (b) Greatest: 9,74,320 and Smallest: 2,03,479
7. (a) Greatest: 98,64,321 and Smallest: 12,34,689 (b) Greatest: 76,54,320 and Smallest: 20,34,567

Revision Exercise

1. (a) 5,63,249 (b) 38,62,539 (c) 56,32,738 (d) 98,75,432
2. (a) 326,542 (b) 8,432,124 (c) 756,329 (d) 6,321,825
3. (a) Six lakhs sevnty-three thousand four hundred and twenty-nine (b) Five lakhs eighty-six thousand three hundred and twenty-one
   (c) Forty-five lakhs thirty-two thousand six hundred and fifty-five (d) Twenty-two lakhs thirty-five thousand and one
4. (a) Three hundred fifty-three thousand and four hundred twenty-nine
   (b) Seven million six hundred fifty-two thousand, three hundred and twelve
   (c) One million six hundred and five thousand, five hundred and ninety-five
   (d) One hundred thirty-five thousand, six hundred and eighty-one

Chapter 2: Roman Numerals

Exercise 2.1

B. (a) VII (b) XVIII (c) XXV (d) XXX (e) XLIX (f) C
C. (a) 6 (b) 9 (c) 25 (d) 27 (e) 10 (f) 61

Revision Exercise

2. (a) 4 (b) 35 (c) 12 (d) 40 (e) 3 (f) 19 (g) 24 (h) 36
3. (a) VIII (b) XXVII (c) XV (d) XXXV (e) XIX (f) XI (g) XXXII (h) X
4. (b) < (c) < (d) < (e) < (f) >
5. (a) IIIX (d) IIV (e) VVI (f) LLII and (h) VXV are not Roman numerals.
6. (b) IX (c) XIV (d) XXIX (e) XL

Chapter 3: Addition and Subtraction

Let's Recap

1. (a) 1435 (b) 58700 (c) 1 (d) 4790 (e) 56835 (f) 9743 (g) 48769
2. (a) 7287 (b) 9759 (c) 10491 (d) 8679 (e) 56756 (f) 48121 (g) 68243 (h) 84383
3. (a) 4122 (b) 6211 (c) 891 (d) 1428 (e) 40076 (f) 31103 (g) 8239 (h) 26679

Exercise 3.1

1. (a) 788989 (b) 286843 (c) 344455 (d) 545135 (e) 577769 (f) 938878
2. (a) 817887 (b) 999869 (c) 728876 (d) 576746 (e) 886266 (f) 899528
3. (a) 693210 (b) 796310 (c) 44952 (d) 160079 (e) 0 (f) 779346
4. (a) Addend = 31140; Sum = 99875 (b) Addend = 473322 (c) Addend = 41532
(d) Addends = 43619, 15203 and 17436; Sum = 76258

Exercise 3.2

1. (a) 262153 (b) 174442 (c) 534332 (d) 231432 (e) 325314 (f) 654314 (g) 322488
(h) 476394 (i) 420988 (j) 287978 (k) 225000 (l) 566473
2. (a) 252231 (b) 32111 (c) 377252 (d) 69000 (e) 268056 (f) 26722 (g) 301653
(h) 325422 (i) 606954
3. (a) 230000 (b) 490000 (c) 240000 (d) 332000 (e) 120005 (f) 136340 (g) 481685
(h) 450000 (i) 156104 (j) 248055
4. (a) Subtrahend = 34442 (b) Subtrahend = 17434 (c) 65789 – 23272 = 42517 (d) 59857 – 22436 = 37421

Exercise 3.3

1. 89397 flowers **2.** Rs 314780 **3.** 87940 bulbs **4.** 39118 reference books **5.** 25459 females **6.** 510875

Revision Exercise

1. (a) 998585 (b) 594229 (c) 796938 (d) 937899 (e) 936630 (f) 813511 (g) 689688 (h) 576746
2. (a) 241948 (b) 171289 (c) 390288 (d) 242105 (e) 500001 (f) 577960 (g) 143210 (h) 292601 (i) 33914
3. (a) 0 (b) 234156 (c) 0 (d) 809341 **4.** (a) Addend = 12434 (b) Subtrahend = 156147
5. 900939 sq. km **6.** 798576 people **7.** Rs 193815 **8.** 61235 girls
9. Rs 264000 **10.** 186375 **11.** 551348

Chapter 4: Multiplication

Let's Recap

1. (a) 0 (b) 6580 (c) 24500 (d) 32000 (e) 83 (f) 194
2. (a) 1533 (b) 4 (c) 18947 (d) 86430
3. (a) 4826 (b) 9306 (c) 28374 (d) 65016 (e) 84206 (f) 36096
(g) 83725 (h) 91962 (i) 12231 (j) 10620 (k) 79130 (l) 95400

Exercise 4.1

1. (a) 0 (b) 5591 (c) 0 (d) 27850 (e) 34770 (f) 476090 (g) 586400 (h) 719200
(i) 2210000 (j) 3551000 (k) 3878000 (l) 1623000 (m) 87190000 (n) 522150000 (o) 31200000 (p) 5896700000
2. (a) 4460 (b) 6390 (c) 48840 (d) 862400 (e) 99600 (f) 80800 (g) 4862000 (h) 2760000
(i) 6000000 (j) 9612000
3. (a) 7 (b) 27 (c) 3 (d) 22 (e) 643

Exercise 4.2

1. (a) 21824 (b) 139859 (c) 35853 (d) 95298 (e) 84420 (f) 39900 (g) 49500 (h) 42368
(i) 186850 (j) 123948 (k) 153315 (l) 138150 (m) 88880 (n) 84777 (o) 990990 (p) 848958
2. (a) 632716 (b) 232715 (c) 865600 (d) 619344 (e) 425852 (f) 714618 (g) 825275 (h) 418180
(i) 908572 (j) 627936 (k) 913900 (l) 986996

Exercise 4.3

1. 78195 sheets 2. Rs 44408 3. 35668 pages 4. 3870 pencils 5. 8760 hours

Revision Exercise

3. (a) 75933 (b) 82000 (c) 120244 (d) 212058 (e) 664872 (f) 644279
(g) 178930 (h) 118446 (i) 84942 (j) 916464 (k) 61620 (l) 837800
4. 24990 pages 5. 571200 g 6. Rs 196150 7. 3850 people 8. 172800 seconds
9. 21072 bars of chocolate 10. 850 apartments 11. 3900 letters 12. 99000 13. 98901

Chapter 5: Division

Let's Recap

1. (a) 8; 8 (b) 60; 420 (c) 120; 120 (d) 0 (e) 0 (f) 1 (g) 361 (h) 200 (i) 64; 9
2. (a) 210 (b) 2320 (c) 517 (d) Q = 1163; R = 2
3. (a) 13210 (b) 21013 (c) Q = 9262; R = 2 (d) 253

Exercise 5.1

1. (a) 164 (b) 136 (c) 229 (d) 137 (e) 116 (f) 108
2. (a) 672 (b) 50 (c) 7 (d) 800 (e) 70 (f) 6
3. (a) 34 (b) 27 (c) 21 (d) 286 (e) 138 (f) 147 (g) 140 (h) 250
(i) 1500 (j) 264 (k) 189 (l) 107 (m) 1103 (n) 2381 (o) 1671
4. (a) Q = 122; R = 5 (b) Q = 325; R = 2 (c) Q = 46; R = 2 (d) Q = 26; R = 5
(e) Q = 258; R = 2 (f) Q = 298; R = 6 (g) Q = 379; R = 4 (h) Q = 128; R = 19
(i) Q = 321; R = 11 (j) Q = 254; R = 9 (k) Q = 479; R = 11 (l) Q = 376; R = 10
(m) Q = 232; R = 8 (n) Q = 179; R = 14 (o) Q = 107; R = 2 (p) Q = 1006; R = 10
(q) Q = 1690; R = 37 (r) Q = 1658; R = 15

Exercise 5.2

1. Rs 115 2. 20 rows 3. 70 pizzas 4. 500 tiles 5. 8250 6. 5680

Revision Exercise

2. (a) 77 (b) 174 (c) 87 (d) 373 (e) 207 (f) 263
(g) 108 (h) 127 (i) 20 (j) 90 (k) 20 (l) 89
3. (a) Q = 219; R = 4 (b) Q = 318; R = 5 (c) Q = 126; R = 8 (d) Q = 96; R = 6 (e) Q = 129; R = 5 (f) Q = 158; R = 45
(g) Q = 83; R = 24 (h) Q = 104; R = 21 (i) Q = 16; R = 69 (j) Q = 56; R = 3 (k) Q = 326; R = 4 (l) Q = 156; R = 11
4. Rs 90 5. 60 boxes 6. 152 seeds 7. 24 sacks 8. 200 mℓ 9. 9240
10. 9420 11. 92 12. 986 13. 623 dozens 14. 319 scores

Chapter 6: Multiples and Factors

Exercise 6.1

1. (a) 8, 16, 24, 32, 40 (b) 9, 18, 27, 36, 45 (c) 10, 20, 30, 40, 50 (d) 11, 22, 33, 44, 55
(e) 12, 24, 36, 48, 60 (f) 15, 30, 45, 60, 75 (g) 20, 40, 60, 80, 100 (h) 22, 44, 66, 88, 110
6. (a) 99 (b) 998
7. Common multiples of 3 and 6 = 6, 12, 18, 24, 30
8. Common multiples of 2 and 4 = 4, 8, 12, 16, 20, 24, 28
9. (a) 20, 40 (b) 63, 126 (c) 35, 70 (d) 24, 48
(e) 36, 72 (f) 90, 180 (g) 30, 60 (h) 60, 120
10. (a) 12, 24, 36 (b) 15, 30, 45

Exercise 6.2

1. (i) (a) T (b) F (c) T (d) T (e) F (f) T (g) T (h) F
(ii) (a) T (b) F (c) T (d) F (e) F (f) T (g) T (h) F
6. (a) 2 and 3 (b) 11 and 3 (c) 1 and 72 (d) 5 and 20 (e) 7 and 5 (f) 1 and 300
7. (a) Multiples: 32 and 64; Factors: 2 and 4 (b) Multiples: 40 and 80; Factors: 2 and 5
(c) Multiples: 25 and 50; Factors: 1 and 5 (d) Multiples: 50 and 100; Factors: 2 and 5
(e) Multiples: 300 and 400; Factors: 2 and 10 (f) Multiples: 150 and 300; Factors: 15 and 3
8. (a) 1, 2 (b) 1, 3 (c) 1 (d) 1, 5 (e) 1, 2 (f) 1, 2, 3, 6 (g) 1, 2, 5, 10 (h) 1, 13

Exercise 6.3

3. (a) 2, 4, 6, 8 (b) 6, 12, 18, 24 (c) 4, 8, 12, 16 (d) 10, 20, 30, 40 (e) 6, 12, 18, 24 (f) 14, 28, 42, 56
4. 8472, 9008, 1340, 8706, 9110 and 3744
5. 39, 282, 636, 8808
6. 48, 732, 9124, 18764 and 99812
7. 50, 360, 4955, 98340 and 49385
8. 2934, 7206, 83184 and 68754
9. 216, 666, 7281, 9999, 1377 and 9036
10. 300, 89100, 20000 and 73600
11. 600, 750, 555 and 1785

Exercise 6.4

1. (a) 83, 89, 97 (b) 127 (c) 151, 157, 163, 167, 173, 179, 181, 191, 193, 197, 199 (d) 25
(e) 21 (f) 3 and 5, 11 and 13, 17 and 19, 149 and 151, 197 and 199
(g) 13 and 17, 19 and 23, 37 and 41, 67 and 71, 79 and 83
2. (a) F (b) T (c) F (d) F (e) T (f) F (g) F (h) F (i) T (j) T

Exercise 6.5

1. (a) F (b) F (c) F (d) T
3. (a) $3\times17=51$ (b) $2\times2\times19=76$ (c) $2\times2\times3\times7=84$ (d) $2\times7\times7=98$
(e) $2\times2\times5\times5=100$ (f) $5\times37=185$ (g) $2\times2\times7\times13=364$ (h) $2\times2\times2\times2\times2\times2\times2\times5=640$
(i) $5\times127=635$ (j) $2\times2\times2\times2\times2\times3\times7=672$
4. (a) $2\times2\times2\times2\times2=32$ (b) $2\times2\times2\times5=40$ (c) $2\times3\times3\times3=54$ (d) $2\times2\times2\times2\times2\times3=96$
(e) $2\times2\times2\times3\times5=120$ (f) $2\times2\times2\times2\times2\times2\times2=128$ (g) $2\times2\times3\times3\times7=252$ (h) $2\times2\times2\times5\times7=280$
(i) $2\times5\times5\times7=350$ (j) $3\times5\times5\times7=525$

Revision Exercise

1. (a) 100 (b) 4, 8, 12, 16, 20, 24, 28, 32, 36, 40, 44, 48 (c) 55, 66, 77, 88, 99
(d) 98 (e) 999 2. 60, 36, 45 3. 26, 16, 46, 56
4. (a) 21, 42, 63 (b) 10, 20, 30 (c) 6, 12, 18 (d) 42, 84, 126
(e) 28, 56, 84 5. 2, 6, 5, 10, 3 6. 7, 5, 10
7. (a) 1, 5 (b) 1, 3 (c) 1, 2, 3, 4, 6, 8, 12, 24 (d) 1, 3, 5, 15
(e) 1, 2, 4, 8 8. 39, 25 9. 54, 219, 444, 1203 10. 126, 162, 306, 324, 144
11. (a) $2\times3\times3\times5\times5=450$ (b) $2\times2\times2\times3=24$ (c) $5\times43=215$ (d) $2\times2\times2\times5\times13=520$ (e) $2\times2\times2\times5\times5=200$

Chapter 7: HCF and LCM

Exercise 7.1

1. (a) 3 (b) 6 (c) 4 (d) 2 (e) 5 (f) 9 (g) 12 (h) 14
(i) 13 (j) 12 (k) 27 (l) 16 (m) 54 (n) 15
2. (a) 15 (b) 18 (c) 7 (d) 15 (e) 16 (f) 42 (g) 12 (h) 26
(i) 28 (j) 16 (k) 24 (l) 65 (m) 33 (n) 21

Exercise 7.2

1. (a) LCM=12 (b) LCM=10 (c) LCM=12
2. (a) 12 (b) 24 (c) 55 (d) 30 (e) 35 (f) 30 (g) 84 (h) 70
(i) 60 (j) 60 (k) 16 (l) 144 (m) 20 (n) 20 (o) 24 (p) 91
3. (a) 48 (b) 120 (c) 336 (d) 360 (e) 1092 (f) 360 (g) 300 (h) 720
(i) 2730 (j) 2520 (k) 2400 (l) 2100

Revision Exercise

2. (a) 12 (b) 81 (c) 20 (d) 3 (e) 1 (f) 1 (g) 12 (h) 15
(i) 6 (j) 17 (k) 18 (l) 14
3. (a) 4 (b) 36 (c) 60 (d) 100 (e) 216 (f) 114 (g) 360 (h) 390
(i) 978 (j) 567 (k) 192 (l) 144
4. Yes 5. No

Chapter 8: Fractional Numbers

Let's Recap

2. $\frac{1}{2}$ and $\frac{1}{3}$ are not equivalent fractions
3. (a) N = 2, D = 3 (b) N = 1, D = 4 (c) N = 4, D = 5
4. (a) $\frac{2}{3}$ (b) $\frac{5}{7}$ (c) $\frac{3}{5}$

Exercise 8.1

1. (a) $\frac{1}{6}$ (b) $\frac{1}{10}$ (c) $\frac{3}{4}$ (d) $\frac{6}{16}$ (e) $\frac{1}{4}$ (f) $\frac{2}{6}$
2. (b) 2 (c) 8 (d) 9 (e) 6 (f) 7
3. (b) 10 (c) 4 (d) 5 (e) 1 (f) 6 (g) 9 (h) 4

Exercise 8.2

1. (a), (b), (d), (e), (g), (h) and (k) are like fractions

2. (a) $\frac{1}{3}$ (b) $\frac{7}{10}$ (c) $\frac{11}{13}$ (d) $\frac{3}{5}$ (e) $\frac{7}{9}$ (f) $\frac{1}{5}$ (g) $\frac{1}{7}$ (h) $\frac{8}{9}$

3. (a) $\frac{1}{4}$ (b) $\frac{1}{6}$ (c) $\frac{3}{11}$ (d) $\frac{6}{7}$ (e) $\frac{7}{8}$ (f) $\frac{1}{2}$ (g) $\frac{1}{3}$ (h) $\frac{7}{10}$

5. (a) $1\frac{2}{3}$ (b) $1\frac{1}{10}$ (c) $1\frac{2}{12}$ (d) $1\frac{1}{7}$ (e) $1\frac{3}{6}$ (f) $2\frac{1}{2}$ (g) $2\frac{2}{3}$ (h) $4\frac{2}{4}$
(i) $4\frac{3}{5}$ (j) $8\frac{2}{6}$ (k) $3\frac{1}{8}$ (l) $6\frac{1}{7}$

6. (a) $\frac{4}{3}$ (b) $\frac{15}{9}$ (c) $\frac{10}{3}$ (d) $\frac{26}{3}$ (e) $\frac{33}{5}$ (f) $\frac{106}{10}$ (g) $\frac{44}{12}$ (h) $\frac{82}{15}$
(i) $\frac{99}{12}$ (j) $\frac{283}{14}$ (k) $\frac{65}{4}$ (l) $\frac{74}{3}$

7. (a) $\frac{2}{6}, \frac{3}{9}, \frac{4}{12}$ (b) $\frac{6}{10}, \frac{9}{15}, \frac{12}{20}$ (c) $\frac{10}{14}, \frac{15}{21}, \frac{20}{28}$ (d) $\frac{8}{18}, \frac{12}{27}, \frac{16}{36}$
(e) $\frac{4}{20}, \frac{6}{30}, \frac{8}{40}$ (f) $\frac{6}{8}, \frac{9}{12}, \frac{12}{16}$ (g) $\frac{8}{14}, \frac{12}{21}, \frac{16}{28}$ (h) $\frac{2}{16}, \frac{3}{24}, \frac{4}{32}$
(i) $\frac{10}{18}, \frac{15}{27}, \frac{20}{36}$ (j) $\frac{14}{18}, \frac{21}{27}, \frac{28}{36}$ (k) $\frac{10}{16}, \frac{15}{24}, \frac{20}{32}$ (l) $\frac{14}{20}, \frac{21}{30}, \frac{28}{40}$

8. (a) $\frac{8}{6}, \frac{12}{9}, \frac{16}{12}$ (b) $\frac{10}{4}, \frac{15}{6}, \frac{20}{8}$ (c) $\frac{24}{10}, \frac{36}{15}, \frac{48}{20}$ (d) $\frac{18}{14}, \frac{27}{21}, \frac{36}{28}$
(e) $\frac{40}{22}, \frac{60}{33}, \frac{80}{44}$ (f) $\frac{14}{10}, \frac{21}{15}, \frac{28}{20}$ (g) $\frac{18}{10}, \frac{27}{15}, \frac{36}{20}$ (h) $\frac{20}{14}, \frac{30}{21}, \frac{40}{28}$

9. (b), (d), (f), (h) and (k) are equivalent fractions.

Exercise 8.3

1. (a) 30 (b) 24 (c) 9 (d) 5 (e) 8 (f) 7 (g) 25 (h) 15 (i) 45

2. (a) $<$ (b) $>$ (c) $<$ (d) $>$ (e) $<$ (f) $>$ (g) $>$ (h) $<$ (i) $<$

3. (a) $\frac{7}{8}, \frac{4}{8}, \frac{3}{8}, \frac{2}{8}, \frac{1}{8}$ (b) $\frac{5}{5}, \frac{4}{5}, \frac{3}{5}, \frac{2}{5}, \frac{1}{5}$ (c) $\frac{24}{16}, \frac{17}{16}, \frac{15}{16}, \frac{10}{16}, \frac{6}{16}$ (d) $\frac{21}{10}, \frac{13}{10}, \frac{9}{10}, \frac{7}{10}, \frac{2}{10}$ (e) $2\frac{2}{4}, 1\frac{1}{4}, \frac{4}{4}, \frac{3}{4}, \frac{1}{4}$

4. (a) $\frac{6}{13}, \frac{6}{10}, \frac{6}{9}, \frac{6}{8}, \frac{6}{7}$ (b) $\frac{1}{3}, \frac{2}{3}, \frac{4}{2}, \frac{6}{2}, \frac{9}{2}$ (c) $\frac{2}{5}, \frac{11}{20}, \frac{13}{20}, \frac{7}{10}, \frac{3}{4}$ (d) $\frac{1}{3}, \frac{2}{5}, \frac{7}{15}, \frac{4}{6}, \frac{8}{10}$
(e) $\frac{1}{8}, \frac{3}{20}, \frac{1}{5}, \frac{2}{10}, \frac{1}{4}$ or $\frac{1}{8}, \frac{3}{20}, \frac{2}{10}, \frac{1}{5}, \frac{1}{4}$

5. (a) $>$ (b) $<$ (c) $>$ (d) $<$ (e) $<$ (f) $>$

Exercise 8.4

1. (a) $\frac{7}{13}$ (b) $\frac{3}{4}$ (c) $\frac{3}{4}$ (d) $\frac{3}{5}$

2. (a) $\frac{1}{3}$ (b) $\frac{4}{5}$ (c) $\frac{1}{2}$ (d) $\frac{5}{6}$ (e) $\frac{1}{2}$ (f) $\frac{2}{3}$ (g) $\frac{1}{4}$ (h) $\frac{1}{3}$ (i) $\frac{1}{2}$ (j) $\frac{1}{3}$

3. (a), (c) and (d) are in their simplest form (b) $\frac{1}{3}$ (e) $\frac{1}{3}$ (f) $\frac{2}{5}$

Exercise 8.5

1. 23 buses 2. 17 apples

Revision Exercise

1. (a) $1\frac{3}{7}$ (b) $1\frac{2}{11}$ (c) $1\frac{8}{15}$ (d) $3\frac{3}{5}$ (e) $3\frac{3}{14}$

2. (a) $\frac{8}{3}$ (b) $\frac{19}{5}$ (c) $\frac{17}{11}$ (d) $\frac{22}{3}$ (e) $\frac{59}{5}$ (f) $\frac{33}{4}$
(g) $\frac{13}{4}$ (h) $\frac{28}{5}$ (i) $\frac{51}{4}$ (j) $\frac{46}{3}$

3. (a) 9 (b) 48 (c) 39 (d) 4 (e) $2\frac{1}{8}$

4. (a) $\frac{3}{30}$ and $\frac{10}{30}$ (b) $\frac{10}{35}$ and $\frac{21}{35}$ (c) $\frac{15}{12}$ and $\frac{40}{12}$ (d) $\frac{12}{10}$ and $\frac{15}{10}$ (e) $\frac{6}{18}$ and $\frac{12}{18}$ (f) $\frac{9}{12}$ and $\frac{10}{12}$
(g) $\frac{8}{20}$ and $\frac{15}{20}$ (h) $\frac{20}{15}$ and $\frac{39}{15}$

5. (a) $\frac{3}{6}$ and $\frac{3}{9}$ (b) $\frac{6}{15}$ and $\frac{6}{21}$ (c) $\frac{16}{18}$ and $\frac{16}{22}$ (d) $\frac{28}{40}$ and $\frac{28}{36}$

6. (a) $\frac{8}{10}, \frac{12}{15}, \frac{16}{20}$ (b) $\frac{14}{16}, \frac{21}{24}, \frac{35}{40}$ (c) $\frac{22}{18}, \frac{33}{27}, \frac{44}{36}$ (d) $\frac{10}{4}, \frac{15}{6}, \frac{20}{8}$ (e) $\frac{22}{16}, \frac{33}{24}, \frac{44}{32}$

7. (a) $\frac{3}{5}$ (b) $\frac{3}{7}$ (c) $\frac{2}{3}$ (d) $\frac{1}{3}$ (e) $\frac{6}{7}$ (f) $\frac{1}{4}$
(g) $\frac{1}{9}$ (h) $\frac{1}{2}$ (i) $\frac{1}{2}$ (j) $\frac{4}{9}$

8. 20 roses 9. 30 boys

Chapter 9: Addition and Subtraction of Fractions

Let's Recap

1. (a) $\frac{3}{5}$ (b) $\frac{5}{7}$ (c) $\frac{7}{9}$ (d) $\frac{7}{11}$ (e) $\frac{8}{13}$ (f) $\frac{9}{16}$

2. (a) $\frac{1}{3}$ (b) $\frac{3}{5}$ (c) $\frac{3}{7}$ (d) $\frac{2}{9}$ (e) $\frac{1}{11}$ (f) $\frac{10}{17}$

Exercise 9.1

1. (a) $\frac{8}{9}$ (b) $\frac{9}{13}$ (c) $\frac{8}{15}$ (d) $\frac{15}{17}$ (e) 1 (f) $\frac{1}{3}$ (g) $\frac{1}{2}$ (h) $\frac{20}{23}$ (i) $\frac{3}{4}$

2. (a) $\frac{5}{12}$ (b) $\frac{2}{5}$ (c) $\frac{13}{21}$ (d) $1\frac{1}{15}$ (e) $\frac{7}{16}$ (f) $\frac{7}{9}$
(g) $\frac{13}{18}$ (h) $\frac{8}{9}$ (i) $\frac{13}{18}$ (j) $1\frac{20}{21}$ (k) $1\frac{26}{45}$ (l) $1\frac{31}{78}$

3. (a) $1\frac{1}{2}$ (b) $3\frac{2}{3}$ (c) $7\frac{6}{9}$ (d) 2 (e) $6\frac{1}{2}$ (f) $10\frac{1}{2}$ (g) $8\frac{4}{7}$ (h) $6\frac{2}{3}$ (i) $9\frac{8}{11}$

4. (a) $5\frac{5}{6}$ (b) $8\frac{11}{12}$ (c) $5\frac{11}{15}$ (d) $5\frac{13}{24}$ (e) $11\frac{15}{28}$ (f) $23\frac{1}{15}$
(g) $7\frac{32}{105}$ (h) $8\frac{1}{2}$ (i) $7\frac{1}{3}$ (j) $7\frac{19}{28}$ (k) $4\frac{7}{15}$ (l) $5\frac{7}{10}$

Exercise 9.2

1. (a) $\frac{1}{5}$ (b) $\frac{1}{9}$ (c) $\frac{4}{7}$ (d) $\frac{1}{7}$ (e) $\frac{3}{11}$ (f) $\frac{1}{2}$ (g) $\frac{3}{17}$ (h) $\frac{9}{17}$ (i) $\frac{1}{2}$

2. (a) $\frac{7}{12}$ (b) $\frac{1}{6}$ (c) $\frac{1}{12}$ (d) $\frac{3}{20}$ (e) $\frac{3}{7}$ (f) $\frac{1}{15}$
(g) $\frac{2}{15}$ (h) $\frac{1}{8}$ (i) $\frac{7}{15}$ (j) $\frac{1}{12}$ (k) $\frac{11}{30}$ (l) $\frac{1}{9}$

3. (a) 2 (b) 3 (c) 7 (d) 8 (e) 1 (f) $2\frac{1}{5}$
(g) $2\frac{3}{11}$ (h) $4\frac{2}{13}$ (i) $3\frac{2}{7}$ (j) $5\frac{1}{3}$ (k) $2\frac{1}{6}$ (l) $5\frac{1}{2}$

4. (a) $2\frac{2}{15}$ (b) $2\frac{1}{4}$ (c) $5\frac{1}{30}$ (d) $2\frac{3}{20}$ (e) $3\frac{1}{10}$ (f) $3\frac{3}{14}$
(g) $2\frac{1}{2}$ (h) $2\frac{11}{72}$ (i) $2\frac{11}{24}$ (j) $2\frac{3}{10}$ (k) $2\frac{8}{15}$ (l) $2\frac{12}{35}$

Exercise 9.3

1. $7\frac{1}{2}$ m 2. $4\frac{9}{10}$ km 3. $\frac{5}{7}$ of chocolates 4. Rs $6\frac{3}{4}$ 5. 45 ℓ 6. Rs $7\frac{1}{4}$

Revision Exercise

1. (a) $\frac{10}{13}$ (b) 1 (c) $\frac{19}{35}$ (d) $3\frac{1}{4}$ (e) $3\frac{3}{7}$ (f) $8\frac{1}{10}$
   (g) 1 (h) $1\frac{5}{14}$ (i) $\frac{7}{8}$ (j) $1\frac{19}{24}$ (k) $2\frac{11}{70}$ (l) $\frac{6}{7}$
2. (a) $\frac{3}{7}$ (b) $\frac{2}{23}$ (c) $\frac{7}{20}$ (d) $\frac{5}{22}$ (e) $3\frac{3}{14}$ (f) $1\frac{1}{5}$
   (g) $\frac{1}{2}$ (h) $\frac{1}{9}$ (i) $\frac{1}{8}$ (j) $\frac{1}{12}$ (k) $\frac{11}{35}$ (l) $1\frac{11}{24}$
3. $\frac{13}{15}$
4. $13\frac{5}{12}$ m
5. 20 plants

Chapter 10: Decimals

Exercise 10.2

1. (a) 0.2 (b) 2.2 (c) 22.2 (d) 63.4 (e) 0.62 (f) 2.61
   (g) 39.41 (h) 0.03 (i) 4.263 (j) 0.718 (k) 0.005 (l) 0.1
2. (a) $\frac{36}{10}$ (b) $\frac{231}{10}$ (c) $\frac{9}{2}$ (d) $\frac{7}{10}$ (e) $\frac{1826}{100}$ (f) $\frac{2103}{100}$
   (g) $\frac{2}{100}$ (h) $\frac{101}{100}$ (i) $\frac{2371}{1000}$ (j) $\frac{38492}{1000}$ (k) $\frac{11001}{1000}$ (l) $\frac{6}{1000}$
3. (a) 30+6+0.2+0.03+0.004; $30+6+\frac{2}{10}+\frac{3}{100}+\frac{4}{1000}$ (b) 6+0.4; $6+\frac{4}{10}$
   (c) 2+0.6+0.01; $2+\frac{6}{10}+\frac{1}{100}$ (d) 1+0.05; $1+\frac{5}{100}$ (e) 0.2+0.003; $\frac{2}{10}+\frac{3}{1000}$
   (f) 70.3+0.007; $\frac{3}{10}+\frac{7}{1000}$ (g) 60+3+0.7+0.01+0.008; $60+3+\frac{7}{10}+\frac{1}{100}+\frac{8}{1000}$
   (h) 9+0.6; $9+\frac{6}{10}$ (i) 20+1+0.3+0.07; $20+1+\frac{3}{10}+\frac{7}{100}$ (j) 400+30+2+0.2+0.03+0.001; $400+30+2+\frac{2}{10}+\frac{3}{100}+\frac{1}{1000}$

Exercise 10.3

1. (a) < (b) > (c) < (d) > (e) < (f) > (g) > (h) < (i) <
2. (a) 344.34, 34.3, 4.43, 4.34, 3.44, 3.43 (b) 8.282, 8.228, 2.822, 2.282, 2.228 (c) 1101, 1.1, 1.001, 0.101, 0.011, 0.01
   (d) 555.55, 55.555, 55.5, 5.555, 5.55, 5.5
3. (a) 2.579, 2.638, 3.961, 281.39, 461.38 (b) 7.77, 7.777, 77.77, 777.7, 777.77 (c) 9.696, 9.699, 9.969, 69.96, 96.69
   (d) 1.001, 1.01, 1.101, 10.01, 10.1, 11.1

Exercise 10.4

1. (a) 0.02 (b) 3.33 (c) 5.86 (d) 8.06 (e) 56.1 (f) 28.34
   (g) 0.12 (h) 3.81 (i) 8.6 (j) 33.63 (k) 0.008 (l) 4.559
   (m) 8.888 (n) 11.111 (o) 0.014 (p) 4.653 (q) 6.497 (r) 4.253
2. (a) 13.3 (b) 0.01 (c) 2.24 (d) 5.95 (e) 22.52 (f) 6.7
   (g) 0.04 (h) 3.89 (i) 1.67 (j) 0.003 (k) 1.008 (l) 4.432
   (m) 4.726 (n) 0.009 (o) 2.014 (p) 2.478 (q) 1.445 (r) 7.307

Exercise 10.5

1. (a) Rs 3.25 (b) Rs 10.10 (c) Rs 4.45 (d) Rs 10.01 (e) Rs 30.03 (f) Rs 99.09
   (g) Rs 99.90 (h) Rs 75.64
2. (a) 0.5 km (b) 0.514 km (c) 0.612 km (d) 0.264 km (e) 0.1 km (f) 0.01 km
   (g) 0.021 km (h) 0.003 km (i) 0.002 km (j) 6.003 km
3. (a) 0.4 m (b) 0.36 m (c) 0.137 m (d) 0.24 m (e) 0.024 m (f) 0.03 m
   (g) 0.003 m (h) 5.691 m (i) 2.302 m (j) 1.001 m
4. (a) 0.25 kg (b) 0.5 kg (c) 0.75 kg (d) 0.333 kg (e) 0.05 kg (f) 0.01 kg
   (g) 0.003 kg (h) 0.001 kg (i) 7.125 kg (j) 10.9 kg
5. (a) 0.2 ℓ (b) 0.5 ℓ (c) 0.785 ℓ (d) 0.25 ℓ (e) 0.05 ℓ (f) 0.005 ℓ
   (g) 0.002 ℓ (h) 2.002 ℓ (i) 5 ℓ (j) 7.008 ℓ

Revision Exercise

2. (a) 0.005 (b) 3.54 (c) 6.032 (d) 35.103
3. (a) 2+0.6+0.07 (b) 40+0.3+0.01+0.004 (c) 6+0.003 (d) 80+8+0.1+0.008 (e) 100+70+0.01

4. (a) 78.638, 78.963, 493.638, 493.64, 493.963 (b) 3.46, 3.64, 4.36, 4.63, 6.34, 6.43 (c) 0.23, 0.32, 2.03, 2.3, 3.02, 3.2
5. (a) 8.45 (b) 9.99 (c) 37.91 (d) 35.53 (e) 14.78 (f) 10.444
6. (a) 4.81 (b) 6.15 (c) 12.27 (d) 14.34 (e) 13.66 (f) 2.787
7. (a) 2.2 (b) 3.35 (c) 4.356 (d) 6.431
8. (a) $\frac{1891}{100}$ (b) $\frac{3543}{100}$ (c) $\frac{45231}{1000}$ (d) $\frac{61237}{1000}$
9. (a) $30+5+0.8; 30+5+\frac{8}{10}$ (b) $60+1+0.2+0.03; 60+1+\frac{2}{10}+\frac{3}{100}$
(c) $5+0.1+0.02+0.003; 5+\frac{1}{10}+\frac{2}{100}+\frac{3}{1000}$ (d) $1+0.8+0.05+0.004; 1+\frac{8}{10}+\frac{5}{100}+\frac{4}{1000}$
10. (a) Rs 5.05 (b) Rs 62.50 (c) 7.5 kg (d) 83.083 ℓ (e) 6.75 km (f) 0.074 km (g) 3.1 ℓ (h) 15.5 ℓ

Chapter 11: Measurement of Length, Mass and Capacity

Let's Recap

1. (a) 3000 m (b) 850 cm (c) 3000 g (d) 1500 g (e) 1800 mℓ (f) 7400 mℓ
2. (a) 7 kg 445 g (b) 5 kg 975 g (c) 21 m 50 cm (d) 2 km 46 m (e) 9 ℓ 230 mℓ (f) 2 ℓ 650 mℓ
3. (a) 12 m 44 cm (b) 6 km 702 m (c) 10 kg 700 g (d) 24 ℓ 648 mℓ
4. (a) 149 m (b) 164 g (c) 95 mℓ (d) 234 mℓ

Exercise 11.1

1. (a) 1,00,000 cm (b) 0.1 m (c) 300 dm (d) 0.04 m (e) 7.18 dm (f) 64.931 m
(g) 100 dag (h) 0.001 hg (i) 6300 cg (j) 46 hg (k) 492000 mg (l) 0.23496 dag
(m) 10 dℓ (n) 0.001 kℓ (o) 7400 ℓ (p) 0.0036 hℓ (q) 6430 cℓ (r) 0.23496 daℓ
2. (a) 604 m (b) 100010 cm (c) 37 m (d) 1386 m (e) 349 m (f) 2.15 m
3. (a) 16160 mg (b) 80080 dg (c) 840300 cg (d) 1480 g (e) 0.325 g (f) 7.2 g
4. (a) 434 cℓ (b) 6.122 ℓ (c) 6030 ℓ (d) 31.9 ℓ (e) 8.1 ℓ (f) 3100 ℓ
5. (a) 3 m 4 cm (b) 3 hm 64 m (c) 36 dam 4 m (d) 6 km 7.4 hm (e) 3 kg 479 g (f) 800 dg 9 cg
(g) 46 dag 8 g 3 dg (h) 4 ℓ 312 mℓ (i) 63 daℓ 9 ℓ 8 dℓ (j) 3 dℓ 9 cℓ 8 mℓ

Exercise 11.2

1. (a) 9 g 9 cg (b) 7 ℓ 68 mℓ (c) 5 km 550 m (d) 10 hℓ 88 ℓ (e) 54 dag 31 dg (f) 41 m 112 mm
(g) 11 dg 54 mg (h) 109 daℓ 162 mℓ (i) 19 kg 650 g (j) 12 m
2. (a) 2 kg 400 g (b) 5 hℓ 6 ℓ (c) 3 cm 2 mm (d) 4 kg 5 hg (e) 2 ℓ 600 mℓ (f) 4 g 445 mg
(g) 259 dm 78 mm (h) 1 ℓ 92 cℓ (i) 15 dag 5 dg (j) 965 ℓ 75 cℓ
3. (a) 6 km 900 m (b) 16 ℓ 404 mℓ (c) 12 g 330 mg (d) 25 hm 12 m (e) 36 dℓ 61 mℓ (f) 71 dag 70 dg
(g) 186 ℓ 348 mℓ (h) 41 kg 850 g (i) 34 km 370 m (j) 226 kℓ 24 daℓ
4. (a) 1 kg 11 g (b) 2 ℓ 110 mℓ (c) 8 km 200 m (d) 4 dag 2 g (e) 2 hg 101 dg (f) 3 dℓ 26 mℓ
(g) 1 dg 64 mg (h) 278 m (i) 278 ℓ (j) 429 g

Exercise 11.3

1. 65 km 350 m 2. 70 kg 50 g 3. 4 ℓ 50 mℓ of water 4. 1 ℓ 650 mℓ of water

Revision Exercise

1. (a) 3004 m (b) 27600 cℓ (c) 0.674 m (d) 560 g (e) 47.84 m (f) 0.21 daℓ
(g) 8 dℓ (h) 67100 cm (i) 30 g
2. (a) 18 m 43 cm (b) 5 km 25 m (c) 6 dag 35 dg (d) 1 g 704 mg (e) 3 hℓ 3 ℓ 42 mℓ (f) 38 ℓ 377 mℓ
3. (a) 2 m 36 cm (b) 6 dam 3 m (c) 42 g 35 mg (d) 14 kg 570 g (e) 5 ℓ 28 mℓ (f) 3 ℓ 28 cℓ
4. (a) 14 m 16 cm (b) 114 kg (c) 212 km (d) 4 dag 30 dg (e) 40 dℓ 90 mℓ (f) 257 ℓ 600 mℓ
5. (a) 23 kg 112 g (b) 11 km 16 dam (c) 10 ℓ 13 mℓ
6. 1 ℓ 200 mℓ of milk 7. 11 m 34 cm 8. 52 km 500 m 9. 150 g 10. 30 minutes 11. 25 ℓ, 5 buckets
12. 16 cℓ 8 mℓ of oil 13. 15 ℓ 225 mℓ

Chapter 12: Time

Let's Recap

1. (a) 42 days (b) 10 days (c) 30 days (d) 72 hours (e) 50 hours (f) 160 hours
(g) 420 min (h) 200 min (i) 600 s (j) 400 s
2. (a) 7 a.m. (b) 5 p.m. (c) 5 p.m. (d) 7 a.m. (e) 9:20 p.m. (f) 1:30 p.m. (g) 7 p.m. (h) 1 a.m.
3. (a) 19 h (b) 42 min (c) 7 h 50 min (d) 8 h 40 min
4. (a) 10 h (b) 31 min (c) 8 h 24 min (d) 26 h 9 min

Exercise 12.1

1. (a) 1:32 (b) 10:20 (c) 11:05 (d) 9:55 (e) 9:40 (f) 5:00
3. (a) 0600 hours (b) 2200 hours (c) 1130 hours (d) 1230 hours (e) 0345 hours
   (f) 0000 hours (g) 0430 hours (h) 1950 hours (i) 1720 hours (j) 1410 hours
4. (a) 4 p.m. (b) 2:30 p.m. (c) 12:45 p.m. (d) 12:45 a.m. (e) 12:20 p.m.
   (f) 8:08 p.m. (g) 1:51 p.m. (h) 3:40 p.m. (i) 4:20 p.m. (j) 1:50 a.m.

Exercise 12.2

1. (a) 30 min 30 s (b) 8 h 35 min (c) 5 h 33 min 35 s (d) 7 h 48 min 29 s
   (e) 5 h 59 min (f) 10 h 21 min 20 s (g) 10 h 10 min 30 s (h) 12 h 45 min 20 s
   (i) 13 h 01 min 07 s (j) 15 h 23 min 11 s
2. (a) 3 h 36 min (b) 2 min 31 s (c) 3 h 22 min 21 s (d) 41 min 20 s
   (e) 3 h 5 min 20 s (f) 3 h 16 min 10 s (g) 4 h 37 min 12 s (h) 8 h 30 min 21 s
   (i) 4 h 55 min 29 s (j) 6 h 21 min 37 s
3. (a) 6 h 08 min (b) 10 min 09 s (c) 8 h 24 min 48 s (d) 8 h 08 min 48 s
   (e) 5 h 37 min 30 s (f) 30 h 51 min 45 s (g) 19 h 01 min 30 s (h) 47 h 32 min 30 s
   (i) 28 h 42 min 40 s (j) 35 h 53 min 20 s
4. (a) 2 h 04 min (b) 3 min 12 s (c) 3 h 21 min 18 s (d) 2 h 06 min 09 s
   (e) 3 h 12 min 07 s (f) 1 h 10 min 05 s (g) 1 h 02 min 03 s (h) 1 h 06 min 04 s
   (i) 1 h 03 min 04 s (j) 1 h 05 min 04 s
5. (a) 40 min 40 s (b) 1 h 53 min 06 s (c) 1 h 46 min 55 s (d) 9 min 50 s
   (e) 12 midnight (f) 10 min (g) 900 s (h) 120 caps

Revision Exercise

1. (a) 0900 hours (b) 1815 hours (c) 0735 hours (d) 1850 hours (e) 0810 hours (f) 0910 hours
2. (a) 5:40 a.m. (b) 1:15 p.m. (c) 5:20 p.m. (d) 1:20 a.m. (e) 12:00 midnight (f) 12:00 noon
3. (a) 96 h (b) 60 h (c) 83 min (d) 374 s (e) 8 min (f) 1 h 10 min
4. (a) 50 min 17 s (b) 4 h 05 min 22 s (c) 2 h 46 min 08 s (d) 16 min 25 s
   (e) 4 h 57 min 58 s (f) 3 h 41 min 16 s (g) 16 min 16 s (h) 6 h 42 min 30 s
   (i) 25 h 27 min 52 s (j) 13 min 14 s (k) 53 min 42 s (l) 1 h 15 min 19 s
   (m) 4 h 14 min 30 s (n) 2 h 48 min 28 s (o) 3 h 28 s (p) 22 h 07 min 04 s
   (q) 8 h 04 min 03 s (r) 2 h 51 min 20 s
5. 48 min 21 s
6. 2 h 03 min 45 s
7. 23 min
8. 120 h

Chapter 13: Unitary Method

Revision Exercise

1. (a) 28 kg (b) Rs 60 (c) Rs 96 (d) 600 mℓ (e) 200 cm (f) Rs 7
   (g) 15 kg (h) 70 ℓ (i) Re 1 (j) Rs 12
2. (a) Rs 1288 (b) Rs 21 (c) Rs 812 (d) 93 students (e) 36 crayons
3. (a) Rs 25 (b) 36 days (c) Rs 60 (d) 208 matchsticks (e) 330 students (f) Rs 210
   (g) 840 sarees (h) 364 days (i) 24 crayons (j) Rs 850

Chapter 14: Geometry

Exercise 14.1

3. (a) square (b) rectangle (c) all (d) two (e) none
4. (a) No, 8 cm < 9 cm (b) Yes (c) No, 3 cm < 4 cm

Exercise 14.2

(a) 9 sq. cm (b) 12 sq. cm (c) 12 sq. cm (d) 18 sq. cm (e) About 5 sq. cm (f) About 12 sq. cm
(g) About 11 sq. cm (h) About 12 sq. cm (i) About 18 sq. cm (j) About 14 sq. cm

Exercise 14.3

2. 320 m
3. 800 m
4. 900 m

Revision Exercise

2. (a) False, a line has no end points (b) False, the opposite sides of a rectangle are equal (c) True
   (d) True (e) True (f) False, the area of a square with each side 1 cm, is 1 sq. cm.
   (g) False, the perimeter of a square is 4 times the length of one of its sides.
3. (a) plane, solid (b) two (c) one (d) one
4. (a) 40° (b) 90° (c) 100° (d) 60° (e) 120° (f) 80°